Alice's adventures in Wonderland

and Through the Looking Glass

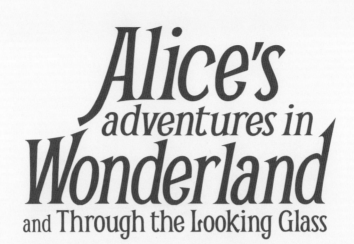

'What do you know about this business?' the King said to Alice.

'Nothing,' said Alice.

'Nothing whatever?' persisted the King.

'Nothing *whatever*,' said Alice.

– *Chapter twelve: alice's evidence*

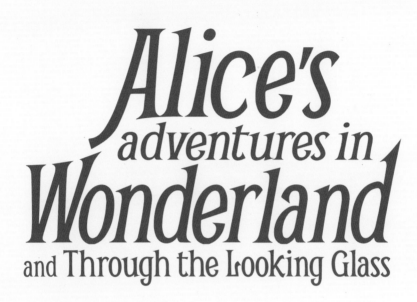

Alice's
adventures in
Wonderland
and Through the Looking Glass

Lewis Carroll

With Illustrations by Sir John Tenniel

ARCTURUS

This edition published in 2016 by Arcturus Publishing Limited
26/27 Bickels Yard, 151–153 Bermondsey Street,
London SE1 3HA

Art Director: Peter Ridley
Design: Jeni Child and Michael Reynolds
Illustrations colourised by Katy Jackson
Front cover image: Private Collection/Bridgeman Images

ISBN: 978-1-78599-253-7
CH004994UK
Supplier 26, Date 0216, Print run 4871

Printed in China

CONTENTS

Alice's Adventures in Wonderland

CONTENTS

Through the Looking Glass

ALICE'S ADVENTURES IN WONDERLAND

All in the golden afternoon
    Full leisurely we glide;
For both our oars, with little skill,
    By little arms are plied,
While little hands make vain pretence
    Our wanderings to guide.

Ah, cruel Three! In such an hour,
    Beneath such dreamy weather,
To beg a tale of breath too weak
    To stir the tiniest feather!
Yet what can one poor voice avail
    Against three tongues together?

Imperious Prima flashes forth
    Her edict 'to begin it' –
In gentler tone Secunda hopes
    'There will be nonsense in it!' –
While Tertia interrupts the tale
    Not more than once a minute.

Anon, to sudden silence won,
    In fancy they pursue
The dream-child moving through a land
    Of wonders wild and new,
In friendly chat with bird or beast –
    And half believe it true.

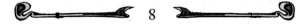

And ever, as the story drained
    The wells of fancy dry,
And faintly strove that weary one
    To put the subject by,
'The rest next time –' 'It *is* next time!'
    The happy voices cry.

Thus grew the tale of Wonderland:
    Thus slowly, one by one,
Its quaint events were hammered out –
    And now the tale is done,
And home we steer, a merry crew,
    Beneath the setting sun.

Alice! a childish story take,
    And with a gentle hand
Lay it where Childhood's dreams are twined
    In Memory's mystic band,
Like pilgrim's wither'd wreath of flowers
    Pluck'd in a far-off land.

'Who cares for you?' said Alice, (she had grown to her full size by this time.) 'You're nothing but a pack of cards!'

– CHAPTER TWELVE: ALICE'S EVIDENCE

CHAPTER ONE

DOWN THE RABBIT-HOLE

*A*lice was beginning to get very tired of sitting by her sister on the bank, and of having nothing to do: once or twice she had peeped into the book her sister was reading, but it had no pictures or conversations in it, 'and what is the use of a book,' thought Alice, 'without pictures or conversation?'

So she was considering in her own mind (as well as she could, for the hot day made her feel very sleepy and stupid), whether the pleasure of making a daisy-chain would be worth the trouble of getting up and picking the daisies, when suddenly a White Rabbit with pink eyes ran close by her.

There was nothing so very remarkable in that; nor did Alice think it so very much out of the way to hear the Rabbit say to itself, 'Oh dear! Oh dear! I shall be too late!' (when she thought it over afterwards, it occurred to her that she ought to have wondered at this, but at the time it all seemed quite natural); but when the Rabbit actually took a watch out of its waistcoat pocket, and looked at it, and then hurried on, Alice started to her feet, for it flashed across her mind that she had never before seen a rabbit with either a waistcoat-pocket, or a watch to take out of it, and burning with curiosity, she ran across the field after it, and fortunately was just in time to see it pop down a large rabbit-hole under the hedge.

In another moment down went Alice after it, never once considering how in the world she was to get out again.

The rabbit-hole went straight on like a tunnel for some way, and then dipped suddenly down, so suddenly that Alice had not a moment to think about stopping herself before she found herself falling down a very deep well.

Either the well was very deep or she fell very slowly, for she had plenty of time as she went down to look about her, and to wonder what was going to happen next. First, she tried to look down and make out what she was coming to, but it was too dark to see anything; then she looked at the sides of the well, and noticed that they were filled with cupboards and pictures hung upon pegs. She took down a jar from one of the shelves as she passed; it was labelled 'ORANGE MARMALADE', but to her great disappointment it was empty: she did not like to drop the jar for fear of killing somebody, so managed to put it into one of the cupboards as she fell past it.

'Well!' thought Alice to herself, 'after such a fall as this, I shall think nothing of tumbling down stairs! How brave they'll all think me at home! Why, I wouldn't say anything about it, even if I fell off the top of the house!' (Which was very likely true.)

Down, down, down. Would the fall *never* come to an end! 'I wonder how many miles I've fallen by this time?' she said aloud. 'I must be getting somewhere near the centre of the earth. Let me see: that would be four thousand miles down, I think –' (for, you see, Alice had learnt several things of this sort in her lessons in the schoolroom, and though this was not a very good opportunity for showing off her knowledge, as there was no one to listen to her, still it was good practice to say it over) '– yes, that's about the right distance – but then I wonder what Latitude or Longitude I've got to?' (Alice had no idea what Latitude was, or Longitude either, but thought they were nice grand words to say.)

Presently she began again. 'I wonder if I shall fall right *through* the earth! How funny it'll seem to come out among the people that walk with their heads downwards! The Antipathies, I think–' (she *was* rather glad there was no one listening, this time, as it didn't sound at all the right word) '– but I shall have to

ask them what the name of the country is, you know. Please, Ma'am, is this New Zealand or Australia?' (and she tried to curtsey as she spoke – fancy *curtseying* as you're falling through the air! Do you think you could manage it!) 'And what an ignorant little girl she'll think me for asking! No, it'll never do to ask: perhaps I shall see it written up somewhere.'

Down, down, down. There was nothing else to do, so Alice soon began talking again. 'Dinah'll miss me very much to-night, I should think!' (Dinah was the cat.) 'I hope they'll remember her saucer of milk at tea-time. Dinah, my dear! I wish you were down here with me! There are no mice in the air, I'm afraid, but you might catch a bat, and that's very like a mouse, you know. But do cats eat bats, I wonder?' And here Alice began to get rather sleepy, and went on saying to herself, in a dreamy sort of way, 'Do cats eat bats? Do cats eat bats?' and sometimes, 'Do bats eat cats?' for, you see, as she couldn't answer either question, it didn't much matter which way she put it. She felt that she was dozing off, and had just begun to dream that she was walking hand in hand with Dinah, and saying to her very earnestly, 'Now, Dinah, tell me the truth: did you ever eat a bat?' when suddenly, thump! thump! down she came upon a heap of sticks and dry leaves, and the fall was over.

Alice was not a bit hurt, and she jumped up on to her feet in a moment: she looked up, but it was all dark overhead; before her was another long passage, and the White Rabbit was still in sight, hurrying down it. There was not a moment to be lost: away went Alice like the wind, and was just in time to hear it say, as it turned a corner, 'Oh my ears and whiskers, how late it's getting!' She was close behind it when she turned the corner, but the Rabbit was no longer to be seen: she found herself in a long, low hall, which was lit up by a row of lamps hanging from the roof.

There were doors all round the hall, but they were all locked; and when Alice had been all the way down one side and up the other, trying every door, she walked sadly down the middle, wondering how she was ever to get out again.

Suddenly she came upon a little three-legged table, all made of solid glass; there was nothing on it except a tiny golden key, and Alice's first thought was that it might belong to one of the doors of the hall; but, alas! either the locks were too large, or the key was too small, but at any rate it would not open any of them. However, on the second time round, she came upon a low curtain she had not noticed before, and behind it was a little door about fifteen inches high: she tried the little golden key in the lock, and to her great delight it fitted!

Alice opened the door and found that it led into a small passage, not much larger than a rat-hole: she knelt down and looked along the passage into the loveliest garden you ever saw. How she longed to get out of that dark hall, and wander about among those beds of bright flowers and those cool fountains, but she could not even get her head through the doorway; 'and even if my head would go through,' thought poor Alice, 'it would be of very little use without my

shoulders. Oh, how I wish I could shut up like a telescope! I think I could, if I only knew how to begin.' For, you see, so many out-of-the-way things had happened lately, that Alice had begun to think that very few things indeed were really impossible.

There seemed to be no use in waiting by the little door, so she went back to the table, half hoping she might find another key on it, or at any rate a book of rules for shutting people up like telescopes: this time she found a little bottle on it, ('which certainly was not here before,' said Alice,) and round the neck of the bottle was a paper label, with the words 'DRINK ME' beautifully printed on it in large letters.

It was all very well to say 'Drink me,' but the wise little Alice was not going to do *that* in a hurry. 'No, I'll look first,' she said, 'and see whether it's marked "*poison*" or not'; for she had read several nice little histories about children who had got burnt, and eaten up by wild beasts and other unpleasant things, all because they *would* not remember the simple rules their friends had taught them: such as, that a red-hot poker will burn you if you hold it too long; and that if you cut your finger *very* deeply with a knife, it usually bleeds; and she had never forgotten that, if you drink much from a bottle marked 'poison,' it is almost certain to disagree with you, sooner or later.

However, the bottle was *not* marked 'poison,' so Alice ventured to taste it, and finding it very nice, (it had, in fact, a sort of mixed flavour of cherry-tart, custard, pineapple, roast turkey, toffee, and hot buttered toast,) she very soon finished it off.

*   *   *   *

*   *   *

*   *   *   *

'What a curious feeling!' said Alice; 'I must be shutting up like a telescope.'

And so it was indeed: she was now only ten inches high, and her face brightened up at the thought that she was now the right size for going through the little door into that lovely garden. First, however, she waited for a few minutes to see if she was going to shrink any further: she felt a little nervous about this; 'for it might end, you know,' said Alice to herself, 'in my going out altogether, like a candle. I wonder what I should be like then?' And she tried to fancy what the flame of a candle is like after the candle is blown out, for she could not remember ever having seen such a thing.

After a while, finding that nothing more happened, she decided on going into the garden at once; but, alas for poor Alice! when she got to the door, she found she had forgotten the little golden key, and when she went back to the table for it, she found she could not possibly reach it: she could see it quite plainly through the glass, and she tried her best to climb up one of the legs of the table, but it was too slippery; and when she had tired herself out with trying, the poor little thing sat down and cried.

'Come, there's no use in crying like that!' said Alice to herself, rather sharply; 'I advise you to leave off this minute!' She generally gave herself very good advice, (though she very seldom followed it), and sometimes she scolded herself so severely as to bring tears into her eyes; and once she remembered trying to box

her own ears for having cheated herself in a game of croquet she was playing against herself, for this curious child was very fond of pretending to be two people. 'But it's no use now,' thought poor Alice, 'to pretend to be two people! Why, there's hardly enough of me left to make one respectable person!'

Soon her eye fell on a little glass box that was lying under the table: she opened it, and found in it a very small cake, on which the words 'EAT ME' were beautifully marked in currants. 'Well, I'll eat it,' said Alice, 'and if it makes me grow larger, I can reach the key; and if it makes me grow smaller, I can creep under the door; so either way I'll get into the garden, and I don't care which happens!'

She ate a little bit, and said anxiously to herself, 'Which way? Which way?' holding her hand on the top of her head to feel which way it was growing, and she was quite surprised to find that she remained the same size: to be sure, this generally happens when one eats cake, but Alice had got so much into the way of expecting nothing but out-of-the-way things to happen, that it seemed quite dull and stupid for life to go on in the common way.

So she set to work, and very soon finished off the cake.

*   *   *   *

*   *   *

*   *   *   *

CHAPTER TWO

THE POOL OF TEARS

'Curiouser and curiouser!' cried Alice (she was so much surprised, that for the moment she quite forgot how to speak good English); 'now I'm opening out like the largest telescope that ever was! Good-bye, feet!' (for when she looked down at her feet, they seemed to be almost out of sight, they were getting so far off). 'Oh, my poor little feet, I wonder who will put on your shoes and stockings for you now, dears? I'm sure I shan't be able! I shall be a great deal too far off to trouble myself about you: you must manage the best way you can; – but I must be kind to them,' thought Alice, 'or perhaps they won't walk the way I want to go! Let me see: I'll give them a new pair of boots every Christmas.'

And she went on planning to herself how she would manage it. 'They must go by the carrier,' she thought; 'and how funny it'll seem, sending presents to one's own feet! And how odd the directions will look!

Alice's Right Foot, Esq.
Hearthrug,
  near the Fender,
    (with Alice's love).

Oh dear, what nonsense I'm talking!'

Just then her head struck against the roof of the hall: in fact she was now more than nine feet high, and she at once took up the little golden key and hurried off to the garden door.

Poor Alice! It was as much as she could do, lying down on one side, to look through into the garden with one eye; but to get through was more hopeless than ever: she sat down and began to cry again.

'You ought to be ashamed of yourself,' said Alice, 'a great girl like you,' (she might well say this), 'to go on crying in this way! Stop this moment, I tell you!' But she went on all the same, shedding gallons of tears, until there was a large pool all round her, about four inches deep and reaching half down the hall.

After a time she heard a little pattering of feet in the distance, and she hastily dried her eyes to see what was coming. It was the White Rabbit returning, splendidly dressed, with a pair of white kid gloves in one hand and a large fan in the other: he came trotting along in a great hurry, muttering to himself as he came, 'Oh! the Duchess, the Duchess! Oh! won't she be savage if I've kept her waiting!' Alice felt so desperate that she was ready to ask help of any one; so, when the Rabbit came near her, she began, in a low, timid voice, 'If you please, sir –' The Rabbit started violently, dropped the white kid gloves and the fan, and scurried away into the darkness as hard as he could go.

Alice took up the fan and gloves, and, as the hall was very hot, she kept fanning herself all the time she went on talking: 'Dear, dear! How queer everything is to-day! And yesterday things went on just as usual. I wonder if I've been changed in the night? Let me think: was I the same when I got up this morning? I almost think I can remember feeling a little different. But if I'm not the same, the next question is, Who in the world am I? Ah *that's* the great puzzle!' And she began thinking over all the children she knew that were of the same age as herself, to see if she could have been changed for any of them.

'I'm sure I'm not Ada,' she said, 'for her hair goes in such long ringlets, and mine doesn't go in ringlets at all; and I'm sure I can't be Mabel, for I know

all sorts of things, and she, oh! she knows such a very little! Besides, *she's* she, and *I'm* I, and – oh dear, how puzzling it all is! I'll try if I know all the things I used to know. Let me see: four times five is twelve, and four times six is thirteen, and four times seven is – oh dear! I shall never get to twenty at that rate! However, the Multiplication Table doesn't signify: let's try Geography. London is the capital of Paris, and Paris is the capital of Rome, and Rome – no, *that's* all wrong, I'm certain! I must have been changed for Mabel! I'll try and say

"*How doth the little –*'" and she crossed her hands on her lap as if she were saying lessons, and began to repeat it, but her voice sounded hoarse and strange, and the words did not come the same as they used to do:–

'*How doth the little crocodile*
Improve his shining tail,
And pour the waters of the Nile
On every golden scale!

'*How cheerfully he seems to grin,*
How neatly spread his claws,
And welcome little fishes in
With gently smiling jaws!'

'I'm sure those are not the right words,' said poor Alice, and her eyes filled with tears again as she went on, 'I must be Mabel after all, and I shall have to go and live in that poky little house, and have next to no toys to play with, and oh! ever so many lessons to learn! No, I've made up my mind about it; if I'm Mabel, I'll stay down here! It'll be no use their putting their heads down and saying "Come up again, dear!" I shall only look up and say "Who am I then? Tell me that first, and then, if I like being that person, I'll come up: if not, I'll stay down here till I'm somebody else" – but, oh dear!' cried Alice, with a sudden burst of tears, 'I do wish they *would* put their heads down! I am so very *tired* of being all alone here!'

As she said this she looked down at her hands, and was surprised to see that she had put on one of the Rabbit's little white kid gloves while she was talking. 'How *can* I have done that?' she thought. 'I must be growing small again.' She got up and went to the table to measure herself by it, and found that, as nearly as she could guess, she was now about two feet high, and was going on shrinking

rapidly: she soon found out that the cause of this was the fan she was holding, and she dropped it hastily, just in time to avoid shrinking away altogether.

'That *was* a narrow escape!' said Alice, a good deal frightened at the sudden change, but very glad to find herself still in existence; 'and now for the garden!' and she ran with all speed back to the little door: but, alas! the little door was shut again, and the little golden key was lying on the glass table as before, 'and things are worse than ever,' thought the poor child, 'for I never was so small as this before, never! And I declare it's too bad, that it is!'

As she said these words her foot slipped, and in another moment, splash! she was up to her chin in salt water. Her first idea was that she had somehow fallen into the sea, 'and in that case I can go back by railway,' she said to herself. (Alice had been to the seaside once in her life, and had come to the general conclusion, that wherever you go to on the English coast you find a number of bathing machines in the sea, some children digging in the sand with wooden spades, then a row of lodging houses, and behind them a railway station.) However, she soon made out that she was in the pool of tears which she had wept when she was nine feet high.

'I wish I hadn't cried so much!' said Alice, as she swam about, trying to find her way out. 'I shall be punished for it now, I suppose, by being drowned in my own tears! That *will* be a queer thing, to be sure! However, everything is queer to-day.'

Just then she heard something splashing about in the pool a little way off, and she swam nearer to make out what it was: at first she thought it must be a walrus or hippopotamus, but then she remembered how small she was now, and she soon made out that it was only a mouse that had slipped in like herself.

'Would it be of any use, now,' thought Alice, 'to speak to this mouse? Everything is so out-of-the-way down here, that I should think very likely it can talk: at any rate, there's no harm in trying.' So she began: 'O Mouse, do you know the way out of this pool? I am very tired of swimming about here, O Mouse!' (Alice thought this must be the right way of speaking to a mouse: she had never done such a thing before, but she remembered having seen in her brother's Latin Grammar, 'A mouse – of a mouse – to a mouse – a mouse – O

mouse!') The Mouse looked at her rather inquisitively, and seemed to her to wink with one of its little eyes, but it said nothing.

'Perhaps it doesn't understand English,' thought Alice; 'I daresay it's a French mouse, come over with William the Conqueror.' (For, with all her knowledge of history, Alice had no very clear notion how long ago anything had happened.) So she began again: 'Où est ma chatte?' which was the first sentence in her French lesson-book. The Mouse gave a sudden leap out of the water, and seemed to quiver all over with fright. 'Oh, I beg your pardon!' cried Alice hastily, afraid that she had hurt the poor animal's feelings. 'I quite forgot you didn't like cats.'

'Not like cats!' cried the Mouse, in a shrill, passionate voice. 'Would *you* like cats if you were me?'

'Well, perhaps not,' said Alice in a soothing tone: 'don't be angry about it. And yet I wish I could show you our cat Dinah: I think you'd take a fancy to cats if you could only see her. She is such a dear quiet thing,' Alice went on, half to herself, as she swam lazily about in the pool, 'and she sits purring so nicely by the fire, licking her paws and washing her face – and she is such a nice soft thing to nurse and she's such a capital one for catching mice – oh, I beg your pardon!' cried Alice again, for this time the Mouse was bristling all over, and she felt certain it must be really offended. 'We won't talk about her any more if you'd rather not.'

'We, indeed!' cried the Mouse, who was trembling down to the end of his tail. 'As if I would talk on such a subject! Our family always *hated* cats: nasty, low, vulgar things! Don't let me hear the name again!'

'I won't indeed!' said Alice, in a great hurry to change the subject of conversation. 'Are you – are you fond – of – of dogs?' The Mouse did not answer, so Alice went on eagerly: 'There is such a nice little dog near our house I should like to show you! A little bright-eyed terrier, you know, with oh, such long curly brown hair! And it'll fetch things when you throw them, and it'll sit up

and beg for its dinner, and all sorts of things – I can't remember half of them – and it belongs to a farmer, you know, and he says it's so useful, it's worth a hundred pounds! He says it kills all the rats and – oh dear!' cried Alice in a sorrowful tone, 'I'm afraid I've offended it again!' For the Mouse was swimming away from her as hard as it could go, and making quite a commotion in the pool as it went.

So she called softly after it, 'Mouse dear! Do come back again, and we won't talk about cats or dogs either, if you don't like them!' When the Mouse heard this, it turned round and swam slowly back to her: its face was quite pale (with passion, Alice thought), and it said in a low trembling voice, 'Let us get to the shore, and then I'll tell you my history, and you'll understand why it is I hate cats and dogs.'

It was high time to go, for the pool was getting quite crowded with the birds and animals that had fallen into it: there were a Duck and a Dodo, a Lory and an Eaglet, and several other curious creatures. Alice led the way, and the whole party swam to the shore.

CHAPTER THREE

A CAUCUS-RACE AND A LONG TALE

They were indeed a queer-looking party that assembled on the bank – the birds with draggled feathers, the animals with their fur clinging close to them, and all dripping wet, cross, and uncomfortable.

The first question of course was, how to get dry again: they had a consultation about this, and after a few minutes it seemed quite natural to Alice to find herself talking familiarly with them, as if she had known them all her life. Indeed, she had quite a long argument with the Lory, who at last turned sulky, and would only say, 'I am older than you, and must know better'; and this Alice would not allow without knowing how old it was, and, as the Lory positively refused to tell its age, there was no more to be said.

At last the Mouse, who seemed to be a person of authority among them, called out, 'Sit down, all of you, and listen to me! *I'll* soon make you dry enough!' They all sat down at once, in a large ring, with the Mouse in the middle. Alice kept her eyes anxiously fixed on it, for she felt sure she would catch a bad cold if she did not get dry very soon.

'Ahem!' said the Mouse with an important air, 'are you all ready? This is the driest thing I know. Silence all round, if you please! "William the Conqueror, whose cause was favoured by the pope, was soon submitted to by the English, who wanted leaders, and had been of late much accustomed to usurpation and conquest. Edwin and Morcar, the earls of Mercia and Northumbria –"'

'Ugh!' said the Lory, with a shiver.

'I beg your pardon!' said the Mouse, frowning, but very politely: 'Did you speak?'

'Not I!' said the Lory hastily.

'I thought you did,' said the Mouse. '– I proceed. "Edwin and Morcar, the earls of Mercia and Northumbria, declared for him, and even Stigand, the patriotic archbishop of Canterbury, found it advisable –"'

'Found *what*?' said the Duck.

'Found *it*,' the Mouse replied rather crossly: 'of course you know what "it" means.'

'I know what "it" means well enough, when I find a thing,' said the Duck: 'it's generally a frog or a worm. The question is, what did the archbishop find?'

The Mouse did not notice this question, but hurriedly went on, '"– found it advisable to go with Edgar Atheling to meet William and offer him the crown. William's conduct at first was moderate. But the insolence of his Normans –" How are you getting on now, my dear?' it continued, turning to Alice as it spoke.

'As wet as ever,' said Alice in a melancholy tone: 'it doesn't seem to dry me at all.'

'In that case,' said the Dodo solemnly, rising to its feet, 'I move that the meeting adjourn, for the immediate adoption of more energetic remedies –'

'Speak English!' said the Eaglet. 'I don't know the meaning of half those long words, and, what's more, I don't believe you do either!' And the Eaglet bent down its head to hide a smile: some of the other birds tittered audibly.

'What I was going to say,' said the Dodo in an offended tone, 'was, that the best thing to get us dry would be a Caucus-race.'

'What *is* a Caucus-race?' said Alice; not that she wanted much to know, but the Dodo had paused as if it thought that *somebody* ought to speak, and no one else seemed inclined to say anything.

CHAPTER THREE: A CAUCUS-RACE AND A LONG TALE

'Why,' said the Dodo, 'the best way to explain it is to do it.' (And, as you might like to try the thing yourself, some winter day, I will tell you how the Dodo managed it.)

First it marked out a race-course, in a sort of circle, ('the exact shape doesn't matter,' it said,) and then all the party were placed along the course, here and there. There was no 'One, two, three, and away,' but they began running

when they liked, and left off when they liked, so that it was not easy to know when the race was over. However, when they had been running half an hour or so, and were quite dry again, the Dodo suddenly called out 'The race is over!' and they all crowded round it, panting, and asking, 'But who has won?'

This question the Dodo could not answer without a great deal of thought, and it sat for a long time with one finger pressed upon its forehead (the position in which you usually see Shakespeare, in the pictures of him), while the rest waited in silence. At last the Dodo said, '*Everybody* has won, and all must have prizes.'

'But who is to give the prizes?' quite a chorus of voices asked.

'Why, *she*, of course,' said the Dodo, pointing to Alice with one finger; and the whole party at once crowded round her, calling out in a confused way, 'Prizes! Prizes!'

Alice had no idea what to do, and in despair she put her hand in her pocket, and pulled out a box of comfits, (luckily the salt water had not got into it), and handed them round as prizes. There was exactly one a-piece all round.

'But she must have a prize herself, you know,' said the Mouse.

'Of course,' the Dodo replied very gravely. 'What else have you got in your pocket?' he went on, turning to Alice.

'Only a thimble,' said Alice sadly.

'Hand it over here,' said the Dodo.

Then they all crowded round her once more, while the Dodo solemnly presented the thimble, saying 'We beg your acceptance of this elegant thimble'; and, when it had finished this short speech, they all cheered.

Alice thought the whole thing very absurd, but they all looked so grave that she did not dare to laugh; and, as she could not think of anything to say, she simply bowed, and took the thimble, looking as solemn as she could.

The next thing was to eat the comfits: this caused some noise and confusion, as the large birds complained that they could not taste theirs, and

the small ones choked and had to be patted on the back. However, it was over at last, and they sat down again in a ring, and begged the Mouse to tell them something more.

'You promised to tell me your history, you know,' said Alice, 'and why it is you hate – C and D,' she added in a whisper, half afraid that it would be offended again.

'Mine is a long and a sad tale!' said the Mouse, turning to Alice, and sighing.

'It *is* a long tail, certainly,' said Alice, looking down with wonder at the Mouse's tail; 'but why do you call it sad?' And she kept on puzzling about it while the Mouse was speaking, so that her idea of the tale was something like this:

'Fury said to a
mouse, That he
met in the
house,
"Let us
both go to
law: I will
prosecute
you. – Come,
I'll take no
denial; We
must have a
trial: For
really this
morning I've
nothing
to do."
Said the
mouse to the
cur, "Such
a trial,
dear Sir,
With
no jury
or judge,
would be
wasting
our
breath."
"I'll be
judge, I'll
be jury"
Said
cunning
old Fury:'
"I'll
try the
whole
cause,
and
condemn
you
to
death."

'You are not attending!' said the Mouse to Alice severely. 'What are you thinking of?'

'I beg your pardon,' said Alice very humbly: 'you had got to the fifth bend, I think?'

'I had *not*!' cried the Mouse, sharply and very angrily.

'A knot!' said Alice, always ready to make herself useful, and looking anxiously about her, 'Oh, do let me help to undo it!'

'I shall do nothing of the sort,' said the Mouse, getting up and walking away. 'You insult me by talking such nonsense!'

'I didn't mean it!' pleaded poor Alice. 'But you're so easily offended, you know!'

The Mouse only growled in reply.

'Please come back and finish your story!' Alice called after it; and the others all joined in chorus, 'Yes, please do!' but the Mouse only shook its head impatiently, and walked a little quicker.

'What a pity it wouldn't stay!' sighed the Lory, as soon as it was quite out of sight; and an old Crab took the opportunity of saying to her daughter 'Ah, my dear! Let this be a lesson to you never to lose *your* temper!' 'Hold your tongue, Ma!' said the young Crab, a little snappishly. 'You're enough to try the patience of an oyster!'

'I wish I had our Dinah here, I know I do!' said Alice aloud, addressing nobody in particular. 'She'd soon fetch it back!'

'And who is Dinah, if I might venture to ask the question?' said the Lory.

Alice replied eagerly, for she was always ready to talk about her pet: 'Dinah's our cat. And she's such a capital one for catching mice you can't think! And oh, I wish you could see her after the birds! Why, she'll eat a little bird as soon as look at it!'

This speech caused a remarkable sensation among the party. Some of the birds hurried off at once: one old Magpie began wrapping itself up very carefully, remarking, 'I really must be getting home; the night-air doesn't suit my throat!'

and a Canary called out in a trembling voice to its children, 'Come away, my dears! It's high time you were all in bed!' On various pretexts they all moved off, and Alice was soon left alone.

'I wish I hadn't mentioned Dinah!' she said to herself in a melancholy tone. 'Nobody seems to like her, down here, and I'm sure she's the best cat in the world! Oh, my dear Dinah! I wonder if I shall ever see you any more!' And here poor Alice began to cry again, for she felt very lonely and low-spirited. In a little while, however, she again heard a little pattering of footsteps in the distance, and she looked up eagerly, half hoping that the Mouse had changed his mind, and was coming back to finish his story.

CHAPTER FOUR

THE RABBIT SENDS IN A LITTLE BILL

*I*t was the White Rabbit, trotting slowly back again, and looking anxiously about as it went, as if it had lost something; and she heard it muttering to itself 'The Duchess! The Duchess! Oh my dear paws! Oh my fur and whiskers! She'll get me executed, as sure as ferrets are ferrets! Where *can* I have dropped them, I wonder?' Alice guessed in a moment that it was looking for the fan and the pair of white kid gloves, and she very good-naturedly began hunting about for them, but they were nowhere to be seen – everything seemed to have changed since her swim in the pool, and the great hall, with the glass table and the little door, had vanished completely.

Very soon the Rabbit noticed Alice, as she went hunting about, and called out to her in an angry tone, 'Why, Mary Ann, what *are* you doing out here? Run home this moment, and fetch me a pair of gloves and a fan! Quick, now!' And Alice was so much frightened that she ran off at once in the direction it pointed to, without trying to explain the mistake it had made.

'He took me for his housemaid,' she said to herself as she ran. 'How surprised he'll be when he finds out who I am! But I'd better take him his fan and gloves – that is, if I can find them.' As she said this, she came upon a neat little house, on the door of which was a bright brass plate with the name 'w. rabbit' engraved upon it. She went in without knocking, and hurried upstairs, in great

fear lest she should meet the real Mary Ann, and be turned out of the house before she had found the fan and gloves.

'How queer it seems,' Alice said to herself, 'to be going messages for a rabbit! I suppose Dinah'll be sending me on messages next!' And she began fancying the sort of thing that would happen: '"Miss Alice! Come here directly, and get ready for your walk!" "Coming in a minute, nurse! But I've got to watch this mouse-hole till Dinah comes back, and see that the mouse doesn't get out." Only I don't think,' Alice went on, 'that they'd let Dinah stop in the house if it began ordering people about like that!'

By this time she had found her way into a tidy little room with a table in the window, and on it (as she had hoped) a fan and two or three pairs of tiny white kid gloves: she took up the fan and a pair of the gloves, and was just going to leave the room, when her eye fell upon a little bottle that stood near the looking-glass. There was no label this time with the words 'DRINK ME,' but nevertheless she uncorked it and put it to her lips. 'I know *something* interesting is sure to happen,' she said to herself, 'whenever I eat or drink anything; so I'll just see what this bottle does. I do hope it'll make me grow large again, for really I'm quite tired of being such a tiny little thing!'

It did so indeed, and much sooner than she had expected: before she had drunk half the bottle, she found her head pressing against the ceiling, and had to stoop to save her neck from being broken. She hastily put down the bottle, saying to herself 'That's quite enough – I hope I shan't grow any more – As it is, I can't get out at the door – I do wish I hadn't drunk quite so much!'

Alas! It was too late to wish that! She went on growing, and growing, and very soon had to kneel down on the floor: in another minute there was not even room for this, and she tried the effect of lying down with one elbow against the door, and the other arm curled round her head. Still she went on growing, and as a last resource, she put one arm out of the window, and one

foot up the chimney, and said to herself 'Now I can do no more, whatever happens. What *will* become of me?'

Luckily for Alice, the little magic bottle had now had its full effect, and she grew no larger: still it was very uncomfortable, and, as there seemed to be no sort of chance of her ever getting out of the room again, no wonder she felt unhappy.

'It was much pleasanter at home,' thought poor Alice, 'when one wasn't always growing larger and smaller, and being ordered about by mice and rabbits. I almost wish I hadn't gone down that rabbit-hole – and yet – and yet – it's rather curious, you know, this sort of life! I do wonder what *can* have happened to me! When I used to read fairy-tales, I fancied that kind of thing never happened, and now here I am in the middle of one! There ought to be a book written about me, that there ought! And when I grow up, I'll write one – but I'm grown up now,' she added in a sorrowful tone; 'at least there's no room to grow up any more *here*.'

'But then,' thought Alice, 'shall I *never* get any older than I am now? That'll be a comfort, one way – never to be an old woman – but then – always to have lessons to learn! Oh, I shouldn't like *that*!'

'Oh, you foolish Alice!' she answered herself. 'How can you learn lessons in here? Why, there's hardly room for *you*, and no room at all for any lesson-books!'

And so she went on, taking first one side and then the other, and making quite a conversation of it altogether; but after a few minutes she heard a voice outside, and stopped to listen.

'Mary Ann! Mary Ann!' said the voice. 'Fetch me my gloves this moment!' Then came a little pattering of feet on the stairs. Alice knew it was the Rabbit coming to look for her, and she trembled till she shook the house, quite forgetting that she was now about a thousand times as large as the Rabbit, and had no reason to be afraid of it.

Presently the Rabbit came up to the door, and tried to open it; but, as the door opened inwards, and Alice's elbow was pressed hard against it, that attempt proved a failure. Alice heard it say to itself 'Then I'll go round and get in at the window.'

'*That* you won't!' thought Alice, and, after waiting till she fancied she heard the Rabbit just under the window, she suddenly spread out her hand, and made a snatch in the air. She did not get hold of anything, but she heard a little shriek and a fall, and a crash of broken glass, from which she concluded that it was just possible it had fallen into a cucumber-frame, or something of the sort.

Next came an angry voice – the Rabbit's – 'Pat! Pat! Where are you?' And then a voice she had never heard before, 'Sure then I'm here! Digging for apples, yer honour!'

'Digging for apples, indeed!' said the Rabbit angrily. 'Here! Come and help me out of this!' (Sounds of more broken glass.)

'Now tell me, Pat, what's that in the window?'

'Sure, it's an arm, yer honour!' (He pronounced it 'arrum.')

'An arm, you goose! Who ever saw one that size? Why, it fills the whole window!'

'Sure, it does, yer honour: but it's an arm for all that.'

'Well, it's got no business there, at any rate: go and take it away!'

There was a long silence after this, and Alice could only hear whispers now and then; such as, 'Sure, I don't like it, yer honour, at all, at all!' 'Do as I tell you, you coward!' and at last she spread out her hand again, and made another snatch in the air. This time there were *two* little shrieks, and more sounds of broken glass. 'What a number of cucumber-frames there must be!' thought Alice.

'I wonder what they'll do next! As for pulling me out of the window, I only wish they *could*! I'm sure I don't want to stay in here any longer!'

She waited for some time without hearing anything more: at last came a rumbling of little cartwheels, and the sound of a good many voices all talking together: she made out the words: 'Where's the other ladder? – Why, I hadn't to bring but one; Bill's got the other – Bill! fetch it here, lad! – Here, put 'em up at this corner – No, tie 'em together first – they don't reach half high enough yet – Oh! they'll do well enough; don't be particular – Here, Bill! catch hold of this rope – Will the roof bear? – Mind that loose slate – Oh, it's coming down! Heads below!' (a loud crash) – 'Now, who did that? – It was Bill, I fancy – Who's to go down the chimney? – Nay, *I* shan't! *You* do it! – *That* I won't, then! – Bill's to go down – Here, Bill! the master says you're to go down the chimney!'

'Oh! So Bill's got to come down the chimney, has he?' said Alice to herself. 'Why, they seem to put everything upon Bill! I wouldn't be in Bill's place for a good deal: this fireplace is narrow, to be sure; but I *think* I can kick a little!'

She drew her foot as far down the chimney as she could, and waited

till she heard a little animal (she couldn't guess of what sort it was) scratching and scrambling about in the chimney close above her: then, saying to herself 'This is Bill,' she gave one sharp kick, and waited to see what would happen next.

The first thing she heard was a general chorus of 'There goes Bill!' then the Rabbit's voice alone – 'Catch him, you by the hedge!' then silence, and then another confusion of voices – 'Hold up his head – Brandy now – Don't choke him – How was it, old fellow? What happened to you? Tell us all about it!'

Last came a little feeble, squeaking voice, ('That's Bill,' thought Alice,) 'Well, I hardly know – No more, thank ye; I'm better now – but I'm a deal too flustered to tell you – all I know is, something comes at me like a Jack-in-the-box, and up I goes like a sky-rocket!'

'So you did, old fellow!' said the others.

'We must burn the house down!' said the Rabbit's voice; and Alice called out as loud as she could, 'If you do, I'll set Dinah at you!'

There was a dead silence instantly, and Alice thought to herself, 'I wonder what they *will* do next! If they had any sense, they'd take the roof off.' After a minute or two, they began moving about again, and Alice heard the Rabbit say, 'A barrowful will do, to begin with.'

'A barrowful of *what*?' thought Alice; but she had not long to doubt, for the next moment a shower of little pebbles came rattling in at the window, and some of them hit her in the face. 'I'll put a stop to this,' she said to herself, and shouted out, 'You'd better not do that again!' which produced another dead silence.

Alice noticed with some surprise that the pebbles were all turning into little cakes as they lay on the floor, and a bright idea came into her head. 'If I eat one of these cakes,' she thought, 'it's sure to make *some* change in my size; and as it can't possibly make me larger, it must make me smaller, I suppose.'

So she swallowed one of the cakes, and was delighted to find that she began shrinking directly. As soon as she was small enough to get through the

door, she ran out of the house, and found quite a crowd of little animals and birds waiting outside. The poor little Lizard, Bill, was in the middle, being held up by two guinea-pigs, who were giving it something out of a bottle. They all made a rush at Alice the moment she appeared; but she ran off as hard as she could, and soon found herself safe in a thick wood.

'The first thing I've got to do,' said Alice to herself, as she wandered about in the wood, 'is to grow to my right size again; and the second thing is to find my way into that lovely garden. I think that will be the best plan.'

It sounded an excellent plan, no doubt, and very neatly and simply arranged; the only difficulty was, that she had not the smallest idea how to set about it; and while she was peering about anxiously among the trees, a little sharp bark just over her head made her look up in a great hurry.

An enormous puppy was looking down at her with large round eyes, and feebly stretching out one paw, trying to touch her. 'Poor little thing!' said Alice, in a coaxing tone, and she tried hard to whistle to it; but she was terribly frightened all the time at the thought that it might be hungry, in which case it would be very likely to eat her up in spite of all her coaxing.

Hardly knowing what she did, she picked up a little bit of stick, and held it out to the puppy; whereupon the puppy jumped into the air off all its feet at once, with a yelp of delight, and rushed at the stick, and made believe to worry it; then Alice dodged behind a great thistle, to keep herself from being run over; and the moment she appeared on the other side, the puppy made another rush at the stick, and tumbled head over heels in its hurry to get hold of it; then Alice, thinking it was very like having a game of play with a cart-horse, and expecting every moment to be trampled under its feet, ran round the thistle again; then the puppy began a series of short charges at the stick, running a very little way forwards each time and a long way back, and barking hoarsely all the while, till at last it sat down a good way off, panting, with its tongue hanging out of its mouth, and its great eyes half shut.

This seemed to Alice a good opportunity for making her escape; so she set off at once, and ran till she was quite tired and out of breath, and till the puppy's bark sounded quite faint in the distance.

'And yet what a dear little puppy it was!' said Alice, as she leant against a buttercup to rest herself, and fanned herself with one of the leaves: 'I should have liked teaching it tricks very much, if – if I'd only been the right size to do it! Oh dear! I'd nearly forgotten that I've got to grow up again! Let me see – how *is* it to be managed? I suppose I ought to eat or drink something or other; but the great question is, what?'

The great question certainly was, what? Alice looked all round her at the flowers and the blades of grass, but she could not see anything that looked like the right thing to eat or drink under the circumstances. There was a large mushroom growing near her, about the same height as herself; and when she had looked under it, and on both sides of it, and behind it, it occurred to her that she might as well look and see what was on top of it.

She stretched herself up on tiptoe, and peeped over the edge of the mushroom, and her eyes immediately met those of a large blue caterpillar, that was sitting on the top with its arms folded, quietly smoking a long hookah, and taking not the smallest notice of her or anything else.

CHAPTER FIVE

ADVICE FROM A CATERPILLAR

*T*he Caterpillar and Alice looked at each other for some time in silence: at last the Caterpillar took the hookah out of its mouth, and addressed her in a languid, sleepy voice.

'Who are *you*?' said the Caterpillar.

This was not an encouraging opening for a conversation. Alice replied, rather shyly, 'I-I hardly know, sir, just at present – at least I know who I *was* when I got up this morning, but I think I must have been changed several times since then.'

'What do you mean by that?' said the Caterpillar sternly. 'Explain yourself!'

'I can't explain *myself*, I'm afraid, sir,' said Alice, 'because I'm not myself, you see.'

'I don't see,' said the Caterpillar.

'I'm afraid I can't put it more clearly,' Alice replied very politely, 'for I can't understand it myself to begin with; and being so many different sizes in a day is very confusing.'

'It isn't,' said the Caterpillar.

'Well, perhaps you haven't found it so yet,' said Alice; 'but when you have to turn into a chrysalis – you will some day, you know – and then after that into a butterfly, I should think you'll feel it a little queer, won't you?'

'Not a bit,' said the Caterpillar.

'Well, perhaps your feelings may be different,' said Alice; 'all I know is, it would feel very queer to *me*.'

'You!' said the Caterpillar contemptuously. 'Who are *you*?'

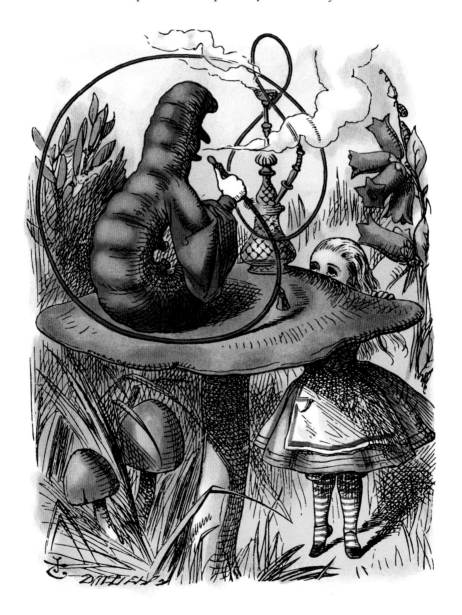

Which brought them back again to the beginning of the conversation. Alice felt a little irritated at the Caterpillar's making such *very* short remarks, and she drew herself up and said, very gravely, 'I think you ought to tell me who *you* are, first.'

'Why?' said the Caterpillar.

Here was another puzzling question; and as Alice could not think of any good reason, and as the Caterpillar seemed to be in a *very* unpleasant state of mind, she turned away.

'Come back!' the Caterpillar called after her. 'I've something important to say!'

This sounded promising, certainly: Alice turned and came back again.

'Keep your temper,' said the Caterpillar.

'Is that all?' said Alice, swallowing down her anger as well as she could.

'No,' said the Caterpillar.

Alice thought she might as well wait, as she had nothing else to do, and perhaps after all it might tell her something worth hearing. For some minutes it puffed away without speaking, but at last it unfolded its arms, took the hookah out of its mouth again, and said, 'So you think you're changed, do you?'

'I'm afraid I am, sir,' said Alice; 'I can't remember things as I used – and I don't keep the same size for ten minutes together!'

'Can't remember *what* things?' said the Caterpillar.

'Well, I've tried to say "*How doth the little busy bee*," but it all came different!' Alice replied in a very melancholy voice.

'Repeat, "*You are old, Father William*,"' said the Caterpillar.

Alice folded her hands, and began:–

> 'You are old, Father William,' the young man said,
> 'And your hair has become very white;
> And yet you incessantly stand on your head –
> Do you think, at your age, it is right?'
>
> 'In my youth,' Father William replied to his son,
> 'I feared it might injure the brain;
> But, now that I'm perfectly sure I have none,
> Why, I do it again and again.'
>
> 'You are old,' said the youth, 'as I mentioned before,
> And have grown most uncommonly fat;
> Yet you turned a back-somersault in at the door –
> Pray, what is the reason of that?'

'In my youth,' said the sage, as he shook his grey locks,
'I kept all my limbs very supple
By the use of this ointment – one shilling the box –
Allow me to sell you a couple?'

'You are old,' said the youth, 'and your jaws are too weak
For anything tougher than suet;
Yet you finished the goose, with the bones and the beak –
Pray how did you manage to do it?'

'In my youth,' said his father, 'I took to the law,
And argued each case with my wife;
And the muscular strength, which it gave to my jaw,
Has lasted the rest of my life.'

'You are old,' said the youth, 'one would hardly suppose
That your eye was as steady as ever;
Yet you balanced an eel on the end of your nose –
What made you so awfully clever?'

'I have answered three questions, and that is enough,'
Said his father; 'don't give yourself airs!
Do you think I can listen all day to such stuff?
Be off, or I'll kick you down stairs!'

'That is not said right,' said the Caterpillar.

'Not *quite* right, I'm afraid,' said Alice, timidly; 'some of the words have got altered.'

'It is wrong from beginning to end,' said the Caterpillar decidedly, and there was silence for some minutes.

The Caterpillar was the first to speak.

'What size do you want to be?' it asked.

'Oh, I'm not particular as to size,' Alice hastily replied; 'only one doesn't like changing so often, you know.'

'I *don't* know,' said the Caterpillar.

Alice said nothing: she had never been so much contradicted in all her life before, and she felt that she was losing her temper.

'Are you content now?' said the Caterpillar.

'Well, I should like to be a *little* larger, sir, if you wouldn't mind,' said Alice: 'three inches is such a wretched height to be.'

'It is a very good height indeed!' said the Caterpillar angrily, rearing itself upright as it spoke (it was exactly three inches high).

'But I'm not used to it!' pleaded poor Alice in a piteous tone. And she thought to herself, 'I wish the creatures wouldn't be so easily offended!'

'You'll get used to it in time,' said the Caterpillar; and put the hookah into its mouth and began smoking again.

This time Alice waited patiently until it chose to speak again. In a minute or two the Caterpillar took the hookah out of its mouth and yawned once or twice, and shook itself. Then it got down off the mushroom, and crawled away into the grass, merely remarking as it went, 'One side will make you grow taller, and the other side will make you grow shorter.'

'One side of *what*? The other side of *what*?' thought Alice to herself.

'Of the mushroom,' said the Caterpillar, just as if she had asked it aloud; and in another moment it was out of sight.

Alice remained looking thoughtfully at the mushroom for a minute, trying to make out which were the two sides of it; and as it was perfectly round, she found this a very difficult question. However, at last she stretched her arms round it as far as they would go, and broke off a bit of the edge with each hand.

'And now which is which?' she said to herself, and nibbled a little of the right-hand bit to try the effect: the next moment she felt a violent blow underneath her chin: it had struck her foot!

She was a good deal frightened by this very sudden change, but she felt that there was no time to be lost, as she was shrinking rapidly; so she set to work at once to eat some of the other bit. Her chin was pressed so closely against her foot, that there was hardly room to open her mouth; but she did it at last, and managed to swallow a morsel of the left-hand bit.

*　　*　　*　　*

*　　*　　*

*　　*　　*　　*

'Come, my head's free at last!' said Alice in a tone of delight, which changed into alarm in another moment, when she found that her shoulders were nowhere to be found: all she could see, when she looked down, was an immense length of neck, which seemed to rise like a stalk out of a sea of green leaves that lay far below her.

'What *can* all that green stuff be?' said Alice. 'And where *have* my shoulders got to? And oh, my poor hands, how is it I can't see you?' She was moving them about as she spoke, but no result seemed to follow, except a little shaking among the distant green leaves.

As there seemed to be no chance of getting her hands up to her head, she tried to get her head down to them, and was delighted to find that her neck would bend about easily in any direction, like a serpent. She had just succeeded in curving it down into a graceful zigzag, and was going to dive in among the leaves, which she found to be nothing but the tops of the trees under which she had been wandering, when a sharp hiss made her draw back in a hurry: a large pigeon had flown into her face, and was beating her violently with its wings.

'Serpent!' screamed the Pigeon.

'I'm *not* a serpent!' said Alice indignantly. 'Let me alone!'

'Serpent, I say again!' repeated the Pigeon, but in a more subdued tone, and added with a kind of sob, 'I've tried every way, and nothing seems to suit them!'

'I haven't the least idea what you're talking about,' said Alice.

'I've tried the roots of trees, and I've tried banks, and I've tried hedges,' the Pigeon went on, without attending to her; 'but those serpents! There's no pleasing them!'

Alice was more and more puzzled, but she thought there was no use in saying anything more till the Pigeon had finished.

'As if it wasn't trouble enough hatching the eggs,' said the Pigeon; 'but I must be on the look-out for serpents night and day! Why, I haven't had a wink of sleep these three weeks!'

'I'm very sorry you've been annoyed,' said Alice, who was beginning to see its meaning.

'And just as I'd taken the highest tree in the wood,' continued the Pigeon, raising its voice to a shriek, 'and just as I was thinking I should be free of them at last, they must needs come wriggling down from the sky! Ugh, Serpent!'

'But I'm *not* a serpent, I tell you!' said Alice. 'I'm a – I'm a –'

'Well, *what* are you?' said the Pigeon. 'I can see you're trying to invent something!'

'I-I'm a little girl,' said Alice, rather doubtfully, as she remembered the number of changes she had gone through that day.

'A likely story indeed!' said the Pigeon in a tone of the deepest contempt. 'I've seen a good many little girls in my time, but never one with such a neck as that! No, no! You're a serpent; and there's no use denying it. I suppose you'll be telling me next that you never tasted an egg!'

'I *have* tasted eggs, certainly,' said Alice, who was a very truthful child; 'but little girls eat eggs quite as much as serpents do, you know.'

'I don't believe it,' said the Pigeon; 'but if they do, why then they're a kind of serpent, that's all I can say.'

This was such a new idea to Alice, that she was quite silent for a minute or two, which gave the Pigeon the opportunity of adding, 'You're looking for eggs, I know *that* well enough; and what does it matter to me whether you're a little girl or a serpent?'

'It matters a good deal to *me*,' said Alice hastily; 'but I'm not looking for eggs, as it happens; and if I was, I shouldn't want yours: I don't like them raw.'

'Well, be off, then!' said the Pigeon in a sulky tone, as it settled down again into its nest. Alice crouched down among the trees as well as she could, for her neck kept getting entangled among the branches, and every now and then she had to stop and untwist it. After a while she remembered that she still held the pieces of mushroom in her hands, and she set to work very carefully, nibbling first at one and then at the other, and growing sometimes taller and sometimes shorter, until she had succeeded in bringing herself down to her usual height.

It was so long since she had been anything near the right size, that it felt quite strange at first; but she got used to it in a few minutes, and began talking to herself, as usual. 'Come, there's half my plan done now! How puzzling all these changes are! I'm never sure what I'm going to be, from one minute to another! However, I've got back to my right size: the next thing is, to get into that beautiful garden – how *is* that to be done, I wonder?' As she said this, she came suddenly upon an open place, with a little house in it about four feet high. 'Whoever lives there,' thought Alice, 'it'll never do to come upon them *this* size: why, I should frighten them out of their wits!' So she began nibbling at the right-hand bit again, and did not venture to go near the house till she had brought herself down to nine inches high.

CHAPTER SIX

PIG AND PEPPER

For a minute or two she stood looking at the house, and wondering what to do next, when suddenly a footman in livery came running out of the wood – (she considered him to be a footman because he was in livery: otherwise, judging by his face only, she would have called him a fish) – and rapped loudly at the door with his knuckles. It was opened by another footman in livery, with a round face, and large eyes like a frog; and both footmen, Alice noticed, had powdered hair that curled all over their heads. She felt very curious to know what it was all about, and crept a little way out of the wood to listen.

The Fish-Footman began by producing from under his arm a great letter, nearly as large as himself, and this he handed over to the other, saying, in a solemn tone, 'For the Duchess. An invitation from the Queen to play croquet.' The Frog-Footman repeated, in the same solemn tone, only changing the order of the words a little, 'From the Queen. An invitation for the Duchess to play croquet.'

Then they both bowed low, and their curls got entangled together.

Alice laughed so much at this, that she had to run back into the wood for fear of their hearing her; and when she next peeped out the Fish-Footman was gone, and the other was sitting on the ground near the door, staring stupidly up into the sky.

Alice went timidly up to the door, and knocked.

'There's no sort of use in knocking,' said the Footman, 'and that for two reasons. First, because I'm on the same side of the door as you are; secondly, because they're making such a noise inside, no one could possibly hear you.' And certainly there was a most extraordinary noise going on within – a constant howling and sneezing, and every now and then a great crash, as if a dish or kettle had been broken to pieces.

'Please, then,' said Alice, 'how am I to get in?'

'There might be some sense in your knocking,' the Footman went on without attending to her, 'if we had the door between us. For instance, if you were *inside*, you might knock, and I could let you out, you know.' He was

looking up into the sky all the time he was speaking, and this Alice thought decidedly uncivil. 'But perhaps he can't help it,' she said to herself; 'his eyes are so *very* nearly at the top of his head. But at any rate he might answer questions. – How am I to get in?' she repeated, aloud.

'I shall sit here,' the Footman remarked, 'till tomorrow –'

At this moment the door of the house opened, and a large plate came skimming out, straight at the Footman's head: it just grazed his nose, and broke to pieces against one of the trees behind him.

'– or next day, maybe,' the Footman continued in the same tone, exactly as if nothing had happened.

'How am I to get in?' asked Alice again, in a louder tone.

'*Are* you to get in at all?' said the Footman. 'That's the first question, you know.'

It was, no doubt: only Alice did not like to be told so. 'It's really dreadful,' she muttered to herself, 'the way all the creatures argue. It's enough to drive one crazy!'

The Footman seemed to think this a good opportunity for repeating his remark, with variations. 'I shall sit here,' he said, 'on and off, for days and days.'

'But what am *I* to do?' said Alice.

'Anything you like,' said the Footman, and began whistling.

'Oh, there's no use in talking to him,' said Alice desperately: 'he's perfectly idiotic!' And she opened the door and went in.

The door led right into a large kitchen, which was full of smoke from one end to the other: the Duchess was sitting on a three-legged stool in the middle, nursing a baby; the cook was leaning over the fire, stirring a large cauldron which seemed to be full of soup.

'There's certainly too much pepper in that soup!' Alice said to herself, as well as she could for sneezing.

There was certainly too much of it in the air. Even the Duchess sneezed occasionally; and as for the baby, it was sneezing and howling alternately

without a moment's pause. The only things in the kitchen that did not sneeze, were the cook, and a large cat which was sitting on the hearth and grinning from ear to ear.

'Please would you tell me,' said Alice, a little timidly, for she was not quite sure whether it was good manners for her to speak first, 'why your cat grins like that?'

'It's a Cheshire cat,' said the Duchess, 'and that's why. Pig!'

She said the last word with such sudden violence that Alice quite jumped; but she saw in another moment that it was addressed to the baby, and not to her, so she took courage, and went on again: –

'I didn't know that Cheshire cats always grinned; in fact, I didn't know that cats *could* grin.'

'They all can,' said the Duchess; 'and most of 'em do.'

'I don't know of any that do,' Alice said very politely, feeling quite pleased to have got into a conversation.

'You don't know much,' said the Duchess; 'and that's a fact.'

Alice did not at all like the tone of this remark, and thought it would be as well to introduce some other subject of conversation. While she was trying to fix on one, the cook took the cauldron of soup off the fire, and at once set to work throwing everything within her reach at the Duchess and the baby – the fire-irons came first; then followed a shower of saucepans, plates, and dishes. The Duchess took no notice of them even when they hit her; and the baby was howling so much already, that it was quite impossible to say whether the blows hurt it or not.

'Oh, *please* mind what you're doing!' cried Alice, jumping up and down in an agony of terror. 'Oh, there goes his *precious* nose'; as an unusually large saucepan flew close by it, and very nearly carried it off.

'If everybody minded their own business,' the Duchess said in a hoarse growl, 'the world would go round a deal faster than it does.'

'Which would *not* be an advantage,' said Alice, who felt very glad to get an opportunity of showing off a little of her knowledge. 'Just think of what work it would make with the day and night! You see the earth takes twenty-four hours to turn round on its axis –'

'Talking of axes,' said the Duchess, 'chop off her head!'

Alice glanced rather anxiously at the cook, to see if she meant to take the hint; but the cook was busily stirring the soup, and seemed not to be listening, so she went on again: 'Twenty-four hours, I *think*; or is it twelve? I –'

'Oh, don't bother *me*,' said the Duchess; 'I never could abide figures!' And with that she began nursing her child again, singing a sort of lullaby to it as she did so, and giving it a violent shake at the end of every line:

'Speak roughly to your little boy,
And beat him when he sneezes:
He only does it to annoy,
Because he knows it teases.'

CHORUS

(In which the cook and the baby joined):–
'Wow! wow! wow!'

While the Duchess sang the second verse of the song, she kept tossing the baby violently up and down, and the poor little thing howled so, that Alice could hardly hear the words:

'I speak severely to my boy,
I beat him when he sneezes;
For he can thoroughly enjoy
The pepper when he pleases!'

CHORUS

(In which the cook and the baby joined):–
'Wow! wow! wow!'

'Here! you may nurse it a bit, if you like!' the Duchess said to Alice, flinging the baby at her as she spoke. 'I must go and get ready to play croquet with the Queen,' and she hurried out of the room. The cook threw a frying-pan after her as she went out, but it just missed her.

Alice caught the baby with some difficulty, as it was a queer-shaped little creature, and held out its arms and legs in all directions, 'just like a star-fish,' thought Alice. The poor little thing was snorting like a steam-engine when she

caught it, and kept doubling itself up and straightening itself out again, so that altogether, for the first minute or two, it was as much as she could do to hold it.

As soon as she had made out the proper way of nursing it, (which was to twist it up into a sort of knot, and then keep tight hold of its right ear and left foot, so as to prevent its undoing itself,) she carried it out into the open air. 'If I don't take this child away with me,' thought Alice, 'they're sure to kill it in a day or two: wouldn't it be murder to leave it behind?' She said the last words out loud, and the little thing grunted in reply (it had left off sneezing by this time). 'Don't grunt,' said Alice; 'that's not at all a proper way of expressing yourself.'

The baby grunted again, and Alice looked very anxiously into its face to see what was the matter with it. There could be no doubt that it had a *very* turn-up nose, much more like a snout than a real baby: altogether Alice did not like the look of the thing at all. 'But perhaps it was only sobbing,' she thought, and looked into its eyes again, to see if there were any tears.

No, there were no tears. 'If you're going to turn into a pig, my dear,' said Alice, seriously, 'I'll have nothing more to do with you. Mind now!' The poor little thing sobbed again (or grunted, it was impossible to say which), and they went on for some while in silence.

Alice was just beginning to think to herself, 'Now, what am I to do with this creature when I get it home?' when it grunted again, so violently, that she looked down into its face in some alarm. This time there could be *no* mistake about it: it was neither more nor less than a pig, and she felt that it would be quite absurd for her to carry it any further.

CHAPTER SIX: PIG AND PEPPER

So she set the little creature down, and felt quite relieved to see it trot away quietly into the wood. 'If it had grown up,' she said to herself, 'it would have made a dreadfully ugly child: but it makes rather a handsome pig, I think.' And she began thinking over other children she knew, who might do very well as pigs, and was just saying to herself, 'if one only knew the right way to change them –' when she was a little startled by seeing the Cheshire Cat sitting on a bough of a tree a few yards off.

The Cat only grinned when it saw Alice. It looked good-natured, she thought: still it had *very* long claws and a great many teeth, so she felt that it ought to be treated with respect.

'Cheshire Puss,' she began, rather timidly, as she did not at all know whether it would like the name: however, it only grinned a little wider. 'Come, it's pleased so far,' thought Alice, and she went on. 'Would you tell me, please, which way I ought to go from here?'

'That depends a good deal on where you want to get to,' said the Cat.

'I don't much care where –' said Alice.

'Then it doesn't matter which way you go,' said the Cat.

'– so long as I get *somewhere*,' Alice added as an explanation.

'Oh, you're sure to do that,' said the Cat, 'if you only walk long enough.'

Alice felt this could not be denied, so she tried another question. 'What sort of people live about here?'

'In *that* direction,' the Cat said, waving its right paw round, 'lives a Hatter: and in that direction,' waving the other paw, 'lives a March Hare. Visit either you like: they're both mad.'

'But I don't want to go among mad people,' Alice remarked.

'Oh, you can't help that,' said the Cat: 'we're all mad here. I'm mad. You're mad.'

'How do you know I'm mad?' said Alice.

'You must be,' said the Cat, 'or you wouldn't have come here.'

Alice didn't think that proved it at all; however, she went on 'And how do you know that you're mad?'

'To begin with,' said the Cat, 'a dog's not mad. You grant that?'

'I suppose so,' said Alice.

'Well, then,' the Cat went on, 'you see, a dog growls when it's angry, and wags its tail when it's pleased. Now *I* growl when I'm pleased, and wag my tail when I'm angry. Therefore I'm mad.'

'*I* call it purring, not growling,' said Alice.

'Call it what you like,' said the Cat. 'Do you play croquet with the Queen to-day?'

'I should like it very much,' said Alice, 'but I haven't been invited yet.'

'You'll see me there,' said the Cat, and vanished.

Alice was not much surprised at this, she was getting so used to queer things happening. While she was looking at the place where it had been, it suddenly appeared again.

'By-the-bye, what became of the baby?' said the Cat. 'I'd nearly forgotten to ask.'

'It turned into a pig,' Alice quietly said, just as if it had come back in a natural way.

'I thought it would,' said the Cat, and vanished again. Alice waited a little, half expecting to see it again, but it did not appear, and after a minute or two she walked on in the direction in which the March Hare was said to live. 'I've seen hatters before,' she said to herself; 'the March Hare will be much the most interesting, and perhaps as this is May it won't be raving mad – at least not so mad as it was in March.' As she said this, she looked up, and there was the Cat again, sitting on a branch of a tree.

'Did you say pig, or fig?' said the Cat.

'I said pig,' replied Alice; 'and I wish you wouldn't keep appearing and vanishing so suddenly: you make one quite giddy.'

'All right,' said the Cat; and this time it vanished quite slowly, beginning with the end of the tail, and ending with the grin, which remained some time after the rest of it had gone.

'Well! I've often seen a cat without a grin,' thought Alice; 'but a grin without a cat! It's the most curious thing I ever saw in all my life!'

She had not gone much farther before she came in sight of the house of the March Hare: she thought it must be the right house, because the chimneys were shaped like ears and the roof was thatched with fur. It was so large a house, that she did not like to go nearer till she had nibbled some more of the left-hand bit of mushroom, and raised herself to about two feet high: even then she walked up towards it rather timidly, saying to herself 'Suppose it should be raving mad after all! I almost wish I'd gone to see the Hatter instead!'

CHAPTER SEVEN

A MAD TEA-PARTY

There was a table set out under a tree in front of the house, and the March Hare and the Hatter were having tea at it: a Dormouse was sitting between them, fast asleep, and the other two were using it as a cushion, resting their elbows on it, and talking over its head. 'Very uncomfortable for the Dormouse,' thought Alice; 'only, as it's asleep, I suppose it doesn't mind.'

The table was a large one, but the three were all crowded together at one corner of it: 'No room! No room!' they cried out when they saw Alice coming. 'There's *plenty* of room!' said Alice indignantly, and she sat down in a large arm-chair at one end of the table.

'Have some wine,' the March Hare said in an encouraging tone.

Alice looked all round the table, but there was nothing on it but tea. 'I don't see any wine,' she remarked.

'There isn't any,' said the March Hare.

'Then it wasn't very civil of you to offer it,' said Alice angrily.

'It wasn't very civil of you to sit down without being invited,' said the March Hare.

'I didn't know it was *your* table,' said Alice; 'it's laid for a great many more than three.'

'Your hair wants cutting,' said the Hatter. He had been looking at Alice for some time with great curiosity, and this was his first speech.

'You should learn not to make personal remarks,' Alice said with some severity; 'it's very rude.'

The Hatter opened his eyes very wide on hearing this; but all he *said* was, 'Why is a raven like a writing-desk?'

'Come, we shall have some fun now!' thought Alice. 'I'm glad they've begun asking riddles. – I believe I can guess that,' she added aloud.

'Do you mean that you think you can find out the answer to it?' said the March Hare.

'Exactly so,' said Alice.

'Then you should say what you mean,' the March Hare went on.

'I do,' Alice hastily replied; 'at least – at least I mean what I say – that's the same thing, you know.'

'Not the same thing a bit!' said the Hatter. 'You might just as well say that "I see what I eat" is the same thing as "I eat what I see"!'

'You might just as well say,' added the March Hare, 'that "I like what I get" is the same thing as "I get what I like"!'

'You might just as well say,' added the Dormouse, who seemed to be talking in his sleep, 'that "I breathe when I sleep" is the same thing as "I sleep when I breathe"!'

'It *is* the same thing with you,' said the Hatter, and here the conversation dropped, and the party sat silent for a minute, while Alice thought over all she could remember about ravens and writing-desks, which wasn't much.

The Hatter was the first to break the silence.

'What day of the month is it?' he said, turning to Alice: he had taken his watch out of his pocket, and was looking at it uneasily, shaking it every now and then, and holding it to his ear.

Alice considered a little, and then said 'The fourth.'

'Two days wrong!' sighed the Hatter. 'I told you butter wouldn't suit the works!' he added, looking angrily at the March Hare.

'It was the *best* butter,' the March Hare meekly replied.

'Yes, but some crumbs must have got in as well,' the Hatter grumbled: 'you shouldn't have put it in with the bread-knife.'

The March Hare took the watch and looked at it gloomily: then he dipped it into his cup of tea, and looked at it again: but he could think of nothing better to say than his first remark, 'It was the *best* butter, you know.'

Alice had been looking over his shoulder with some curiosity. 'What a funny watch!' she remarked. 'It tells the day of the month, and doesn't tell what o'clock it is!'

'Why should it?' muttered the Hatter. 'Does *your* watch tell you what year it is?'

'Of course not,' Alice replied very readily: 'but that's because it stays the same year for such a long time together.'

'Which is just the case with *mine*,' said the Hatter.

Alice felt dreadfully puzzled. The Hatter's remark seemed to have no sort of meaning in it, and yet it was certainly English. 'I don't quite understand you,' she said, as politely as she could.

'The Dormouse is asleep again,' said the Hatter, and he poured a little hot tea upon its nose.

The Dormouse shook its head impatiently, and said, without opening its eyes, 'Of course, of course; just what I was going to remark myself.'

'Have you guessed the riddle yet?' the Hatter said, turning to Alice again.

'No, I give it up,' Alice replied: 'what's the answer?'

'I haven't the slightest idea,' said the Hatter.

'Nor I,' said the March Hare.

Alice sighed wearily. 'I think you might do something better with the time,' she said, 'than waste it in asking riddles that have no answers.'

'If you knew Time as well as I do,' said the Hatter, 'you wouldn't talk about wasting *it*. It's *him*.'

'I don't know what you mean,' said Alice.

'Of course you don't!' the Hatter said, tossing his head contemptuously. 'I dare say you never even spoke to Time!'

'Perhaps not,' Alice cautiously replied: 'but I know I have to beat time when I learn music.'

'Ah! that accounts for it,' said the Hatter. 'He won't stand beating. Now, if you only kept on good terms with him, he'd do almost anything you liked with the clock. For instance, suppose it were nine o'clock in the morning, just time to begin lessons: you'd only have to whisper a hint to Time, and round goes the clock in a twinkling! Half-past one, time for dinner!'

('I only wish it was,' the March Hare said to itself in a whisper.)

'That would be grand, certainly,' said Alice thoughtfully: 'but then – I shouldn't be hungry for it, you know.'

'Not at first, perhaps,' said the Hatter: 'but you could keep it to half-past one as long as you liked.'

'Is that the way *you* manage?' Alice asked.

The Hatter shook his head mournfully. 'Not I!' he replied. 'We quarrelled last March – just before *he* went mad, you know –' (pointing with his teaspoon at the March Hare,) '– it was at the great concert given by the Queen of Hearts, and I had to sing:

> *"Twinkle, twinkle, little bat!*
> *How I wonder what you're at!"*

You know the song, perhaps?'

'I've heard something like it,' said Alice.

'It goes on, you know,' the Hatter continued, 'in this way:–

"Up above the world you fly,
Like a tea-tray in the sky.
Twinkle, twinkle –"'

Here the Dormouse shook itself, and began singing in its sleep *'Twinkle,*
twinkle, twinkle, twinkle –' and went on so long that they had to pinch it to
make it stop.

'Well, I'd hardly finished the first verse,' said the Hatter, 'when the Queen
jumped up and bawled out, "He's murdering the time! Off with his head!"'

'How dreadfully savage!' exclaimed Alice.

'And ever since that,' the Hatter went on in a mournful tone, 'he won't do a
thing I ask! It's always six o'clock now.'

A bright idea came into Alice's head. 'Is that the reason so many tea-things
are put out here?' she asked.

'Yes, that's it,' said the Hatter with a sigh: 'it's always tea-time, and we've no
time to wash the things between whiles.'

'Then you keep moving round, I suppose?' said Alice.

'Exactly so,' said the Hatter: 'as the things get used up.'

'But what happens when you come to the beginning again?' Alice ventured to ask.

'Suppose we change the subject,' the March Hare interrupted, yawning. 'I'm
getting tired of this. I vote the young lady tells us a story.'

'I'm afraid I don't know one,' said Alice, rather alarmed at the proposal.

'Then the Dormouse shall!' they both cried. 'Wake up, Dormouse!' And they
pinched it on both sides at once.

The Dormouse slowly opened his eyes. 'I wasn't asleep,' he said in a hoarse,
feeble voice: 'I heard every word you fellows were saying.'

'Tell us a story!' said the March Hare.

'Yes, please do!' pleaded Alice.

'And be quick about it,' added the Hatter, 'or you'll be asleep again before it's done.'

'Once upon a time there were three little sisters,' the Dormouse began in a great hurry; 'and their names were Elsie, Lacie, and Tillie; and they lived at the bottom of a well –'

'What did they live on?' said Alice, who always took a great interest in questions of eating and drinking.

'They lived on treacle,' said the Dormouse, after thinking a minute or two.

'They couldn't have done that, you know,' Alice gently remarked; 'they'd have been ill.'

'So they were,' said the Dormouse; '*very* ill.'

Alice tried to fancy to herself what such an extraordinary way of living would be like, but it puzzled her too much, so she went on: 'But why did they live at the bottom of a well?'

'Take some more tea,' the March Hare said to Alice, very earnestly.

'I've had nothing yet,' Alice replied in an offended tone, 'so I can't take more.'

'You mean you can't take *less*,' said the Hatter: 'it's very easy to take more than nothing.'

'Nobody asked *your* opinion,' said Alice.

'Who's making personal remarks now?' the Hatter asked triumphantly.

Alice did not quite know what to say to this: so she helped herself to some tea and bread-and-butter, and then turned to the Dormouse, and repeated her question. 'Why did they live at the bottom of a well?'

The Dormouse again took a minute or two to think about it, and then said, 'It was a treacle-well.'

'There's no such thing!' Alice was beginning very angrily, but the Hatter and the March Hare went 'Sh! sh!' and the Dormouse sulkily remarked, 'If you can't be civil, you'd better finish the story for yourself.'

'No, please go on!' Alice said very humbly: 'I won't interrupt again. I dare say there may be *one*.'

'One, indeed!' said the Dormouse indignantly. However, he consented to go on. 'And so these three little sisters – they were learning to draw, you know –'

'What did they draw?' said Alice, quite forgetting her promise.

'Treacle,' said the Dormouse, without considering at all this time.

'I want a clean cup,' interrupted the Hatter: 'let's all move one place on.'

He moved on as he spoke, and the Dormouse followed him: the March Hare moved into the Dormouse's place, and Alice rather unwillingly took the place of the March Hare. The Hatter was the only one who got any advantage from the change: and Alice was a good deal worse off than before, as the March Hare had just upset the milk-jug into his plate.

Alice did not wish to offend the Dormouse again, so she began very cautiously: 'But I don't understand. Where did they draw the treacle from?'

'You can draw water out of a water-well,' said the Hatter; 'so I should think you could draw treacle out of a treacle-well – eh, stupid?'

'But they were *in* the well,' Alice said to the Dormouse, not choosing to notice this last remark.

'Of course they were,' said the Dormouse; '– well in.'

This answer so confused poor Alice, that she let the Dormouse go on for some time without interrupting it.

'They were learning to draw,' the Dormouse went on, yawning and rubbing its eyes, for it was getting very sleepy; 'and they drew all manner of things – everything that begins with an M –'

'Why with an M?' said Alice.

'Why not?' said the March Hare.

Alice was silent.

The Dormouse had closed its eyes by this time, and was going off into a doze; but, on being pinched by the Hatter, it woke up again with a little shriek,

and went on: '– that begins with an M, such as mouse-traps, and the moon, and memory, and muchness – you know you say things are "much of a muchness" – did you ever see such a thing as a drawing of a muchness?'

'Really, now you ask me,' said Alice, very much confused, 'I don't think –'

'Then you shouldn't talk,' said the Hatter.

This piece of rudeness was more than Alice could bear: she got up in great disgust, and walked off; the Dormouse fell asleep instantly, and neither of the others took the least notice of her going, though she looked back once or twice, half hoping that they would call after her: the last time she saw them, they were trying to put the Dormouse into the teapot.

'At any rate I'll never go *there* again!' said Alice as she picked her way through the wood. 'It's the stupidest tea-party I ever was at in all my life!'

Just as she said this, she noticed that one of the trees had a door leading right into it. 'That's very curious!' she thought. 'But everything's curious today. I think I may as well go in at once.' And in she went.

Once more she found herself in the long hall, and close to the little glass table. 'Now, I'll manage better this time,' she said to herself, and began by taking the little golden key, and unlocking the door that led into the garden. Then she set to work nibbling at the mushroom (she had kept a piece of it in her pocket) till she was about a foot high: then she walked down the little passage: and *then* – she found herself at last in the beautiful garden, among the bright flower-beds and the cool fountains.

CHAPTER EIGHT

THE QUEEN'S CROQUET-GROUND

A large rose-tree stood near the entrance of the garden: the roses growing on it were white, but there were three gardeners at it, busily painting them red. Alice thought this a very curious thing, and she went nearer to watch them, and just as she came up to them she heard one of them say, 'Look out now, Five! Don't go splashing paint over me like that!'

'I couldn't help it,' said Five in a sulky tone; 'Seven jogged my elbow.'

On which Seven looked up and said, 'That's right, Five! Always lay the blame on others!'

'*You'd* better not talk!' said Five. 'I heard the Queen say only yesterday you deserved to be beheaded!'

'What for?' said the one who had spoken first.

'That's none of *your* business, Two!' said Seven.

'Yes it *is* his business!' said Five, 'and I'll tell him – it was for bringing the cook tulip-roots instead of onions.'

Seven flung down his brush, and had just begun 'Well, of all the unjust things –' when his eye chanced to fall upon Alice, as she stood watching them, and he checked himself suddenly: the others looked round also, and all of them bowed low.

'Would you tell me,' said Alice, a little timidly 'why you are painting those roses?'

Five and Seven said nothing, but looked at Two. Two began in a low voice, 'Why the fact is, you see, Miss, this here ought to have been a *red* rose-tree, and we put a white one in by mistake; and if the Queen was to find out, we should all have our heads cut off, you know. So you see, Miss, we're doing our best, afore she comes, to –' At this moment Five, who had been anxiously looking across the garden, called out 'The Queen! The Queen!' and the three gardeners instantly threw themselves flat upon their faces. There was a sound of many footsteps, and Alice looked round, eager to see the Queen.

First came ten soldiers carrying clubs; these were all shaped like the three gardeners, oblong and flat, with their hands and feet at the corners: next the ten courtiers; these were ornamented all over with diamonds, and walked two and two, as the soldiers did. After these came the royal children; there were ten of them, and the little dears came jumping merrily along hand in hand, in couples: they were all ornamented with hearts. Next came the guests, mostly Kings and Queens, and among them Alice recognised the White Rabbit: it was talking in a hurried nervous manner, smiling at everything that was said, and went by without noticing her. Then followed the Knave of Hearts, carrying the King's crown on a crimson velvet cushion; and, last of all this procession, came THE KING AND QUEEN OF HEARTS.

Alice was rather doubtful whether she ought not to lie down on her face like the three gardeners, but she could not remember ever having heard of such a

rule at processions; 'and besides, what would be the use of a procession,' thought she, 'if people had all to lie down upon their faces, so that they couldn't see it?' So she stood still where she was, and waited.

When the procession came opposite to Alice, they all stopped and looked at her, and the Queen said severely 'Who is this?' She said it to the Knave of Hearts, who only bowed and smiled in reply.

'Idiot!' said the Queen, tossing her head impatiently; and, turning to Alice, she went on, 'What's your name, child?'

'My name is Alice, so please your Majesty,' said Alice very politely; but she added, to herself, 'Why, they're only a pack of cards, after all. I needn't be afraid of them!'

'And who are *these*?' said the Queen, pointing to the three gardeners who were lying round the rose-tree; for, you see, as they were lying on their faces, and the pattern on their backs was the same as the rest of the pack, she could not tell whether they were gardeners, or soldiers, or courtiers, or three of her own children.

'How should I know?' said Alice, surprised at her own courage. 'It's no business of *mine*.'

The Queen turned crimson with fury, and, after glaring at her for a moment like a wild beast, screamed 'Off with her head! Off –'

'Nonsense!' said Alice, very loudly and decidedly, and the Queen was silent.

The King laid his hand upon her arm, and timidly said 'Consider, my dear: she is only a child!'

The Queen turned angrily away from him, and said to the Knave 'Turn them over!'

The Knave did so, very carefully, with one foot.

'Get up!' said the Queen, in a shrill, loud voice, and the three gardeners instantly jumped up, and began bowing to the King, the Queen, the royal children, and everybody else.

'Leave off that!' screamed the Queen. 'You make me giddy.' And then, turning to the rose-tree, she went on, 'What *have* you been doing here?'

'May it please your Majesty,' said Two, in a very humble tone, going down on one knee as he spoke, 'we were trying –'

'*I* see!' said the Queen, who had meanwhile been examining the roses. 'Off with their heads!' and the procession moved on, three of the soldiers remaining behind to execute the unfortunate gardeners, who ran to Alice for protection.

'You shan't be beheaded!' said Alice, and she put them into a large flower-pot that stood near. The three soldiers wandered about for a minute or two, looking for them, and then quietly marched off after the others.

'Are their heads off?' shouted the Queen.

'Their heads are gone, if it please your Majesty!' the soldiers shouted in reply.

'That's right!' shouted the Queen. 'Can you play croquet?'

The soldiers were silent, and looked at Alice, as the question was evidently meant for her.

'Yes!' shouted Alice.

'Come on, then!' roared the Queen, and Alice joined the procession, wondering very much what would happen next.

'It's – it's a very fine day!' said a timid voice at her side. She was walking by the White Rabbit, who was peeping anxiously into her face.

'Very,' said Alice: '– where's the Duchess?'

'Hush! Hush!' said the Rabbit in a low, hurried tone. He looked anxiously over his shoulder as he spoke, and then raised himself upon tiptoe, put his mouth close to her ear, and whispered 'She's under sentence of execution.'

'What for?' said Alice.

'Did you say "What a pity!"?' the Rabbit asked.

'No, I didn't,' said Alice: 'I don't think it's at all a pity. I said "What for?"'

'She boxed the Queen's ears –' the Rabbit began. Alice gave a little scream of

CHAPTER EIGHT: THE QUEEN'S CROQUET-GROUND

laughter. 'Oh, hush!' the Rabbit whispered in a frightened tone. 'The Queen will hear you! You see, she came rather late, and the Queen said –'

'Get to your places!' shouted the Queen in a voice of thunder, and people began running about in all directions, tumbling up against each other; however, they got settled down in a minute or two, and the game began. Alice thought she had never seen such a curious croquet-ground in all her life; it was all ridges and furrows; the balls were live hedgehogs, the mallets live flamingoes, and

the soldiers had to double themselves up and to stand on their hands and feet, to make the arches.

The chief difficulty Alice found at first was in managing her flamingo: she succeeded in getting its body tucked away, comfortably enough, under her arm, with its legs hanging down, but generally, just as she had got its neck nicely straightened out, and was going to give the hedgehog a blow with its head, it *would* twist itself round and look up in her face, with such a puzzled expression that she could not help bursting out laughing: and when she had got its head down, and was going to begin again, it was very provoking to find that the hedgehog had unrolled itself, and was in the act of crawling away: besides all this, there was generally a ridge or furrow in the way wherever she wanted to

send the hedgehog to, and, as the doubled-up soldiers were always getting up and walking off to other parts of the ground, Alice soon came to the conclusion that it was a very difficult game indeed.

The players all played at once without waiting for turns, quarrelling all the while, and fighting for the hedgehogs; and in a very short time the Queen was in a furious passion, and went stamping about, and shouting 'Off with his head!' or 'Off with her head!' about once in a minute.

Alice began to feel very uneasy: to be sure, she had not as yet had any dispute with the Queen, but she knew that it might happen any minute, 'and then,' thought she, 'what would become of me? They're dreadfully fond of beheading people here; the great wonder is, that there's any one left alive!'

She was looking about for some way of escape, and wondering whether she could get away without being seen, when she noticed a curious appearance in the air: it puzzled her very much at first, but, after watching it a minute or two, she made it out to be a grin, and she said to herself 'It's the Cheshire Cat: now I shall have somebody to talk to.'

'How are you getting on?' said the Cat, as soon as there was mouth enough for it to speak with.

Alice waited till the eyes appeared, and then nodded. 'It's no use speaking to it,' she thought, 'till its ears have come, or at least one of them.' In another minute the whole head appeared, and then Alice put down her flamingo, and began an account of the game, feeling very glad she had someone to listen to her. The Cat seemed to think that there was enough of it now in sight, and no more of it appeared.

'I don't think they play at all fairly,' Alice began, in rather a complaining tone, 'and they all quarrel so dreadfully one can't hear oneself speak – and they don't seem to have any rules in particular; at least, if there are, nobody attends to them – and you've no idea how confusing it is all the things being alive; for instance, there's the arch I've got to go through next walking about at the other end of

the ground – and I should have croqueted the Queen's hedgehog just now, only it ran away when it saw mine coming!'

'How do you like the Queen?' said the Cat in a low voice.

'Not at all,' said Alice: 'she's so extremely –' Just then she noticed that the Queen was close behind her, listening: so she went on, '– likely to win, that it's hardly worth while finishing the game.'

The Queen smiled and passed on.

'Who are you talking to?' said the King, coming up to Alice, and looking at the Cat's head with great curiosity.

'It's a friend of mine – a Cheshire Cat,' said Alice: 'allow me to introduce it.'

'I don't like the look of it at all,' said the King: 'however, it may kiss my hand if it likes.'

'I'd rather not,' the Cat remarked.

'Don't be impertinent,' said the King, 'and don't look at me like that!' He got behind Alice as he spoke.

'A cat may look at a king,' said Alice. 'I've read that in some book, but I don't remember where.'

'Well, it must be removed,' said the King very decidedly, and he called to the Queen, who was passing at the moment, 'My dear! I wish you would have this cat removed!'

The Queen had only one way of settling all difficulties, great or small. 'Off with his head!' she said, without even looking round.

'I'll fetch the executioner myself,' said the King eagerly, and he hurried off.

Alice thought she might as well go back, and see how the game was going on, as she heard the Queen's voice in the distance, screaming with passion. She had already heard her sentence three of the players to be executed for having missed their turns, and she did not like the look of things at all, as the game was in such confusion that she never knew whether it was her turn or not. She went in search of her hedgehog.

The hedgehog was engaged in a fight with another hedgehog, which seemed to Alice an excellent opportunity for croqueting one of them with the other: the only difficulty was, that her flamingo was gone across to the other side of the garden, where Alice could see it trying in a helpless sort of way to fly up into a tree.

By the time she had caught the flamingo and brought it back, the fight was over, and both the hedgehogs were out of sight: 'but it doesn't matter much,' thought Alice, 'as all the arches are gone from this side of the ground.' So she tucked it away under her arm, that it might not escape again, and went back for a little more conversation with her friend.

When she got back to the Cheshire Cat, she was surprised to find quite a large crowd collected round it: there was a dispute going on between the executioner, the King, and the Queen, who were all talking at once, while all the rest were quite silent, and looked very uncomfortable.

The moment Alice appeared, she was appealed to by all three to settle the question, and they repeated their arguments to her, though, as they all spoke at once, she found it very hard indeed to make out exactly what they said.

The executioner's argument was, that you couldn't cut off a head unless there was a body to cut it off from: that he had never had to do such a thing before, and he wasn't going to begin at *his* time of life.

The King's argument was, that anything that had a head could be beheaded, and that you weren't to talk nonsense.

The Queen's argument was, that if something wasn't done about it in less than no time she'd have everybody executed, all round. (It was this last remark that had made the whole party look so grave and anxious.)

Alice could think of nothing else to say but 'It belongs to the Duchess: you'd better ask *her* about it.'

'She's in prison,' the Queen said to the executioner: 'fetch her here.' And the executioner went off like an arrow.

The Cat's head began fading away the moment he was gone, and, by the time he had come back with the Duchess, it had entirely disappeared; so the King and the executioner ran wildly up and down looking for it, while the rest of the party went back to the game.

CHAPTER NINE

THE MOCK TURTLE'S STORY

'You can't think how glad I am to see you again, you dear old thing!' said the Duchess, as she tucked her arm affectionately into Alice's, and they walked off together.

Alice was very glad to find her in such a pleasant temper, and thought to herself that perhaps it was only the pepper that had made her so savage when they met in the kitchen.

'When *I'm* a Duchess,' she said to herself, (not in a very hopeful tone though), I won't have any pepper in my kitchen *at all*. Soup does very well without – Maybe it's always pepper that makes people hot-tempered,' she went on, very much pleased at having found out a new kind of rule, 'and vinegar that makes them sour – and camomile that makes them bitter – and – and barley-sugar and such things that make children sweet-tempered. I only wish people knew *that*: then they wouldn't be so stingy about it, you know –'

She had quite forgotten the Duchess by this time, and was a little startled when she heard her voice close to her ear. 'You're thinking about something, my dear, and that makes you forget to talk. I can't tell you just now what the moral of that is, but I shall remember it in a bit.'

'Perhaps it hasn't one,' Alice ventured to remark.

'Tut, tut, child!' said the Duchess. 'Everything's got a moral, if only you can find it.' And she squeezed herself up closer to Alice's side as she spoke.

Alice did not much like keeping so close to her: first, because the Duchess was *very* ugly; and secondly, because she was exactly the right height to rest her chin upon Alice's shoulder, and it was an uncomfortably sharp chin. However, she did not like to be rude, so she bore it as well as she could.

'The game's going on rather better now,' she said, by way of keeping up the conversation a little.

' 'Tis so,' said the Duchess: 'and the moral of *that* is – "Oh, 'tis love, 'tis love, that makes the world go round!"'

'Somebody said,' Alice whispered, 'that it's done by everybody minding their own business!'

'Ah, well! It means much the same thing,' said the Duchess, digging her sharp little chin into Alice's shoulder as she added, 'and the moral of that is – "Take care of the sense, and the sounds will take care of themselves."'

'How fond she is of finding morals in things!' Alice thought to herself.

'I dare say you're wondering why I don't put my arm round your waist,' the Duchess said after a pause: 'the reason is, that I'm doubtful about the temper of your flamingo. Shall I try the experiment?'

'He might bite,' Alice cautiously replied, not feeling at all anxious to have the experiment tried.

'Very true,' said the Duchess: 'flamingoes and mustard both bite. And the moral of that is – "Birds of a feather flock together."'

'Only mustard isn't a bird,' Alice remarked.

'Right, as usual,' said the Duchess: 'what a clear way you have of putting things!'

'It's a mineral, I *think*,' said Alice.

'Of course it is,' said the Duchess, who seemed ready to agree to everything that Alice said; 'there's a large mustard-mine near here. And the moral of that is – "The more there is of mine, the less there is of yours."'

'Oh, I know!' exclaimed Alice, who had not attended to this last remark, 'it's a vegetable. It doesn't look like one, but it is.'

'I quite agree with you,' said the Duchess; 'and the moral of that is – "Be what you would seem to be" – or if you'd like it put more simply – "Never imagine yourself not to be otherwise than what it might appear to others that what you were or might have been was not otherwise than what you had been would have appeared to them to be otherwise."'

'I think I should understand that better,' Alice said very politely, 'if I had it written down: but I can't quite follow it as you say it.'

'That's nothing to what I could say if I chose,' the Duchess replied, in a pleased tone.

'Pray don't trouble yourself to say it any longer than that,' said Alice.

'Oh, don't talk about trouble!' said the Duchess. 'I make you a present of everything I've said as yet.'

'A cheap sort of present!' thought Alice. 'I'm glad they don't give birthday presents like that!' But she did not venture to say it out loud.

'Thinking again?' the Duchess asked, with another dig of her sharp little chin.

'I've a right to think,' said Alice sharply, for she was beginning to feel a little worried.

'Just about as much right,' said the Duchess, 'as pigs have to fly; and the m –'

But here, to Alice's great surprise, the Duchess's voice died away, even in the middle of her favourite word 'moral,' and the arm that was linked into hers began to tremble. Alice looked up, and there stood the Queen in front of them, with her arms folded, frowning like a thunderstorm.

'A fine day, your Majesty!' the Duchess began in a low, weak voice.

'Now, I give you fair warning,' shouted the Queen, stamping on the ground as she spoke; 'either you or your head must be off, and that in about half no time! Take your choice!'

The Duchess took her choice, and was gone in a moment.

'Let's go on with the game,' the Queen said to Alice; and Alice was too much frightened to say a word, but slowly followed her back to the croquet-ground.

The other guests had taken advantage of the Queen's absence, and were resting in the shade: however, the moment they saw her, they hurried back to the game, the Queen merely remarking that a moment's delay would cost them their lives.

All the time they were playing the Queen never left off quarrelling with the other players, and shouting 'Off with his head!' or 'Off with her head!' Those whom she sentenced were taken into custody by the soldiers, who of course had to leave off being arches to do this, so that by the end of half an hour or so there

were no arches left, and all the players, except the King, the Queen, and Alice, were in custody and under sentence of execution.

Then the Queen left off, quite out of breath, and said to Alice, 'Have you seen the Mock Turtle yet?'

'No,' said Alice. 'I don't even know what a Mock Turtle is.'

'It's the thing Mock Turtle Soup is made from,' said the Queen.

'I never saw one, or heard of one,' said Alice.

'Come on, then,' said the Queen, 'and he shall tell you his history.'

As they walked off together, Alice heard the King say in a low voice, to the company generally, 'You are all pardoned.' 'Come, *that's* a good thing!' she said to herself, for she had felt quite unhappy at the number of executions the Queen had ordered.

They very soon came upon a Gryphon, lying fast asleep in the sun. (If you don't know what a Gryphon is, look at the picture.) 'Up, lazy thing!' said the Queen,

'and take this young lady to see the Mock Turtle, and to hear his history. I must go back and see after some executions I have ordered'; and she walked off, leaving Alice alone with the Gryphon. Alice did not quite like the look of the creature, but on the whole she thought it would be quite as safe to stay with it as to go after that savage Queen: so she waited.

The Gryphon sat up and rubbed its eyes: then it watched the Queen till she was out of sight: then it chuckled. 'What fun!' said the Gryphon, half to itself, half to Alice.

'What *is* the fun?' said Alice.

'Why, *she*,' said the Gryphon. 'It's all her fancy, that: they never executes nobody, you know. Come on!'

'Everybody says "come on!" here,' thought Alice, as she went slowly after it: 'I never was so ordered about in all my life, never!'

They had not gone far before they saw the Mock Turtle in the distance, sitting sad and lonely on a little ledge of rock, and, as they came nearer, Alice could hear him sighing as if his heart would break. She pitied him deeply. 'What is his sorrow?' she asked the Gryphon, and the Gryphon answered, very nearly in the same words as before, 'It's all his fancy, that: he hasn't got no sorrow, you know. Come on!'

So they went up to the Mock Turtle, who looked at them with large eyes full of tears, but said nothing.

'This here young lady,' said the Gryphon, 'she wants for to know your history, she do.'

'I'll tell it her,' said the Mock Turtle in a deep, hollow tone: 'sit down, both of you, and don't speak a word till I've finished.'

So they sat down, and nobody spoke for some minutes. Alice thought to herself, 'I don't see how he can *ever* finish, if he doesn't begin.' But she waited patiently.

'Once,' said the Mock Turtle at last, with a deep sigh, 'I was a real Turtle.'

These words were followed by a very long silence, broken only by an occasional exclamation of 'Hjckrrh!' from the Gryphon, and the constant heavy sobbing of the Mock Turtle. Alice was very nearly getting up and saying, 'Thank you, sir, for your interesting story,' but she could not help thinking there *must* be more to come, so she sat still and said nothing.

'When we were little,' the Mock Turtle went on at last, more calmly, though still sobbing a little now and then, 'we went to school in the sea. The master was an old Turtle – we used to call him Tortoise –'

'Why did you call him Tortoise, if he wasn't one?' Alice asked.

'We called him Tortoise because he taught us,' said the Mock Turtle angrily: 'really you are very dull!'

'You ought to be ashamed of yourself for asking such a simple question,' added the Gryphon; and then they both sat silent and looked at poor Alice, who felt ready to sink into the earth. At last the Gryphon said to the Mock Turtle, 'Drive on, old fellow! Don't be all day about it!' and he went on in these words:

'Yes, we went to school in the sea, though you mayn't believe it –'

'I never said I didn't!' interrupted Alice.

'You did,' said the Mock Turtle.

'Hold your tongue!' added the Gryphon, before Alice could speak again. The Mock Turtle went on.

'We had the best of educations – in fact, we went to school every day –'

'*I've* been to a day-school, too,' said Alice; 'you needn't be so proud as all that.'

'With extras?' asked the Mock Turtle a little anxiously.

'Yes,' said Alice, 'we learned French and music.'

'And washing?' said the Mock Turtle.

'Certainly not!' said Alice indignantly.

'Ah! then yours wasn't a really good school,' said the Mock Turtle in a tone of great relief. 'Now at *ours* they had at the end of the bill, "French, music, *and washing* – extra."'

'You couldn't have wanted it much,' said Alice; 'living at the bottom of the sea.'

'I couldn't afford to learn it,' said the Mock Turtle with a sigh. 'I only took the regular course.'

'What was that?' inquired Alice.

'Reeling and Writhing, of course, to begin with,' the Mock Turtle replied; 'and then the different branches of Arithmetic – Ambition, Distraction, Uglification, and Derision.'

'I never heard of "Uglification,"' Alice ventured to say. 'What is it?'

The Gryphon lifted up both its paws in surprise. 'What! Never heard of uglifying!' it exclaimed. 'You know what to beautify is, I suppose?'

'Yes,' said Alice doubtfully: 'it means – to – make – anything – prettier.'

'Well, then,' the Gryphon went on, 'if you don't know what to uglify is, you *are* a simpleton.'

Alice did not feel encouraged to ask any more questions about it, so she turned to the Mock Turtle, and said 'What else had you to learn?'

'Well, there was Mystery,' the Mock Turtle replied, counting off the subjects on his flappers, '– Mystery, ancient and modern, with Seaography: then Drawling – the Drawling-master was an old conger-eel, that used to come once a week: *he* taught us Drawling, Stretching, and Fainting in Coils.'

'What was *that* like?' said Alice.

'Well, I can't show it you myself,' the Mock Turtle said: 'I'm too stiff. And the Gryphon never learnt it.'

'Hadn't time,' said the Gryphon: 'I went to the Classical master, though. He was an old crab, *he* was.'

'I never went to him,' the Mock Turtle said with a sigh: 'he taught Laughing and Grief, they used to say.'

'So he did, so he did,' said the Gryphon, sighing in his turn; and both creatures hid their faces in their paws.

'And how many hours a day did you do lessons?' said Alice, in a hurry to change the subject.

'Ten hours the first day,' said the Mock Turtle: 'nine the next, and so on.'

'What a curious plan!' exclaimed Alice.

'That's the reason they're called lessons,' the Gryphon remarked: 'because they lessen from day to day.'

This was quite a new idea to Alice, and she thought it over a little before she made her next remark. 'Then the eleventh day must have been a holiday?'

'Of course it was,' said the Mock Turtle.

'And how did you manage on the twelfth?' Alice went on eagerly.

'That's enough about lessons,' the Gryphon interrupted in a very decided tone: 'tell her something about the games now.'

CHAPTER TEN

THE LOBSTER QUADRILLE

*T*he Mock Turtle sighed deeply, and drew the back of one flapper across his eyes. He looked at Alice, and tried to speak, but for a minute or two sobs choked his voice. 'Same as if he had a bone in his throat,' said the Gryphon: and it set to work shaking him and punching him in the back. At last the Mock Turtle recovered his voice, and, with tears running down his cheeks, he went on again: –

'You may not have lived much under the sea –' ('I haven't,' said Alice) – 'and perhaps you were never even introduced to a lobster –' (Alice began to say 'I once tasted –' but checked herself hastily, and said 'No, never') '– so you can have no idea what a delightful thing a Lobster Quadrille is!'

'No, indeed,' said Alice. 'What sort of a dance is it?'

'Why,' said the Gryphon, 'you first form into a line along the sea-shore –'

'Two lines!' cried the Mock Turtle. 'Seals, turtles, salmon, and so on; then, when you've cleared all the jellyfish out of the way –'

'*That* generally takes some time,' interrupted the Gryphon.

'– you advance twice –'

'Each with a lobster as a partner!' cried the Gryphon.

'Of course,' the Mock Turtle said: 'advance twice, set to partners –'

'– change lobsters, and retire in same order,' continued the Gryphon.

'Then, you know,' the Mock Turtle went on, 'you throw the –'

'The lobsters!' shouted the Gryphon, with a bound into the air.

'– as far out to sea as you can –'

'Swim after them!' screamed the Gryphon.

'Turn a somersault in the sea!' cried the Mock Turtle, capering wildly about.

'Change lobsters again!' yelled the Gryphon.

'Back to land again, and that's all the first figure,' said the Mock Turtle, suddenly dropping his voice; and the two creatures, who had been jumping about like mad things all this time, sat down again very sadly and quietly, and looked at Alice.

'It must be a very pretty dance,' said Alice timidly.

'Would you like to see a little of it?' said the Mock Turtle.

'Very much indeed,' said Alice.

'Come, let's try the first figure!' said the Mock Turtle to the Gryphon.

'We can do without lobsters, you know. Which shall sing?'

'Oh, *you* sing,' said the Gryphon. 'I've forgotten the words.'

So they began solemnly dancing round and round Alice, every now and then treading on her toes when they passed too close, and waving their forepaws to mark the time, while the Mock Turtle sang this, very slowly and sadly:

> *"Will you walk a little faster?" said a whiting to a snail.*
> *"There's a porpoise close behind us, and he's treading on my tail.*
> *See how eagerly the lobsters and the turtles all advance!*
> *They are waiting on the shingle – will you come and join the dance?*
> *Will you, won't you, will you, won't you, will you join the dance?*
> *Will you, won't you, will you, won't you, won't you join the dance?*
>
> *"You can really have no notion how delightful it will be*
> *When they take us up and throw us, with the lobsters, out to sea!"*
> *But the snail replied "Too far, too far!" and gave a look askance –*
> *Said he thanked the whiting kindly, but he would not join the dance.*
> *Would not, could not, would not, could not, would not join the dance.*
> *Would not, could not, would not, could not, could not join the dance.*
>
> *"What matters it how far we go?" his scaly friend replied.*
> *"There is another shore, you know, upon the other side.*
> *The further off from England the nearer is to France –*
> *Then turn not pale, beloved snail, but come and join the dance.*
> *Will you, won't you, will you, won't you, will you join the dance?*
> *Will you, won't you, will you, won't you, won't you join the dance?"*

'Thank you, it's a very interesting dance to watch,' said Alice, feeling very glad that it was over at last: 'and I do so like that curious song about the whiting!'

'Oh, as to the whiting,' said the Mock Turtle, 'they – you've seen them, of course?'

'Yes,' said Alice, 'I've often seen them at dinn –' she checked herself hastily.

'I don't know where Dinn may be,' said the Mock Turtle, 'but if you've seen them so often, of course you know what they're like.'

'I believe so,' Alice replied thoughtfully. 'They have their tails in their mouths – and they're all over crumbs.'

'You're wrong about the crumbs,' said the Mock Turtle: 'crumbs would all wash off in the sea. But they *have* their tails in their mouths; and the reason is –' here the Mock Turtle yawned and shut his eyes.– 'Tell her about the reason and all that,' he said to the Gryphon.

'The reason is,' said the Gryphon, 'that they *would* go with the lobsters to the dance. So they got thrown out to sea. So they had to fall a long way. So they got their tails fast in their mouths. So they couldn't get them out again. That's all.'

'Thank you,' said Alice, 'it's very interesting. I never knew so much about a whiting before.'

'I can tell you more than that, if you like,' said the Gryphon. 'Do you know why it's called a whiting?'

'I never thought about it,' said Alice. 'Why?'

'*It does the boots and shoes,*' the Gryphon replied very solemnly.

Alice was thoroughly puzzled. 'Does the boots and shoes!' she repeated in a wondering tone.

'Why, what are *your* shoes done with?' said the Gryphon. 'I mean what makes them so shiny?'

Alice looked down at them, and considered a little before she gave her answer. 'They're done with blacking, I believe.'

'Boots and shoes under the sea,' the Gryphon went on in a deep voice, 'are done with whiting. Now you know.'

'And what are they made of?' Alice asked in a tone of great curiosity.

'Soles and eels, of course,' the Gryphon replied rather impatiently: 'any shrimp could have told you that.'

'If I'd been the whiting,' said Alice, whose thoughts were still running on the song, 'I'd have said to the porpoise, "Keep back, please: we don't want *you* with us!"'

'They were obliged to have him with them,' the Mock Turtle said: 'no wise fish would go anywhere without a porpoise.'

'Wouldn't it really?' said Alice in a tone of great surprise.

'Of course not,' said the Mock Turtle: 'why, if a fish came to *me*, and told me he was going a journey, I should say "With what porpoise?"'

'Don't you mean "purpose"?' said Alice.

'I mean what I say,' the Mock Turtle replied in an offended tone. And the Gryphon added 'Come, let's hear some of *your* adventures.'

'I could tell you my adventures – beginning from this morning,' said Alice a little timidly: 'but it's no use going back to yesterday, because I was a different person then.' 'Explain all that,' said the Mock Turtle.

'No, no! The adventures first,' said the Gryphon in an impatient tone: 'explanations take such a dreadful time.'

So Alice began telling them her adventures from the time when she first saw the White Rabbit. She was a little nervous about it just at first, the two creatures got so close to her, one on each side, and opened their eyes and mouths so *very* wide, but she gained courage as she went on. Her listeners were perfectly quiet till she got to the part about her repeating '*You are old, Father William*,' to the Caterpillar, and the words all coming different, and then the Mock Turtle drew a long breath, and said 'That's very curious.'

'It's all about as curious as it can be,' said the Gryphon.

'It all came different!' the Mock Turtle repeated thoughtfully. 'I should like to hear her try and repeat something now. Tell her to begin.' He looked at the Gryphon as if he thought it had some kind of authority over Alice.

'Stand up and repeat "*'Tis the voice of the sluggard,*"' said the Gryphon.

'How the creatures order one about, and make one repeat lessons!' thought Alice; 'I might as well be at school at once.' However, she got up, and began to repeat it, but her head was so full of the Lobster Quadrille, that she hardly knew what she was saying, and the words came very queer indeed:–

> *"'Tis the voice of the Lobster; I heard him declare,*
> *"You have baked me too brown, I must sugar my hair."*
> *As a duck with its eyelids, so he with his nose*
> *Trims his belt and his buttons, and turns out his toes.'*

'That's different from what I used to say when I was a child,' said the Gryphon.

'Well, I never heard it before,' said the Mock Turtle; 'but it sounds uncommon nonsense.'

Alice said nothing; she had sat down with her face in her hands, wondering if anything would *ever* happen in a natural way again.

'I should like to have it explained,' said the Mock Turtle.

'She can't explain it,' said the Gryphon hastily. 'Go on with the next verse.'

'But about his toes?' the Mock Turtle persisted. 'How *could* he turn them out with his nose, you know?'

'It's the first position in dancing,' Alice said; but was dreadfully puzzled by the whole thing, and longed to change the subject.

'Go on with the next verse,' the Gryphon repeated impatiently: 'it begins "*I passed by his garden.*"'

Alice did not dare to disobey, though she felt sure it would all come wrong, and she went on in a trembling voice:

> *'I passed by his garden, and marked, with one eye,*
> *How the Owl and the Panther were sharing a pie –'*

'What is the use of repeating all that stuff,' the Mock Turtle interrupted, 'if you don't explain it as you go on? It's by far the most confusing thing I ever heard!'

'Yes, I think you'd better leave off,' said the Gryphon: and Alice was only too glad to do so.

'Shall we try another figure of the Lobster Quadrille?' the Gryphon went on. 'Or would you like the Mock Turtle to sing you a song?'

'Oh, a song, please, if the Mock Turtle would be so kind,' Alice replied, so eagerly that the Gryphon said, in a rather offended tone, 'Hm! No accounting for tastes! Sing her "*Turtle Soup*," will you, old fellow?'

The Mock Turtle sighed deeply, and began, in a voice sometimes choked with sobs, to sing this:–

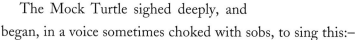

'Beautiful Soup, so rich and green,
Waiting in a hot tureen!
Who for such dainties would not stoop?
Soup of the evening, beautiful Soup!
Soup of the evening, beautiful Soup!
 Beau – ootiful Soo – oop!
 Beau – ootiful Soo – oop!
Soo – oop of the e – e – evening,
 Beautiful, beautiful Soup!

'Beautiful Soup! Who cares for fish,
Game, or any other dish?
Who would not give all else for two
pennyworth only of beautiful Soup?
Pennyworth only of beautiful Soup?
Beau – ootiful Soo – oop!
Beau – ootiful Soo – oop!
Soo – oop of the e – e – evening,
Beautiful, beauti – FUL SOUP!'

'Chorus again!' cried the Gryphon, and the Mock Turtle had just begun to repeat it, when a cry of 'The trial's beginning!' was heard in the distance.

'Come on!' cried the Gryphon, and, taking Alice by the hand, it hurried off, without waiting for the end of the song.

'What trial is it?' Alice panted as she ran; but the Gryphon only answered 'Come on!' and ran the faster, while more and more faintly came, carried on the breeze that followed them, the melancholy words:–

'Soo – oop of the e – e – evening,
Beautiful, beautiful Soup!'

CHAPTER ELEVEN

WHO STOLE THE TARTS?

The King and Queen of Hearts were seated on their throne when they arrived, with a great crowd assembled about them – all sorts of little birds and beasts, as well as the whole pack of cards: the Knave was standing before them, in chains, with a soldier on each side to guard him; and near the King was the White Rabbit, with a trumpet in one hand, and a scroll of parchment in the other. In the very middle of the court was a table, with a large dish of tarts upon it: they looked so good, that it made Alice quite hungry to look at them – 'I wish they'd get the trial done,' she thought, 'and hand round the refreshments!' But there seemed to be no chance of this, so she began looking at everything about her, to pass away the time.

Alice had never been in a court of justice before, but she had read about them in books, and she was quite pleased to find that she knew the name of nearly everything there. 'That's the judge,' she said to herself, 'because of his great wig.'

The judge, by the way, was the King; and as he wore his crown over the wig, (look at the frontispiece if you want to see how he did it,) he did not look at all comfortable, and it was certainly not becoming.

'And that's the jury-box,' thought Alice, 'and those twelve creatures,' (she was obliged to say 'creatures' you see, because some of them were animals, and some were birds,) 'I suppose they are the jurors.' She said this last word two or three times over to herself, being rather proud of it: for she thought, and rightly

too, that very few little girls of her age knew the meaning of it at all. However, 'jury-men' would have done just as well.

The twelve jurors were all writing very busily on slates. 'What are they doing?' Alice whispered to the Gryphon. 'They can't have anything to put down yet, before the trial's begun.'

'They're putting down their names,' the Gryphon whispered in reply, 'for fear they should forget them before the end of the trial.'

'Stupid things!' Alice began in a loud, indignant voice, but she stopped hastily, for the White Rabbit cried out, 'Silence in the court!' and the King put on his spectacles and looked anxiously round, to make out who was talking.

Alice could see, as well as if she were looking over their shoulders, that all the jurors were writing down 'stupid things!' on their slates, and she could even make out that one of them didn't know how to spell 'stupid,' and that he had to ask his neighbour to tell him. 'A nice muddle their slates'll be in before the trial's over!' thought Alice.

One of the jurors had a pencil that squeaked. This of course, Alice could *not* stand, and she went round the court and got behind him, and very soon found an opportunity of taking it away. She did it so quickly that the poor little juror (it was Bill, the Lizard) could not make out at all what had become of it; so, after hunting all about for it, he was obliged to write with one finger for the rest of the day; and this was of very little use, as it left no mark on the slate.

'Herald, read the accusation!' said the King.

On this the White Rabbit blew three blasts on the trumpet, and then unrolled the parchment scroll, and read as follows:–

> *'The Queen of Hearts, she made some tarts,*
> *All on a summer day:*
> *The Knave of Hearts, he stole those tarts,*
> *And took them quite away!'*

'Consider your verdict,' the King said to the jury.

'Not yet, not yet!' the Rabbit hastily interrupted. 'There's a great deal to come before that!'

'Call the first witness,' said the King; and the White Rabbit blew three blasts on the trumpet, and called out, 'First witness!'

The first witness was the Hatter. He came in with a teacup in one hand and a piece of bread-and-butter in the other. 'I beg pardon, your Majesty,' he began, 'for bringing these in: but I hadn't quite finished my tea when I was sent for.'

'You ought to have finished,' said the King. 'When did you begin?'

The Hatter looked at the March Hare, who had followed him into the court, arm-in-arm with the Dormouse. 'Fourteenth of March, I *think* it was,' he said.

'Fifteenth,' said the March Hare.

'Sixteenth,' added the Dormouse.

'Write that down,' the King said to the jury, and the jury eagerly wrote down all three dates on their slates, and then added them up, and reduced the answer to shillings and pence.

'Take off your hat,' the King said to the Hatter.

'It isn't mine,' said the Hatter.

'*Stolen!*' the King exclaimed, turning to the jury, who instantly made a memorandum of the fact.

'I keep them to sell,' the Hatter added as an explanation: 'I've none of my own. I'm a hatter.'

Here the Queen put on her spectacles, and began staring at the Hatter, who turned pale and fidgeted.

'Give your evidence,' said the King; 'and don't be nervous, or I'll have you executed on the spot.'

This did not seem to encourage the witness at all: he kept shifting from one foot to the other, looking uneasily at the Queen, and in his confusion he bit a large piece out of his teacup instead of the bread-and-butter.

Just at this moment Alice felt a very curious sensation, which puzzled her a good deal until she made out what it was: she was beginning to grow larger again, and she thought at first she would get up and leave the court; but on second thoughts she decided to remain where she was as long as there was room for her.

'I wish you wouldn't squeeze so,' said the Dormouse, who was sitting next to her. 'I can hardly breathe.'

'I can't help it,' said Alice very meekly: 'I'm growing.'

'You have no right to grow *here*,' said the Dormouse.

'Don't talk nonsense,' said Alice more boldly: 'you know you're growing too.'

'Yes, but *I* grow at a reasonable pace,' said the Dormouse: 'not in that ridiculous fashion.' And he got up very sulkily and crossed over to the other side of the court.

All this time the Queen had never left off staring at the Hatter, and, just as the Dormouse crossed the court, she said to one of the officers of the court, 'Bring me the list of the singers in the last concert!' on which the wretched Hatter trembled so, that he shook both his shoes off.

'Give your evidence,' the King repeated angrily, 'or I'll have you executed, whether you're nervous or not.'

'I'm a poor man, your Majesty,' the Hatter began, in a trembling voice, '– and I hadn't begun my tea – not above a week or so – and what with the bread-and-butter getting so thin – and the twinkling of the tea –'

'The twinkling of the *what*?' said the King.

'It *began* with the tea,' the Hatter replied.

'Of course twinkling begins with a T!' said the King sharply. 'Do you take me for a dunce? Go on!'

'I'm a poor man,' the Hatter went on, 'and most things twinkled after that – only the March Hare said –'

'I didn't!' the March Hare interrupted in a great hurry.

'You did!' said the Hatter.

'I deny it!' said the March Hare.

'He denies it,' said the King: 'leave out that part.'

'Well, at any rate, the Dormouse said –' the Hatter went on, looking anxiously round to see if he would deny it too: but the Dormouse denied nothing, being fast asleep.

'After that,' continued the Hatter, 'I cut some more bread-and-butter –'

'But what did the Dormouse say?' one of the jury asked.

'That I can't remember,' said the Hatter.

'You *must* remember,' remarked the King, 'or I'll have you executed.'

The miserable Hatter dropped his teacup and bread-and-butter, and went down on one knee. 'I'm a poor man, your Majesty,' he began.

'You're a *very* poor *speaker*,' said the King.

Here one of the guinea-pigs cheered, and was immediately suppressed by the officers of the court. (As that is rather a hard word, I will just explain to you how it was done. They had a large canvas bag, which tied up at the mouth with strings: into this they slipped the guinea-pig, head first, and then sat upon it.)

'I'm glad I've seen that done,' thought Alice. 'I've so often read in the newspapers, at the end of trials, "There was some attempt at applause, which was immediately suppressed by the officers of the court," and I never understood what it meant till now.'

'If that's all you know about it, you may stand down,' continued the King.

'I can't go no lower,' said the Hatter: 'I'm on the floor as it is.'

'Then you may *sit* down,' the King replied.

Here the other guinea-pig cheered, and was suppressed.

'Come, that finishes the guinea-pigs!' thought Alice. 'Now we shall get on better.'

'I'd rather finish my tea,' said the Hatter, with an anxious look at the Queen, who was reading the list of singers.

'You may go,' said the King, and the Hatter hurriedly left the court, without even waiting to put his shoes on.

'– and just take his head off outside,' the Queen added to one of the officers: but the Hatter was out of sight before the officer could get to the door.

'Call the next witness!' said the King.

The next witness was the Duchess's cook. She carried the pepper-box in her hand, and Alice guessed who it was, even before she got into the court, by the way people near the door began sneezing all at once.

'Give your evidence,' said the King.

'Shan't,' said the cook.

The King looked anxiously at the White Rabbit, who said in a low voice, 'Your Majesty must cross-examine *this* witness.'

'Well, if I must, I must,' the King said, with a melancholy air, and, after folding his arms and frowning at the cook till his eyes were nearly out of sight, he said in a deep voice, 'What are tarts made of?'

'Pepper, mostly,' said the cook.

'Treacle,' said a sleepy voice behind her.

'Collar that Dormouse,' the Queen shrieked out. 'Behead that Dormouse! Turn that Dormouse out of court! Suppress him! Pinch him! Off with his whiskers!'

For some minutes the whole court was in confusion, getting the Dormouse turned out, and, by the time they had settled down again, the cook had disappeared.

'Never mind!' said the King, with an air of great relief. 'Call the next witness.' And he added in an undertone to the Queen, 'Really, my dear, *you* must cross-examine the next witness. It quite makes my forehead ache!'

Alice watched the White Rabbit as he fumbled over the list, feeling very curious to see what the next witness would be like, '– for they haven't got much evidence *yet*,' she said to herself. Imagine her surprise, when the White Rabbit read out, at the top of his shrill little voice, the name 'Alice!'

CHAPTER TWELVE

ALICE'S EVIDENCE

'Here!' cried Alice, quite forgetting in the flurry of the moment how large she had grown in the last few minutes, and she jumped up in such a hurry that she tipped over the jury-box with the edge of her skirt, upsetting all the jurymen on to the heads of the crowd below, and there they lay sprawling about, reminding her very much of a globe of goldfish she had accidentally upset the week before.

'Oh, I *beg* your pardon!' she exclaimed in a tone of great dismay, and began picking them up again as quickly as she could, for the accident of the goldfish kept running in her head, and she had a vague sort of idea that they must be collected at once and put back into the jury-box, or they would die.

'The trial cannot proceed,' said the King in a very grave voice, 'until all the jurymen are back in their proper places – *all*,' he repeated with great emphasis, looking hard at Alice as he said so.

Alice looked at the jury-box, and saw that, in her haste, she had put the Lizard in head downwards, and the poor little thing was waving its tail about in a melancholy way, being quite unable to move. She soon got it out again, and put it right; 'not that it signifies much,' she said to herself; 'I should think it would be *quite* as much use in the trial one way up as the other.'

As soon as the jury had a little recovered from the shock of being upset, and

their slates and pencils had been found and handed back to them, they set to work very diligently to write out a history of the accident, all except the Lizard, who seemed too much overcome to do anything but sit with its mouth open, gazing up into the roof of the court.

'What do you know about this business?' the King said to Alice.

'Nothing,' said Alice.

'Nothing whatever?' persisted the King.

'Nothing *whatever*,' said Alice.

'That's very important,' the King said, turning to the jury. They were just beginning to write this down on their slates, when the White Rabbit interrupted: '*Un*important, your Majesty means, of course,' he said in a very respectful tone, but frowning and making faces at him as he spoke.

'*Un*important, of course, I meant,' the King hastily said, and went on to himself in an undertone, 'important – unimportant – unimportant – important –' as if he were trying which word sounded best.

Some of the jury wrote it down 'important,' and some 'unimportant.' Alice could see this, as she was near enough to look over their slates; 'but it doesn't matter a bit,' she thought to herself.

At this moment the King, who had been for some time busily writing in his note-book, called out 'Silence!' and read out from his book, 'Rule Forty-two. *All persons more than a mile high to leave the court.*'

Everybody looked at Alice.

'*I'm* not a mile high,' said Alice.

'You are,' said the King.

'Nearly two miles high,' added the Queen.

'Well, I shan't go, at any rate,' said Alice: 'besides, that's not a regular rule: you invented it just now.'

'It's the oldest rule in the book,' said the King.

'Then it ought to be Number One,' said Alice.

The King turned pale, and shut his note-book hastily. 'Consider your verdict,' he said to the jury, in a low trembling voice.

'There's more evidence to come yet, please your Majesty,' said the White Rabbit, jumping up in a great hurry; 'this paper has just been picked up.'

'What's in it?' said the Queen.

'I haven't opened it yet,' said the White Rabbit, 'but it seems to be a letter, written by the prisoner to – to somebody.'

'It must have been that,' said the King, 'unless it was written to nobody, which isn't usual, you know.'

'Who is it directed to?' said one of the jurymen.

'It isn't directed at all,' said the White Rabbit; 'in fact, there's nothing written on the *outside*.' He unfolded the paper as he spoke, and added 'It isn't a letter, after all: it's a set of verses.'

'Are they in the prisoner's handwriting?' asked another of the jurymen.

'No, they're not,' said the White Rabbit, 'and that's the queerest thing about it.' (The jury all looked puzzled.)

'He must have imitated somebody else's hand,' said the King. (The jury all brightened up again.)

'Please your Majesty,' said the Knave; 'I didn't write it, and they can't prove I did: there's no name signed at the end.'

'If you didn't sign it,' said the King, 'that only makes the matter worse. You *must* have meant some mischief, or else you'd have signed your name like an honest man.'

There was a general clapping of hands at this: it was the first really clever thing the King had said that day.

'That *proves* his guilt,' said the Queen.

'It proves nothing of the sort!' said Alice. 'Why, you don't even know what they're about!'

'Read them,' said the King.

The White Rabbit put on his spectacles. 'Where shall I begin, please your Majesty?' he asked.

'Begin at the beginning,' the King said gravely, 'and go on till you come to the end: then stop.'

These were the verses the White Rabbit read:–

'They told me you had been to her,
And mentioned me to him:
She gave me a good character,
But said I could not swim.

He sent them word I had not gone
(We know it to be true):
If she should push the matter on,
What would become of you?

I gave her one, they gave him two,
You gave us three or more;
They all returned from him to you,
Though they were mine before.

If I or she should chance to be
Involved in this affair,
He trusts to you to set them free,
Exactly as we were.

My notion was that you had been
(Before she had this fit)
An obstacle that came between
Him, and ourselves, and it.

Don't let him know she liked them best,
For this must ever be
A secret, kept from all the rest,
Between yourself and me.'

'That's the most important piece of evidence we've heard yet,' said the King, rubbing his hands; 'so now let the jury –'

'If any one of them can explain it,' said Alice, (she had grown so large in the last few minutes that she wasn't a bit afraid of interrupting him,) 'I'll give him sixpence. *I* don't believe there's an atom of meaning in it.'

The jury all wrote down on their slates, '*She* doesn't believe there's an atom of meaning in it,' but none of them attempted to explain the paper.

'If there's no meaning in it,' said the King, 'that saves a world of trouble, you know, as we needn't try to find any. And yet I don't know,' he went on, spreading out the verses on his knee, and looking at them with one eye; 'I seem to see some meaning in them, after all. "– *said I could not swim –*" you can't swim, can you?' he added, turning to the Knave.

The Knave shook his head sadly. 'Do I look like it?' he said. (Which

he certainly did not, being made entirely of cardboard.)

'All right, so far,' said the King, and he went on muttering over the verses to himself: '"*We know it to be true* –" that's the jury, of course – "*I gave her one, they gave him two* –" why, that must be what he did with the tarts, you know –'

'But, it goes on "*they all returned from him to you*,"' said Alice.

'Why, there they are!' said the King triumphantly, pointing to the tarts on the table. 'Nothing can be clearer than *that*. Then again – "*before she had this fit*–" you never had fits, my dear, I think?' he said to the Queen.

'Never!' said the Queen furiously, throwing an inkstand at the Lizard as she spoke. (The unfortunate little Bill had left off writing on his slate with one finger, as he found it made no mark; but he now hastily began again, using the ink, that was trickling down his face, as long as it lasted.)

'Then the words don't *fit* you,' said the King, looking round the court with a smile. There was a dead silence.

'It's a pun!' the King added in an offended tone, and everybody laughed. 'Let the jury consider their verdict,' the King said, for about the twentieth time that day.

'No, no!' said the Queen. 'Sentence first – verdict afterwards.'

'Stuff and nonsense!' said Alice loudly. 'The idea of having the sentence first!'

'Hold your tongue!' said the Queen, turning purple.

'I won't!' said Alice.

'Off with her head!' the Queen shouted at the top of her voice. Nobody moved.

'Who cares for you?' said Alice, (she had grown to her full size by this time.) 'You're nothing but a pack of cards!'

At this the whole pack rose up into the air, and came flying down upon her: she gave a little scream, half of fright and half of anger, and tried to beat them off, and found herself lying on the bank, with her head in the lap of her sister, who was gently brushing away some dead leaves that had fluttered down from the trees upon her face.

'Wake up, Alice dear!' said her sister; 'Why, what a long sleep you've had!'

'Oh, I've had such a curious dream!' said Alice, and she told her sister, as well as she could remember them, all these strange Adventures of hers that you have just been reading about; and when she had finished, her sister kissed her, and said, 'It was a curious dream, dear, certainly: but now run in to your tea; it's getting late.' So Alice got up and ran off, thinking while she ran, as well she might, what a wonderful dream it had been.

*　　*　　*　　*

*　　*　　*

*　　*　　*　　*

But her sister sat still just as she left her, leaning her head on her hand, watching the setting sun, and thinking of little Alice and all her wonderful Adventures, till she too began dreaming after a fashion, and this was her dream:–

First, she dreamed of little Alice herself, and once again the tiny hands were clasped upon her knee, and the bright eager eyes were looking up into hers – she could hear the very tones of her voice, and see that queer little toss of her head to keep back the wandering hair that *would* always get into her eyes – and still as

she listened, or seemed to listen, the whole place around her became alive with the strange creatures of her little sister's dream.

The long grass rustled at her feet as the White Rabbit hurried by – the frightened Mouse splashed his way through the neighbouring pool – she could hear the rattle of the teacups as the March Hare and his friends shared their never-ending meal, and the shrill voice of the Queen ordering off her unfortunate guests to execution – once more the pig-baby was sneezing on the Duchess's knee, while plates and dishes crashed around it – once more the shriek of the Gryphon, the squeaking of the Lizard's slate-pencil, and the choking of the suppressed guinea-pigs, filled the air, mixed up with the distant sobs of the miserable Mock Turtle.

So she sat on, with closed eyes, and half believed herself in Wonderland, though she knew she had but to open them again, and all would change to dull reality – the grass would be only rustling in the wind, and the pool rippling to the waving of the reeds – the rattling teacups would change to tinkling sheep-bells, and the Queen's shrill cries to the voice of the shepherd boy – and the sneeze of the baby, the shriek of the Gryphon, and all the other queer noises, would change (she knew) to the confused clamours of the busy farm-yard – while the lowing of the cattle in the distance would take the place of the Mock Turtle's heavy sobs.

Lastly, she pictured to herself how this same little sister of hers would, in the after-time, be herself a grown woman; and how she would keep, through all her riper years, the simple and loving heart of her childhood: and how she would gather about her other little children, and make *their* eyes bright and eager with many a strange tale, perhaps even with the dream of Wonderland of long ago: and how she would feel with all their simple sorrows, and find a pleasure in all their simple joys, remembering her own child-life, and the happy summer days.

THE END

'Would you tell me, please, which way I ought
to go from here?'

– Chapter six: Pig and Pepper

EVERY CHILD WHO LOVES
Alice

DEAR CHILD

Please to fancy, if you can, that you are reading a real letter, from a real friend whom you have seen, and whose voice you can seem to yourself to hear wishing you, as I do now with all my heart, a happy Easter.

Do you know that delicious dreamy feeling when one first wakes on a summer morning, with the twitter of birds in the air, and the fresh breeze coming in at the open window – when, lying lazily with eyes half-shut, one sees as in a dream green boughs waving, or waters rippling in a golden light? It is a pleasure very near to sadness, bringing tears to one's eyes like a beautiful picture or poem. And is not that a Mother's gentle hand that undraws your curtains, and a Mother's sweet voice that summons you to rise? To rise and forget, in the bright sunlight, the ugly dreams that frightened you so when all was dark – to rise and enjoy another happy day, first kneeling to thank that unseen Friend, who sends you the beautiful sun?

Are these strange words from a writer of such tales as 'Alice'? And is this a strange letter to find in a book of nonsense? It may be so. Some perhaps may blame me for thus mixing together things grave and gay; others may smile and think it odd that any one should speak of solemn things at all, except in church and on a Sunday: but I think – nay, I am sure – that some children will read this gently and lovingly, and in the spirit in which I have written it.

For I do not believe God means us thus to divide life into two halves – to wear a grave face on Sunday, and to think it out-of-place to even so much as mention Him on a week-day. Do you think He cares to see only kneeling figures, and to hear only tones of prayer – and that He does not also love to see the lambs leaping in the sunlight, and to hear the merry voices of the children, as they roll among the

hay? Surely their innocent laughter is as sweet in His ears as the grandest anthem that ever rolled up from the 'dim religious light' of some solemn cathedral?

And if I have written anything to add to those stories of innocent and healthy amusement that are laid up in books for the children I love so well, it is surely something I may hope to look back upon without shame and sorrow (as how much of life must then be recalled!) when my turn comes to walk through the valley of shadows.

This Easter sun will rise on you, dear child, feeling your 'life in every limb', and eager to rush out into the fresh morning air – and many an Easter-day will come and go, before it finds you feeble and gray-headed, creeping wearily out to bask once more in the sunlight – but it is good, even now, to think sometimes of that great morning when the 'Sun of Righteousness shall arise with healing in his wings'.

Surely your gladness need not be the less for the thought that you will one day see a brighter dawn than this – when lovelier sights will meet your eyes than any waving trees or rippling waters – when angel-hands shall undraw your curtains, and sweeter tones than ever loving Mother breathed shall wake you to a new and glorious day – and when all the sadness, and the sin, that darkened life on this little earth, shall be forgotten like the dreams of a night that is past!

Your affectionate friend,
LEWIS CARROLL

Easter, 1876

CHRISTMAS GREETINGS

FROM A FAIRY TO A CHILD

Lady dear, if Fairies may
    For a moment lay aside
Cunning tricks and elfish play,
    'Tis at happy Christmas-tide.

We have heard the children say –
    Gentle children, whom we love –
Long ago, on Christmas Day,
    Came a message from above.

Still, as Christmas-tide comes round,
    They remember it again –
Echo still the joyful sound,
    'Peace on earth, good-will to men.'

Yet the hearts must child-like be
    Where such heavenly guests abide.
Unto children, in their glee,
    All the year is Christmas-tide.

Thus, forgetting tricks and play
    For a moment, Lady dear,
We would wish you, if we may,
    Merry Christmas, glad New Year.

Christmas, 1887

She thought she had never seen such a strange-looking
soldier in all her life.

He was dressed in tin armour, which seemed to fit him
very badly, and he had a queer-shaped little deal box
fastened across his shoulders, upside-down, and with the
lid hanging open. Alice looked at it with great curiosity.

– *Chapter eight: 'It's My Own Invention'*

THROUGH THE LOOKING GLASS

and what Alice found there

RED

WHITE

DRAMATIS PERSONÆ

(As arranged before commencement of game)

WHITE		RED	
PIECES	PAWNS	PAWNS	PIECES
Tweedledee	Daisy	Daisy	Humpty Dumpty
Unicorn	Haigha	Messenger	Carpenter
Sheep	Oyster	Oyster	Walrus
W.Queen	'Lily'	Tiger-lily	R.Queen
W.King	Fawn	Rose	R.King
Aged man	Oyster	Oyster	Crow
W.Knight	Hatta	Frog	R.Knight
Tweedledum	Daisy	Daisy	Lion

White Pawn (Alice) to play, and win in eleven moves

'Where do you come from?' said the Red Queen.
'And where are you going? Look up, speak nicely, and
don't twiddle your fingers all the time.'

– Chapter two: The Garden of Live Flowers

PREFACE

As the chess-problem, given on a previous page, has puzzled some of my readers, it may be well to explain that it is correctly worked out, so far as the *moves* are concerned. The *alternation* of Red and White is perhaps not so strictly observed as it might be, and the 'castling' of the three Queens is merely a way of saying that they entered the palace: but the 'check' of the White King at move 6, the capture of the Red Knight at move 7, and the final 'checkmate' of the Red King, will be found, by any one who will take the trouble to set the pieces and play the moves as directed, to be strictly in accordance with the laws of the game.

The new words, in the poem *Jabberwocky* (see p.144), have given rise to some differences of opinion as to their pronunciation: so it may be well to give instructions on *that* point also. Pronounce 'slithy' as if it were the two words 'sly, the': make the 'g' *hard* in 'gyre' and 'gimble': and pronounce 'rath' to rhyme with 'bath.'

Child of the pure unclouded brow
And dreaming eyes of wonder!
Though time be fleet, and I and thou
Are half a life asunder,
Thy loving smile will surely hail
The love-gift of a fairy-tale.

I have not seen thy sunny face,
Nor heard thy silver laughter;
No thought of me shall find a place
In thy young life's hereafter –
Enough that now thou wilt not fail
To listen to my fairy-tale.

A tale begun in other days,
When summer suns were glowing –
A simple chime, that served to time
The rhythm of our rowing –
Whose echoes live in memory yet,
Though envious years would say 'forget.'

Come, hearken then, ere voice of dread,
With bitter tidings laden,
Shall summon to unwelcome bed
A melancholy maiden!
We are but older children, dear,
Who fret to find our bedtime near.

Without, the frost, the blinding snow,
The storm-wind's moody madness —
Within, the firelight's ruddy glow,
And childhood's nest of gladness.
The magic words shall hold thee fast:
Thou shalt not heed the raving blast.

And though the shadow of a sigh
May tremble through the story,
For 'happy summer days' gone by,
And vanish'd summer glory —
It shall not touch with breath of bale
The pleasance of our fairy-tale.

'Well, "*toves*" are something like badgers – they're something like
lizards – and they're something like corkscrews.'

'They must be very curious-looking creatures.'

'They are that,' said Humpty Dumpty: 'also they make their nests
under sun-dials – also they live on cheese.'

– *Chapter six: Humpty Dumpty*

CHAPTER ONE

LOOKING-GLASS HOUSE

One thing was certain, that the *white* kitten had had nothing to do with it: it was the black kitten's fault entirely. For the white kitten had been having its face washed by the old cat for the last quarter of an hour (and bearing it pretty well, considering); so you see that it *couldn't* have had any hand in the mischief.

The way Dinah washed her children's faces was this: first she held the poor thing down by its ear with one paw, and then with the other paw she rubbed its face all over, the wrong way, beginning at the nose: and just now, as I said, she was hard at work on the white kitten, which was lying quite still and trying to purr – no doubt feeling that it was all meant for its good.

But the black kitten had been finished with earlier in the afternoon, and so, while Alice was sitting curled up in a corner of the great arm-chair, half talking to herself and half asleep, the kitten had been having a grand game of romps with the ball of worsted Alice had been trying to wind up, and had been rolling it up and down till it had all come undone again; and there it was, spread over the hearth-rug, all knots and tangles, with the kitten running after its own tail in the middle.

'Oh, you wicked wicked little thing!' cried Alice, catching up the kitten, and giving it a little kiss to make it understand that it was in disgrace. 'Really, Dinah ought to have taught you better manners! You *ought*, Dinah, you know you ought!'

she added, looking reproachfully at the old cat, and speaking in as cross a voice as she could manage – and then she scrambled back into the arm-chair, taking the kitten and the worsted with her, and began winding up the ball again. But she didn't get on very fast, as she was talking all the time, sometimes to the kitten, and sometimes to herself. Kitty sat very demurely on her knee, pretending to watch the progress of the winding, and now and then putting out one paw and gently touching the ball, as if it would be glad to help if it might.

'Do you know what to-morrow is, Kitty?' Alice began. 'You'd have guessed if you'd been up in the window with me – only Dinah was making you tidy, so you couldn't. I was watching the boys getting in sticks for the bonfire – and it wants plenty of sticks, Kitty! Only it got so cold, and it snowed so, they had to leave off. Never mind, Kitty, we'll go and see the bonfire to-morrow.' Here Alice wound two or three turns of the worsted round the kitten's neck, just to see how it would look: this led to a scramble, in which the ball rolled down upon the floor, and yards and yards of it got unwound again.

'Do you know, I was so angry, Kitty,' Alice went on as soon as they were comfortably settled again, 'when I saw all the mischief you had been doing, I was very nearly opening the window, and putting you out into the snow! And you'd have deserved it, you little mischievous darling! What have you got to say for yourself? Now don't interrupt me!' she went on, holding up one finger. 'I'm going to tell you all your faults. Number one: you squeaked twice while Dinah was washing your face this morning. Now you can't deny it, Kitty: I heard you! What's that you say?' (pretending that the kitten was speaking.) 'Her paw went into your eye? Well, that's *your* fault, for keeping your eyes open – if you'd shut

CHAPTER ONE: LOOKING-GLASS HOUSE

them tight up, it wouldn't have happened. Now don't make any more excuses, but listen! Number two: you pulled Snowdrop away by the tail just as I had put down the saucer of milk before her! What, you were thirsty, were you? How do you know she wasn't thirsty too? Now for Number three: you unwound every bit of the worsted while I wasn't looking!

'That's three faults, Kitty, and you've not been punished for any of them yet. You know I'm saving up all your punishments for Wednesday week – Suppose they had saved up all my punishments!' she went on, talking more to herself than the kitten. 'What *would* they do at the end of the year? I should be sent to prison, I suppose, when the day came. Or – let me see – suppose each punishment was to be going without a dinner: then, when the miserable day came, I should have to go without fifty dinners at once! Well, I shouldn't mind *that* much! I'd far rather go without them than eat them!

'Do you hear the snow against the window-panes, Kitty? How nice and soft it sounds! Just as if some one was kissing the window all over outside. I wonder if the snow *loves* the trees and fields, that it kisses them so gently? And then it covers them up snug, you know, with a white quilt; and perhaps it says, "Go to sleep, darlings, till the summer comes again." And when they wake up in the summer, Kitty, they dress themselves all in green, and dance about – whenever the wind blows – oh, that's very pretty!' cried Alice, dropping the ball of worsted to clap her hands. 'And I do so *wish* it was true! I'm sure the woods look sleepy in the autumn, when the leaves are getting brown.

'Kitty, can you play chess? Now, don't smile, my dear, I'm asking it seriously. Because, when we were playing just now, you watched just as if you understood it: and when I said "Check!" you purred! Well, it *was* a nice check, Kitty, and really I might have won, if it hadn't been for that nasty Knight, that came wriggling down among my pieces. Kitty, dear, let's pretend –' And here I wish I could tell you half the things Alice used to say, beginning with her favourite phrase 'Let's pretend.' She had had quite a long argument with her sister only the day before – all because Alice had begun with 'Let's pretend we're kings and queens;' and her sister, who liked being very exact, had argued that they couldn't, because there were only two of them, and Alice had been reduced at last to say, 'Well, *you* can be one of them then, and *I'll* be all the rest.' And once she had really frightened her old nurse by shouting suddenly in her ear, 'Nurse!

Do let's pretend that I'm a hungry hyæna, and you're a bone!'

But this is taking us away from Alice's speech to the kitten. 'Let's pretend that you're the Red Queen, Kitty! Do you know, I think if you sat up and folded your arms, you'd look exactly like her. Now do try, there's a dear!' And Alice got the Red Queen off the table, and set it up before the kitten as a model for it to imitate: however, the thing didn't succeed, principally, Alice said, because the kitten wouldn't fold its arms properly. So, to punish it, she held it up to the Looking glass, that it might see how sulky it was – 'and if you're not

good directly,' she added, 'I'll put you through the Looking-glass House. How would you like *that*?

'Now, if you'll only attend, Kitty, and not talk so much, I'll tell you all my ideas about Looking-glass House. First, there's the room you can see through the glass – that's just the same as our drawing-room, only the things go the other way. I can see all of it when I get upon a chair – all but the bit just behind the fireplace. Oh! I do so wish I could see *that* bit! I want so much to know whether they've a fire in the winter: you never *can* tell, you know, unless our fire smokes, and then smoke comes up in that room too – but that may be only pretence, just to make it look as if they had a fire. Well then, the books are something like our books, only the words go the wrong way; I know that, because I've held up one of our books to the glass, and then they hold up one in the other room.

'How would you like to live in Looking-glass House, Kitty? I wonder if they'd give you milk in there? Perhaps Looking-glass milk isn't good to drink – But oh, Kitty! now we come to the passage. You can just see a little *peep* of the passage in Looking-glass House, if you leave the door of our drawing-room wide open: and it's very like our passage as far as you can see, only you know it may be quite different on beyond. Oh, Kitty! how nice it would be if we could only get through into Looking-glass House! I'm sure it's got, oh! such beautiful things in it! Let's pretend there's a way of getting through into it, somehow, Kitty. Let's pretend the glass has got all soft like gauze, so that we can get through. Why, it's turning into a sort of mist now, I declare! It'll be easy enough to get through –' She was up on the chimney-piece while she said this, though she hardly knew how she had got there. And certainly the glass was beginning to melt away, just like a bright silvery mist.

In another moment Alice was through the glass, and had jumped lightly down into the Looking-glass room. The very first thing she did was to look whether there was a fire in the fireplace, and she was quite pleased to find that

there was a real one, blazing away as brightly as the one she had left behind. 'So I shall be as warm here as I was in the old room,' thought Alice: 'warmer, in fact, because there'll be no one here to scold me away from the fire. Oh, what fun it'll be, when they see me through the glass in here, and can't get at me!'

Then she began looking about and noticed that what could be seen from the old room was quite common and uninteresting, but that all the rest was as different as possible. For instance, the pictures on the wall next to the fire seemed to be all alive, and the very clock on the chimney-piece (you know you can only see the back of it in the Looking glass) had got the face of a little old man, and grinned at her.

'They don't keep this room so tidy as the other,' Alice thought to herself, as she noticed several of the chessmen down in the hearth among the cinders: but in another moment, with a little 'Oh!' of surprise, she was down on her hands and knees watching them. The chessmen were walking about, two and two!

'Here are the Red King and the Red Queen,' Alice said (in a whisper, for fear of frightening them), 'and there are the White King and the White Queen sitting on the edge of the shovel – and here are two Castles walking arm in arm – I don't think they can hear me,' she went on, as she put her head closer down, 'and I'm nearly sure they can't see me. I feel somehow as if I were invisible –'

Here something began squeaking on the table behind Alice, and made her turn her head just in time to see one of the White Pawns roll over and begin kicking: she watched it with great curiosity to see what would happen next.

'It is the voice of my child!' the White Queen cried out as she rushed past the King, so violently that she knocked him over among the cinders. 'My precious Lily! My imperial kitten!' and she began scrambling wildly up the side of the fender.

'Imperial fiddlestick!' said the King, rubbing his nose, which had been hurt by the fall. He had a right to be a *little* annoyed with the Queen, for he was covered with ashes from head to foot.

Alice was very anxious to be of use, and, as the poor little Lily was nearly screaming herself into a fit, she hastily picked up the Queen and set her on the table by the side of her noisy little daughter.

The Queen gasped, and sat down: the rapid journey through the air had quite taken away her breath and for a minute or two she could do nothing but hug the little Lily in silence. As soon as she had recovered her breath a little, she called out to the White King, who was sitting sulkily among the ashes, 'Mind the volcano!'

'What volcano?' said the King, looking up anxiously into the fire, as if he thought that was the most likely place to find one.

'Blew – me – up,' panted the Queen, who was still a little out of breath. 'Mind you come up – the regular way – don't get blown up!'

Alice watched the White King as he slowly struggled up from bar to bar, till at last she said, 'Why, you'll be hours and hours getting to the table, at that rate. I'd far better help you, hadn't I?' But the King took no notice of the question: it was quite clear that he could neither hear her nor see her.

So Alice picked him up very gently, and lifted him across more slowly than she had lifted the Queen, that she mightn't take his breath away: but, before she put him on the table, she thought she might as well dust him a little, he was so covered in ashes.

She said afterwards that she had never seen in all her life such a face as the King made, when he found himself held in the air by an invisible hand, and being dusted: he was far too much astonished to cry out, but his eyes and mouth

went on getting larger and larger, and rounder and rounder, till her hand shook so with laughing that she nearly let him drop upon the floor.

'Oh! *please* don't make such faces, my dear!' she cried out, quite forgetting that the King couldn't hear her. 'You make me laugh so that I can hardly hold you! And don't keep your mouth so wide open! All the ashes will get into it – there, now I think you're tidy enough!' she added, as she smoothed his hair, and set him upon the table near the Queen.

The King immediately fell flat on his back, and lay perfectly still: and Alice was a little alarmed at what she had done, and went round the room to see if she could find any water to throw over him. However, she could find nothing but a bottle of ink, and when she got back with it she found he had recovered, and he and the Queen were talking together in a frightened whisper – so low, that Alice could hardly hear what they said.

The King was saying, 'I assure you, my dear, I turned cold to the very ends of my whiskers!'

To which the Queen replied, 'You haven't got any whiskers.'

'The horror of that moment,' the King went on, 'I shall never, *never* forget!'

'You will, though,' the Queen said, 'if you don't make a memorandum of it.'

Alice looked on with great interest as the King took an enormous memorandum-book out of his pocket, and began writing. A sudden thought struck her, and she took hold of the end of the pencil, which came some way over his shoulder, and began writing for him.

The poor King looked puzzled and unhappy, and struggled with the pencil for some time without saying anything; but Alice was too strong for him, and at last he panted out, 'My dear! I really *must* get a thinner pencil. I can't manage this one a bit; it writes all manner of things that I don't intend –'

'What manner of things?' said the Queen, looking over the book (in which Alice had put '*The White Knight is sliding down the poker. He balances very badly*'). 'That's not a memorandum of *your* feelings!'

There was a book lying near Alice on the table, and while she sat watching the White King (for she was still a little anxious about him, and had the ink all ready to throw over him, in case he fainted again), she turned over the leaves, to find some part that she could read, '– for it's all in some language I don't know,' she said to herself.

It was like this.

JABBERWOCKY

'Twas brillig, and the slithy toves
Did gyre and gimble in the wabe;
All mimsy were the borogoves,
And the mome raths outgrabe.

She puzzled over this for some time, but at last a bright thought struck her.

'Why, it's a Looking-glass book, of course! And if I hold it up to a glass, the words will all go the right way again.'

This was the poem that Alice read.

JABBERWOCKY

'Twas brillig, and the slithy toves
Did gyre and gimble in the wabe;
All mimsy were the borogoves,
And the mome raths outgrabe.

'Beware the Jabberwock, my son!
The jaws that bite, the claws that catch!
Beware the Jubjub bird, and shun
The frumious Bandersnatch!'

He took his vorpal sword in hand:
Long time the manxome foe he sought –
So rested he by the Tumtum tree,
And stood awhile in thought.

And as in uffish thought he stood,
The Jabberwock, with eyes of flame,
Came whiffling through the tulgey wood,
And burbled as it came!

One, two! One, two! And through and through
The vorpal blade went snicker-snack!
He left it dead, and with its head
He went galumphing back.

CHAPTER ONE: LOOKING-GLASS HOUSE

'And has thou slain the Jabberwock?
Come to my arms, my beamish boy!
A frabjous day! Callooh! Callay!'
He chortled in his joy.

'Twas brillig, and the slithy toves
Did gyre and gimble in the wabe;
All mimsy were the borogoves,
And the mome raths outgrabe.

'It seems very pretty,' she said when she had finished it, 'but it's *rather* hard to understand!' (You see she didn't like to confess, even to herself, that she couldn't make it out at all.) 'Somehow it seems to fill my head with ideas – only I don't exactly know what they are! However, *somebody* killed *something*: that's clear, at any rate –'

'But oh!' thought Alice, suddenly jumping up, 'if I don't make haste I shall have to go back through the Looking glass, before I've seen what the rest of the house is like! Let's have a look at the garden first!' She was out of the room in a moment, and ran down stairs – or, at least, it wasn't exactly running, but a new invention for getting down stairs quickly and easily, as Alice said to herself. She just kept the tips of her fingers on the hand-rail, and floated gently down without even touching the stairs with her feet; then she floated on through the hall, and would have gone straight out at the door in the same way, if she hadn't caught hold of the door-post. She was getting a little giddy with so much floating in the air, and was rather glad to find herself walking again in the natural way.

CHAPTER TWO

THE GARDEN OF LIVE FLOWERS

'*I* should see the garden far better,' said Alice to herself, 'if I could get to the top of that hill: and here's a path that leads straight to it – at least, no, it doesn't do that –' (after going a few yards along the path, and turning several sharp corners), 'but I suppose it will at last. But how curiously it twists! It's more like a corkscrew than a path! Well, *this* turn goes to the hill, I suppose – no, it doesn't! This goes straight back to the house! Well then, I'll try it the other way.'

And so she did: wandering up and down, and trying turn after turn, but always coming back to the house, do what she would. Indeed, once, when she turned a corner rather more quickly than usual, she ran against it before she could stop herself.

'It's no use talking about it,' Alice said, looking up at the house and pretending it was arguing with her. 'I'm *not* going in again yet. I know I should have to get through the Looking glass again – back into the old room – and there'd be an end of all my adventures!'

So, resolutely turning her back upon the house, she set out once more down the path, determined to keep straight on till she got to the hill. For a few minutes all went on well, and she was just saying, 'I really *shall* do it this time –' when the path gave a sudden twist and shook itself (as she described it afterwards), and the next moment she found herself actually walking in at the door.

'Oh, it's too bad!' she cried. 'I never saw such a house for getting in the way! Never!'

However, there was the hill full in sight, so there was nothing to be done but start again. This time she came upon a large flower-bed, with a border of daisies, and a willow-tree growing in the middle.

'O Tiger-lily,' said Alice, addressing herself to one that was waving gracefully about in the wind, 'I *wish* you could talk!'

'We *can* talk,' said the Tiger-lily: 'when there's anybody worth talking to.'

Alice was so astonished that she could not speak for a minute: it quite seemed to take her breath away. At length, as the Tiger-lily only went on waving about, she spoke again, in a timid voice – almost in a whisper. 'And can *all* the flowers talk?'

'As well as *you* can,' said the Tiger-lily. 'And a great deal louder.'

'It isn't manners for us to begin, you know,' said the Rose, 'and I really was wondering when you'd speak! Said I to myself, "Her face has got *some* sense in it, though it's not a clever one!" Still, you're the right colour, and that goes a long way.'

'I don't care about the colour,' the Tiger-lily remarked. 'If only her petals curled up a little more, she'd be all right.'

Alice didn't like being criticised, so she began asking questions. 'Aren't you sometimes frightened at being planted out here, with nobody to take care of you?'

'There's the tree in the middle,' said the Rose: 'what else is it good for?'

'But what could it do, if any danger came?' Alice asked.

'It could bark,' said the Rose.

'It says "Bough-wough!"' cried a Daisy: 'that's why its branches are called boughs!'

'Didn't you know *that*?' cried another Daisy, and here they all began shouting together, till the air seemed quite full of little shrill voices. 'Silence, every one

of you!' cried the Tiger-lily, waving itself passionately from side to side, and trembling with excitement. 'They know I can't get at them!' it panted, bending its quivering head towards Alice, 'or they wouldn't dare to do it!'

'Never mind!' Alice said in a soothing tone, and stooping down to the daisies, who were just beginning again, she whispered, 'If you don't hold your tongues, I'll pick you!'

There was silence in a moment, and several of the pink daisies turned white.

'That's right!' said the Tiger-lily. 'The daisies are worst of all. When one speaks, they all begin together, and it's enough to make one wither to hear the way they go on!'

'How is it you can all talk so nicely?' Alice said, hoping to get it into a better temper by a compliment. 'I've been in many gardens before, but none of the flowers could talk.'

'Put your hand down, and feel the ground,' said the Tiger-lily. 'Then you'll know why.'

Alice did so. 'It's very hard,' she said, 'but I don't see what that has to do with it.'

'In most gardens,' the Tiger-lily said, 'they make the beds too soft – so that the flowers are always asleep.'

This sounded a very good reason, and Alice was quite pleased to know it. 'I never thought of that before!' she said.

'It's *my* opinion that you never think *at all*,' the Rose said in a rather severe tone.

'I never saw anybody looked stupider,' a Violet said, so suddenly, that Alice quite jumped; for it hadn't spoken before.

'Hold *your* tongue!' cried the Tiger-lily. 'As if *you* ever saw anybody! You keep your head under the leaves, and snore away there, till you know no more what's going on in the world, than if you were a bud!'

'Are there any more people in the garden besides me?' Alice said, not choosing to notice the Rose's last remark.

'There's one other flower in the garden that can move about like you,' said the Rose. 'I wonder how you do it –' ('You're always wondering,' said the Tiger-lily), 'but she's more bushy than you are.'

'Is she like me?' Alice asked eagerly, for the thought crossed her mind, 'There's another little girl in the garden, somewhere!'

'Well, she has the same awkward shape as you,' the Rose said, 'but she's redder – and her petals are shorter, I think.'

'Her petals are done up close, almost like a dahlia,' the Tiger-lily interrupted: 'not tumbled about anyhow, like yours.'

'But that's not *your* fault,' the Rose added kindly: 'you're beginning to fade,

you know – and then one can't help one's petals getting a little untidy.'

Alice didn't like this idea at all: so, to change the subject, she asked 'Does she ever come out here?'

'I daresay you'll see her soon,' said the Rose. 'She's one of the thorny kind.'

'Where does she wear the thorns?' Alice asked with some curiosity.

'Why, all round her head, of course,' the Rose replied. 'I was wondering *you* hadn't got some too. I thought it was the regular rule.'

'She's coming!' cried the Larkspur. 'I hear her footstep, thump, thump, along the gravel-walk!'

Alice looked round eagerly, and found that it was the Red Queen. 'She's grown a good deal!' was her first remark. She had indeed: when Alice first found her in the ashes, she had been only three inches high – and here she was, half a head taller than Alice herself!

'It's the fresh air that does it,' said the Rose: 'wonderfully fine air it is, out here.'

'I think I'll go and meet her,' said Alice, for though the flowers were interesting enough, she felt that it would be far grander to have a talk with a real Queen.

'You can't possibly do that,' said the Rose, '*I* should advise you to walk the other way.'

This sounded nonsense to Alice, so she said nothing, but set off at once towards the Red Queen. To her surprise, she lost sight of her in a moment, and found herself walking in at the front-door again.

A little provoked, she drew back, and after looking everywhere for the Queen (whom she spied out at last, a long way off), she thought she would try the plan, this time, of walking in the opposite direction.

It succeeded beautifully. She had not been walking a minute before she found herself face to face with the Red Queen, and full in sight of the hill she had been so long aiming at.

'Where do you come from?' said the Red Queen. 'And where are you going? Look up, speak nicely, and don't twiddle your fingers all the time.'

Alice attended to all these directions, and explained, as well as she could, that she had lost her way.

'I don't know what you mean by *your* way,' said the Queen: 'all the ways about here belong to *me* – but why did you come out here at all?' she added in a kinder tone. 'Curtsey while you're thinking what to say, it saves time.'

Alice wondered a little at this, but she was too much in awe of the Queen to disbelieve it. 'I'll try it when I go home,' she thought to herself, 'the next time I'm a little late for dinner.'

'It's time for you to answer now,' the Queen said, looking at her watch: 'open your mouth a *little* wider when you speak, and always say "your Majesty."'

'I only wanted to see what the garden was like, your Majesty –'

'That's right,' said the Queen, patting her on the head, which Alice didn't like at all, 'though, when you say "garden," – *I've* seen gardens, compared with which this would be a wilderness.'

Alice didn't dare to argue the point, but went on: '– and I thought I'd try and find my way to the top of that hill –'

'When you say "hill,"' the Queen interrupted, '*I* could show you hills, in comparison with which you'd call that a valley.'

'No, I shouldn't,' said Alice, surprised into contradicting her at last: 'a hill *can't* be a valley, you know. That would be nonsense –'

The Red Queen shook her head. 'You may call it "nonsense" if you like,' she said, 'but *I've* heard nonsense, compared with which that would be as sensible as a dictionary!'

Alice curtseyed again, as she was afraid from the Queen's tone that she was a *little* offended: and they walked on in silence till they got to the top of the little hill.

For some minutes Alice stood without speaking, looking out in all directions over the country – and a most curious country it was. There were a number of tiny little brooks running straight across it from side to side, and the ground between was divided up into squares by a number of little green hedges, that reached from brook to brook.

'I declare it's marked out just like a large chessboard!' Alice said at last. 'There ought to be some men moving about somewhere – and so there are!' she added in a tone of delight, and her heart began to beat quick with excitement as she went on. 'It's a great huge game of chess that's being played – all over the world – if this *is* the world at all, you know. Oh, what fun it is! How I *wish* I was one of them! I wouldn't mind being a Pawn, if only I might join – though of course I should *like* to be a Queen, best.'

She glanced rather shyly at the real Queen as she said this, but her companion only smiled pleasantly, and said, 'That's easily managed. You can be the White Queen's Pawn, if you like, as Lily's too young to play: and you're in the Second Square to begin

with: when you get to the Eighth Square you'll be a Queen –' Just at this moment, somehow or other, they began to run.

Alice never could quite make out, in thinking it over afterwards, how it was that they began: all she remembers is, that they were running hand in hand, and the Queen went so fast that it was all she could do to keep up with her: and still the Queen kept crying 'Faster! Faster!' but Alice felt she *could not* go faster, though she had no breath left to say so.

The most curious part of the thing was, that the trees and other things round them never changed their places at all: however fast they went, they never seemed to pass anything. 'I wonder if all the things move along with us?' thought poor puzzled Alice. And the Queen seemed to guess her thoughts, for she cried, 'Faster! Don't try to talk!'

Not that Alice had any idea of doing *that*. She felt as if she would never be able to talk again, she was getting so much out of breath: and still the Queen cried 'Faster! Faster!' and dragged her along. 'Are we nearly there?' Alice managed to pant out at last.

'Nearly there!' the Queen repeated. 'Why, we passed it ten minutes ago! Faster!' And they ran on for a time in silence, with the wind whistling in Alice's ears, and almost blowing her hair off her head, she fancied.

'Now! Now!' cried the Queen. 'Faster! Faster!' And they went so fast that at last they seemed to skim through the air, hardly touching the ground with their feet, till suddenly, just as Alice was getting quite exhausted, they stopped, and she found herself sitting on the ground, breathless and giddy.

The Queen propped her up against a tree, and said kindly, 'You may rest a little now.'

Alice looked round her in great surprise. 'Why, I do believe we've been under this tree the whole time! Everything's just as it was!'

'Of course it is,' said the Queen: 'what would you have it?'

'Well, in *our* country,' said Alice, still panting a little, 'you'd generally get to somewhere else – if you ran very fast for a long time, as we've been doing.'

'A slow sort of country!' said the Queen. 'Now, *here*, you see, it takes all the running *you* can do, to keep in the same place. If you want to get somewhere else, you must run at least twice as fast as that!'

'I'd rather not try, please!' said Alice. 'I'm quite content to stay here – only I *am* so hot and thirsty!'

'I know what you'd like!' the Queen said good-naturedly, taking a little box out of her pocket. 'Have a biscuit?'

Alice thought it would not be civil to say 'No,' though it wasn't at all what she wanted. So she took it, and ate it as well as she could: and it was *very* dry; and she thought she had never been so nearly choked in all her life.

'While you're refreshing yourself,' said the Queen, 'I'll just take the measurements.' And she took a ribbon out of her pocket, marked in inches, and began measuring the ground, and sticking little pegs in here and there.

'At the end of two yards,' she said, putting in a peg to mark the distance, 'I shall give you your directions – have another biscuit?'

'No, thank you,' said Alice: 'one's *quite* enough!'

'Thirst quenched, I hope?' said the Queen.

Alice did not know what to say to this, but luckily the Queen did not wait for an answer, but went on. 'At the end of *three* yards I shall repeat them – for fear of your forgetting them. At the end of *four*, I shall say good-bye. And at the end of *five*, I shall go!'

She had got all the pegs put in by this time, and Alice looked on with great interest as she returned to the tree, and then began slowly walking down the row.

At the two-yard peg she faced round, and said, 'A pawn goes two squares in its first move, you know. So you'll go *very* quickly through the Third Square – by railway, I should think – and you'll find yourself in the Fourth Square in no time. Well, *that* square belongs to Tweedledum and Tweedledee – the Fifth is mostly water – the Sixth belongs to Humpty Dumpty – But you make no remark?'

'I – I didn't know I had to make one – just then,' Alice faltered out.

'You *should* have said,' the Queen went on in a tone of grave reproof, '"It's extremely kind of you to tell me all this" – however, we'll suppose it said – the Seventh Square is all forest – however, one of the Knights will show you the way – and in the Eighth Square we shall be Queens together, and it's all feasting and fun!' Alice got up and curtseyed, and sat down again.

At the next peg the Queen turned again, and this time she said, 'Speak in French when you can't think of the English for a thing – turn out your toes as you walk – and remember who you are!' She did not wait for Alice to curtsey this time, but walked on quickly to the next peg, where she turned for a moment to say 'good-bye,' and then hurried on to the last.

How it happened, Alice never knew, but exactly as she came to the last peg, she was gone. Whether she vanished into the air, or whether she ran quickly into the wood ('and she *can* run very fast!' thought Alice), there was no way of guessing, but she was gone, and Alice began to remember that she was a Pawn, and that it would soon be time for her to move.

CHAPTER THREE

LOOKING-GLASS INSECTS

O f course the first thing to do was to make a grand survey of the country she was going to travel through. 'It's something very like learning geography,' thought Alice, as she stood on tiptoe in hopes of being able to see a little further. 'Principal rivers – there *are* none. Principal mountains – I'm on the only one, but I don't think it's got any name. Principal towns – why, what *are* those creatures, making honey down there? They can't be bees – nobody ever saw bees a mile off, you know –' and for some time she stood silent, watching one of them that was bustling about among the flowers, poking its proboscis into them, 'just as if it was a regular bee,' thought Alice.

However, this was anything but a regular bee: in fact, it was an elephant – as Alice soon found out, though the idea quite took her breath away at first. 'And what enormous flowers they must be!' was her next idea. 'Something like cottages with the roofs taken off, and stalks put to them – and what quantities of honey they must make! I think I'll go down and – no, I won't go *just* yet,' she went on, checking herself just as she was beginning to run down the hill, and trying to find some excuse for turning shy so suddenly. 'It'll never do to go down among them without a good long branch to brush them away – and what fun it'll be when they ask me how I liked my walk. I shall say – "Oh, I liked it well enough –"' (here came the favourite little toss of the head), '"only it was so dusty and hot, and the elephants did tease so!"'

'I think I'll go down the other way,' she said after a pause: 'and perhaps I may visit the elephants later on. Besides, I do so want to get into the Third Square!'

So with this excuse she ran down the hill and jumped over the first of the six little brooks.

*   *   *   *   *   *

*   *   *   *   *

*   *   *   *   *   *

'Tickets, please!' said the Guard, putting his head in at the window. In a moment everybody was holding out a ticket: they were about the same size as the people, and quite seemed to fill the carriage.

'Now then! Show your ticket, child!' the Guard went on, looking angrily at Alice. And a great many voices all said together ('like the chorus of a song,' thought Alice), 'Don't keep him waiting, child! Why, his time is worth a thousand pounds a minute!'

'I'm afraid I haven't got one,' Alice said in a frightened tone: 'there wasn't a ticket-office where I came from.' And again the chorus of voices went on. 'There wasn't room for one where she came from. The land there is worth a thousand pounds an inch!'

'Don't make excuses,' said the Guard: 'you should have bought one from the engine-driver.' And once more the chorus of voices went on with 'The man that drives the engine. Why, the smoke alone is worth a thousand pounds a puff!'

Alice thought to herself, 'Then there's no use in speaking.' The voices didn't join in this time, as she hadn't spoken, but, to her great surprise, they all *thought* in chorus (I hope you understand what *thinking in chorus* means – for I must confess that *I* don't), 'Better say nothing at all. Language is worth a thousand pounds a word!'

'I shall dream about a thousand pounds to-night, I know I shall!' thought Alice.

CHAPTER THREE: LOOKING-GLASS INSECTS

All this time the Guard was looking at her, first through a telescope, then through a microscope, and then through an opera-glass. At last he said, 'You're travelling the wrong way,' and shut up the window and went away.

'So young a child,' said the gentleman sitting opposite to her (he was dressed in white paper), 'ought to know which way she's going, even if she doesn't know her own name!'

A Goat, that was sitting next to the gentleman in white, shut his eyes and said in a loud voice, 'She ought to know her way to the ticket-office, even if she doesn't know her alphabet!'

There was a Beetle sitting next the Goat (it was a very queer carriage-full of passengers altogether), and, as the rule seemed to be that they should all speak in turn, *he* went on with 'She'll have to go back from here as luggage!'

Alice couldn't see who was sitting beyond the Beetle, but a hoarse voice spoke next. 'Change engines –' it said, and there it choked and was obliged to leave off.

'It sounds like a horse,' Alice thought to herself. And an extremely small voice, close to her ear, said,

'You might make a joke on that – something about "horse" and "hoarse," you know.'

CHAPTER THREE: LOOKING-GLASS INSECTS

Then a very gentle voice in the distance said, 'She must be labelled "Lass, with care," you know –'

And after that other voices went on ('What a number of people there are in the carriage!' thought Alice), saying, 'She must go by post, as she's got a head on her –' 'She must be sent as a message by the telegraph –' 'She must draw the train herself the rest of the way –,' and so on.

But the gentleman dressed in white paper leaned forwards and whispered in her ear, 'Never mind what they all say, my dear, but take a return-ticket every time the train stops.'

'Indeed I shan't!' Alice said rather impatiently. 'I don't belong to this railway journey at all – I was in a wood just now – and I wish I could get back there!'

'You might make a joke on that,' said the little voice close to her ear: 'something about "you would if you could," you know.'

'Don't tease so,' said Alice, looking about in vain to see where the voice came from; 'if you're so anxious to have a joke made, why don't you make one yourself?'

The little voice sighed deeply: it was *very* unhappy, evidently, and Alice would have said something pitying to comfort it, 'if it would only sigh like other people!' she thought. But this was such a wonderfully small sigh, that she wouldn't have heard it at all, if it hadn't come *quite* close to her ear. The consequence of this was that it tickled her ear very much, and quite took off her thoughts from the unhappiness of the poor little creature.

'I know you are a friend,' the little voice went on; 'a dear friend, and an old friend. And you won't hurt me, though I am an insect.'

'What kind of insect?' Alice inquired a little anxiously. What she really wanted to know was, whether it could sting or not, but she thought this wouldn't be quite a civil question to ask.

'What, then you don't –' the little voice began, when it was drowned by a shrill scream from the engine, and everybody jumped up in alarm, Alice among the rest.

The Horse, who had put his head out of the window, quietly drew it in and said, 'It's only a brook we have to jump over.' Everybody seemed satisfied with this, though Alice felt a little nervous at the idea of trains jumping at all. 'However, it'll take us into the Fourth Square, that's some comfort!' she said to herself. In another moment she felt the carriage rise straight up into the air, and in her fright she caught at the thing nearest to her hand, which happened to be the Goat's beard.

*   *   *   *   *   *

*   *   *   *   *

*   *   *   *   *   *

But the beard seemed to melt away as she touched it, and she found herself sitting quietly under a tree – while the Gnat (for that was the insect she had been talking to) was balancing itself on a twig just over her head, and fanning her with its wings.

It certainly was a *very* large Gnat: 'about the size of a chicken,' Alice thought. Still, she couldn't feel nervous with it, after they had been talking together so long.

'– then you don't like all insects?' the Gnat went on, as quietly as if nothing had happened.

'I like them when they can talk,' Alice said. 'None of them ever talk, where *I* come from.'

'What sort of insects do you rejoice in, where *you* come from?' the Gnat inquired.

'I don't *rejoice* in insects at all,' Alice explained, 'because I'm rather afraid of them – at least the large kinds. But I can tell you the names of some of them.'

'Of course they answer to their names?' the Gnat remarked carelessly.

'I never knew them do it.'

'What's the use of their having names,' the Gnat said, 'if they won't answer to them?'

'No use to them,' said Alice; 'but it's useful to the people that name them, I suppose. If not, why do things have names at all?'

'I can't say,' the Gnat replied. 'Further on, in the wood down there, they've got no names – however, go on with your list of insects: you're wasting time.'

'Well, there's the Horse-fly,' Alice began, counting off the names on her fingers.

'All right,' said the Gnat: 'half way up that bush, you'll see a Rocking-horse-fly, if you look. It's made entirely of wood, and gets about by swinging itself from branch to branch.'

'What does *it* live on?' Alice asked, with great curiosity.

'Sap and sawdust,' said the Gnat. 'Go on with the list.'

Alice looked at the Rocking-horse-fly with great interest, and made up her mind that it must have been just repainted, it looked so bright and sticky; and then she went on.

'And there's the Dragon-fly.'

'Look on the branch above your head,' said the Gnat, 'and there you'll find a Snap-dragon-fly. Its body is made of plum-pudding, its wings of holly-leaves, and its head is a raisin burning in brandy.'

'And what does it live on?' Alice asked, as before.

'Frumenty and mince-pie,' the Gnat replied; 'and it makes its nest in a Christmas-box.'

'And then there's the Butterfly,' Alice went on, after she had taken a good look at the insect with its head on fire, and had thought to herself, 'I wonder if that's the reason insects are so fond of flying into candles – because they want to turn into Snap-dragon-flies!'

'Crawling at your feet,' said the Gnat (Alice drew her feet back in some alarm), 'you may observe a Bread-and-Butterfly. Its wings are thin slices of Bread-and-butter, its body is a crust, and its head is a lump of sugar.'

'And what does it live on?'

'Weak tea with cream in it.'

A new difficulty came into Alice's head. 'Supposing it couldn't find any?' she suggested.

'Then it would die, of course.'

'But that must happen very often,' Alice remarked thoughtfully.

'It always happens,' said the Gnat.

After this, Alice was silent for a minute or two, pondering. The Gnat amused itself meanwhile by humming round and round her head: at last it settled again and remarked, 'I suppose you don't want to lose your name?'

'No, indeed,' Alice said, a little anxiously.

'And yet I don't know,' the Gnat went on in a careless tone: 'only think how convenient it would be if you could manage to go home without it! For instance, if the governess wanted to call you to your lessons, she would call out

"Come here –," and there she would have to leave off, because there wouldn't be any name for her to call, and of course you wouldn't have to go, you know.'

'That would never do, I'm sure,' said Alice: 'the governess would never think of excusing me lessons for that. If she couldn't remember my name, she'd call me "Miss!" as the servants do.'

'Well, if she said "Miss," and didn't say anything more,' the Gnat remarked, 'of course you'd miss your lessons. That's a joke. I wish *you* had made it.'

'Why do you wish *I* had made it?' Alice asked. 'It's a very bad one.'

But the Gnat only sighed deeply, while two large tears came rolling down its cheeks.

'You shouldn't make jokes,' Alice said, 'if it makes you so unhappy.'

Then came another of those melancholy little sighs, and this time the poor Gnat really seemed to have sighed itself away, for, when Alice looked up, there was nothing whatever to be seen on the twig, and, as she was getting quite chilly with sitting still so long, she got up and walked on.

She very soon came to an open field, with a wood on the other side of it: it looked much darker than the last wood, and Alice felt a *little* timid about going into it. However, on second thoughts, she made up her mind to go on: 'for I certainly won't go *back*,' she thought to herself, and this was the only way to the Eighth Square.

'This must be the wood,' she said thoughtfully to herself, 'where things have no names. I wonder what'll become of *my* name when I go in? I shouldn't like to lose it at all – because they'd have to give me another, and it would be almost certain to be an ugly one. But then the fun would be, trying to find the creature

that had got my old name! That's just like the advertisements, you know, when people lose dogs – "*answers to the name of 'Dash:' had on a brass collar*" – just fancy calling everything you met "Alice," till one of them answered! Only they wouldn't answer at all, if they were wise.'

She was rambling on in this way when she reached the wood: it looked very cool and shady. 'Well, at any rate it's a great comfort,' she said as she stepped under the trees, 'after being so hot, to get into the – into the – into *what*?' she went on, rather surprised at not being able to think of the word. 'I mean to get under the – under the – under *this*, you know!' putting her hand on the trunk of the tree. 'What *does* it call itself, I wonder? I do believe it's got no name – why, to be sure it hasn't!'

She stood silent for a minute, thinking: then she suddenly began again. 'Then it really *has* happened, after all! And now, who am I? I *will* remember, if I can! I'm determined to do it!' But being determined didn't help her much, and all she could say, after a great deal of puzzling, was, 'L, I *know* it begins with L!'

Just then a Fawn came wandering by: it looked at Alice with its large gentle eyes, but didn't seem at all frightened. 'Here then! Here then!' Alice said, as she held out her hand and tried to stroke it; but it only started back a little, and then stood looking at her again.

'What do you call yourself?' the Fawn said at last. Such a soft sweet voice it had!

'I wish I knew!' thought poor Alice. She answered, rather sadly, 'Nothing, just now.'

'Think again,' it said: 'that won't do.'

Alice thought, but nothing came of it. 'Please, would you tell me what *you* call yourself?' she said timidly. 'I think that might help a little.'

'I'll tell you, if you'll come a little further on,' the Fawn said. 'I can't remember here.'

So they walked on together through the wood, Alice with her arms clasped lovingly round the soft neck of the Fawn, till they came out into another open

field, and here the Fawn gave a sudden bound into the air, and shook itself free from Alice's arms. 'I'm a Fawn!' it cried out in a voice of delight, 'and, dear me! you're a human child!' A sudden look of alarm came into its beautiful brown eyes, and in another moment it had darted away at full speed.

Alice stood looking after it, almost ready to cry with vexation at having lost her dear little fellow-traveller so suddenly. 'However, I know my name now,' she said, 'that's *some* comfort. Alice – Alice – I won't forget it again. And now, which of these finger-posts ought I to follow, I wonder?'

It was not a very difficult question to answer, as there was only one road through the wood, and the two fingerposts both pointed along it. 'I'll settle it,' Alice said to herself, 'when the road divides and they point different ways.'

But this did not seem likely to happen. She went on and on, a long way, but wherever the road divided there were sure to be two finger-posts pointing the same way, one marked 'TO TWEEDLEDUM'S HOUSE,' and the other 'TO THE HOUSE OF TWEEDLEDEE.'

'I do believe,' said Alice at last, 'that they live in the same house! I wonder I never thought of that before – But I can't stay there long. I'll just call and say "How d'you do?" and ask them the way out of the wood. If I could only get to the Eighth Square before it gets dark!' So she wandered on, talking to herself as she went, till, on turning a sharp corner, she came upon two fat little men, so suddenly that she could not help starting back, but in another moment she recovered herself, feeling sure that they must be –

CHAPTER FOUR

TWEEDLEDUM AND TWEEDLEDEE

They were standing under a tree, each with an arm round the other's neck, and Alice knew which was which in a moment, because one of them had 'DUM' embroidered on his collar, and the other 'DEE.' 'I suppose they've each got "TWEEDLE" round at the back of the collar,' she said to herself.

They stood so still that she quite forgot they were alive, and she was just looking round to see if the word 'TWEEDLE' was written at the back of each collar, when she was startled by a voice coming from the one marked 'DUM.'

'If you think we're wax-works,' he said, 'you ought to pay, you know. Wax-works weren't made to be looked at for nothing. Nohow!'

'Contrariwise,' added the one marked 'DEE,' 'if you think we're alive, you ought to speak.'

'I'm sure I'm very sorry,' was all Alice could say; for the words of the old song kept ringing through her head like the ticking of a clock, and she could hardly help saying them out loud:–

> *'Tweedledum and Tweedledee*
> *Agreed to have a battle;*
> *For Tweedledum said Tweedledee*
> *Had spoiled his nice new rattle.*

Just then flew down a monstrous crow,
As black as a tar-barrel;
Which frightened both the heroes so,
They quite forgot their quarrel.'

'I know what you're thinking about,' said Tweedledum: 'but it isn't so, nohow.'

'Contrariwise,' continued Tweedledee, 'if it was so, it might be; and if it were so, it would be; but as it isn't, it ain't. That's logic.'

'I was thinking,' Alice said very politely, 'which is the best way out of this wood: it's getting so dark. Would you tell me, please?'

But the fat little men only looked at each other and grinned.

They looked so exactly like a couple of great schoolboys, that Alice couldn't help pointing her finger at Tweedledum, and saying 'First Boy!'

'Nohow!' Tweedledum cried out briskly, and shut his mouth up again with a snap.

'Next Boy!' said Alice, passing on to Tweedledee, though she felt quite certain he would only shout out 'Contrariwise!' and so he did.

'You've begun wrong!' cried Tweedledum. 'The first thing in a visit is to say "How d'ye do?" and shake hands!' And here the two brothers gave each other a hug, and then they held out the two hands that were free, to shake hands with her.

Alice did not like shaking hands with either of them first, for fear of hurting the other one's feelings; so, as the best way out of the difficulty, she took hold of both hands at once: the next moment they were dancing round in a ring. This seemed quite natural (she remembered afterwards), and she was not even surprised to hear music playing: it seemed to come from the tree under which they were dancing and it was done (as well as she could make it out) by the branches rubbing one across the other, like fiddles and fiddle-sticks.

'But it certainly was funny,' (Alice said afterwards, when she was telling her sister the history of all this,) 'to find myself singing "*Here we go round the mulberry bush.*" I don't know when I began it, but somehow I felt as if I'd been singing it a long long time!'

The other two dancers were fat, and very soon out of breath. 'Four times round is enough for one dance,' Tweedledum panted out, and they left off dancing as suddenly as they had begun: the music stopped at the same moment.

Then they let go of Alice's hands, and stood looking at her for a minute: there was a rather awkward pause, as Alice didn't know how to begin a conversation with people she had just been dancing with. 'It would never do to say "How d'ye do?" *now*,' she said to herself: 'we seem to have got beyond that, somehow!'

'I hope you're not much tired?' she said at last.

'Nohow. And thank you *very* much for asking,' said Tweedledum.

'So *much* obliged!' added Tweedledee. 'You like poetry?'

'Ye-es, pretty well – *some* poetry,' Alice said doubtfully. 'Would you tell me which road leads out of the wood?'

'What shall I repeat to her?' said Tweedledee, looking round at Tweedledum with great solemn eyes, and not noticing Alice's question.

'"*The Walrus and the Carpenter*" is the longest,' Tweedledum replied, giving his brother an affectionate hug.

Tweedledee began instantly:

'The sun was shining –'

Here Alice ventured to interrupt him. 'If it's *very* long,' she said, as politely as she could, 'would you please tell me first which road –'

Tweedledee smiled gently, and began again:

> *'The sun was shining on the sea,*
> *Shining with all his might:*
> *He did his very best to make*
> *The billows smooth and bright –*
> *And this was odd, because it was*
> *The middle of the night.*
>
> *The moon was shining sulkily,*
> *Because she thought the sun*
> *Had got no business to be there*
> *After the day was done –*
> *"It's very rude of him," she said,*
> *"To come and spoil the fun!"*
>
> *The sea was wet as wet could be,*
> *The sands were dry as dry.*
> *You could not see a cloud, because*
> *No cloud was in the sky:*
> *No birds were flying overhead –*
> *There were no birds to fly.*

The Walrus and the Carpenter
Were walking close at hand;
They wept like anything to see
Such quantities of sand:
"If this were only cleared away,"
They said, "it would be grand!"

"If seven maids with seven mops
Swept it for half a year,
Do you suppose," the Walrus said,
"That they could get it clear?"
"I doubt it," said the Carpenter,
And shed a bitter tear.

"O Oysters, come and walk with us!"
The Walrus did beseech.
"A pleasant walk, a pleasant talk,
Along the briny beach:
We cannot do with more than four,
To give a hand to each."

The eldest Oyster looked at him.
But never a word he said:
The eldest Oyster winked his eye,
And shook his heavy head –
Meaning to say he did not choose
To leave the oyster-bed.

But four young oysters hurried up,
All eager for the treat:
Their coats were brushed, their faces washed,
Their shoes were clean and neat –
And this was odd, because, you know,
They hadn't any feet.

Four other Oysters followed them,
And yet another four;
And thick and fast they came at last,
And more, and more, and more –
All hopping through the frothy waves,
And scrambling to the shore.

The Walrus and the Carpenter
Walked on a mile or so,
And then they rested on a rock
Conveniently low:
And all the little Oysters stood
And waited in a row.

"The time has come," the Walrus said,
"To talk of many things:
Of shoes – and ships – and sealing wax –
Of cabbages – and kings –
And why the sea is boiling hot –
And whether pigs have wings."

"But wait a bit," the Oysters cried,
"Before we have our chat;
For some of us are out of breath,
And all of us are fat!"
"No hurry!" said the Carpenter.
They thanked him much for that.

"A loaf of bread," the Walrus said,
"Is what we chiefly need:
Pepper and vinegar besides
Are very good indeed –
Now if you're ready, Oysters dear,
We can begin to feed."

"But not on us!" the Oysters cried,
Turning a little blue,
"After such kindness, that would be
A dismal thing to do!"
"The night is fine," the Walrus said.
"Do you admire the view?"

"It was so kind of you to come!
And you are very nice!"
The Carpenter said nothing but
"Cut us another slice:
I wish you were not quite so deaf –
I've had to ask you twice!"

"It seems a shame," the Walrus said,
"To play them such a trick,
After we've brought them out so far,
And made them trot so quick!"
The Carpenter said nothing but
"The butter's spread too thick!"

"I weep for you," the Walrus said,
"I deeply sympathize."
With sobs and tears he sorted out
Those of the largest size,
Holding his pocket-handkerchief
Before his streaming eyes.

"O Oysters," said the Carpenter.
"You've had a pleasant run!
Shall we be trotting home again?"
But answer came there none –
And this was scarcely odd, because
They'd eaten every one.'

'I like the Walrus best,' said Alice: 'because you see he was a *little* sorry for the poor oysters.'

'He ate more than the Carpenter, though,' said Tweedledee. 'You see he held his handkerchief in front, so that the Carpenter couldn't count how many he took: contrariwise.'

'That was mean!' Alice said indignantly. 'Then I like the Carpenter best – if he didn't eat so many as the Walrus.'

'But he ate as many as he could get,' said Tweedledum.

This was a puzzler. After a pause, Alice began, 'Well! They were *both* very unpleasant characters –' Here she checked herself in some alarm, at hearing something that sounded to her like the puffing of a large steam-engine in the wood near them, though she feared it was more likely to be a wild beast. 'Are there any lions or tigers about here?' she asked timidly.

'It's only the Red King snoring,' said Tweedledee.

'Come and look at him!' the brothers cried, and they took each one of Alice's hands, and led her up to where the King was sleeping.

'Isn't he a *lovely* sight?' said Tweedledum.

Alice couldn't say honestly that he was. He had a tall red night-cap on, with a tassel, and he was lying crumpled up into a sort of untidy heap, and snoring loud – 'fit to snore his head off!' as Tweedledum remarked.

'I'm afraid he'll catch cold with lying on the damp grass,' said Alice, who was a very thoughtful little girl.

'He's dreaming now,' said Tweedledee: 'and what do you think he's dreaming about?'

Alice said 'Nobody can guess that.'

'Why, about *you!*' Tweedledee exclaimed, clapping his hands triumphantly. 'And if he left off dreaming about you, where do you suppose you'd be?'

'Where I am now, of course,' said Alice.

'Not you!' Tweedledee retorted contemptuously. 'You'd be nowhere. Why, you're only a sort of thing in his dream!'

'If that there King was to wake,' added Tweedledum, 'you'd go out – bang! – just like a candle!'

'I shouldn't!' Alice exclaimed indignantly. 'Besides, if *I'm* only a sort of thing in his dream, what are *you*, I should like to know?'

'Ditto,' said Tweedledum.

'Ditto, ditto!' cried Tweedledee.

He shouted this so loud that Alice couldn't help saying, 'Hush! You'll be waking him, I'm afraid, if you make so much noise.'

'Well, it's no use *your* talking about waking him,' said Tweedledum, 'when you're only one of the things in his dream. You know very well you're not real.'

'I *am* real!' said Alice, and began to cry.

'You won't make yourself a bit realler by crying,' Tweedledee remarked: 'there's nothing to cry about.'

'If I wasn't real,' Alice said – half-laughing through her tears, it all seemed so ridiculous – 'I shouldn't be able to cry.'

'I hope you don't suppose those are real tears?' Tweedledum interrupted in a tone of great contempt.

'I know they're talking nonsense,' Alice thought to herself: 'and it's foolish to cry about it.' So she brushed away her tears, and went on as cheerfully as she could, 'At any rate I'd better be getting out of the wood, for really its coming on very dark. Do you think it's going to rain?'

Tweedledum spread a large umbrella over himself and his brother, and looked up into it. 'No, I don't think it is,' he said: 'at least – not under *here*. Nohow.'

'But it may rain *outside*?'

'It may – if it chooses,' said Tweedledee: 'we've no objection. Contrariwise.'

'Selfish things!' thought Alice, and she was just going to say 'Good-night' and leave them, when Tweedledum sprang out from under the umbrella, and seized her by the wrist.

'Do you see *that*?' he said, in a voice choking with passion, and his eyes grew large and yellow all in a moment, as he pointed with a trembling finger at a small white thing lying under the tree.

'It's only a rattle,' Alice said, after a careful examination of the little white thing. 'Not a rattle-*snake*, you know,' she added hastily, thinking that he was frightened: 'only an old rattle – quite old and broken.'

'I knew it was!' cried Tweedledum, beginning to stamp about wildly and tear his hair. 'It's spoilt, of course!' Here he looked at Tweedledee, who immediately sat down on the ground, and tried to hide himself under the umbrella.

Alice laid her hand upon his arm, and said in a soothing tone, 'You needn't be so angry about an old rattle.'

'But it isn't old!' Tweedledum cried, in a greater fury than ever. 'It's new, I tell you – I bought it yesterday – my nice new RATTLE!' and his voice rose to a perfect scream.

All this time Tweedledee was trying his best to fold up the umbrella, with himself in it: which was such an extraordinary thing to do, that it quite took off Alice's attention from the angry brother. But he couldn't quite succeed, and it ended in his rolling over, bundled up in the umbrella, with only his head out: and there he lay, opening and shutting his mouth and his large eyes – 'looking more like a fish than anything else,' Alice thought.

'Of course you agree to have a battle?' Tweedledum said in a calmer tone.

'I suppose so,' the other sulkily replied, as he crawled out of the umbrella: 'only *she* must help us to dress up, you know.'

So the two brothers went off hand-in-hand into the wood, and returned in a minute with their arms full of things – such as bolsters, blankets, hearth-rugs, table-cloths, dish-covers and coal-scuttles. 'I hope you're a good hand at pinning and tying strings?' Tweedledum remarked. 'Every one of these things has got to go on, somehow or other.'

Alice said afterwards she had never seen such a fuss made about anything in all her life – the way those two bustled about – and the quantity of things they put on – and the trouble they gave her in tying strings and fastening buttons – 'Really they'll be more like bundles of old clothes than anything else, by the time they're ready!' she said to herself, as she arranged a bolster round the neck of Tweedledee, 'to keep his head from being cut off,' as he said.

'You know,' he added very gravely, 'it's one of the most serious things that can

possibly happen to one in a battle – to get one's head cut off.'

Alice laughed loud: but she managed to turn it into a cough, for fear of hurting his feelings.

'Do I look very pale?' said Tweedledum, coming up to have his helmet tied on. (He called it a helmet, though it certainly looked much more like a saucepan.)

'Well – yes – a *little*,' Alice replied gently.

'I'm very brave generally,' he went on in a low voice: 'only to-day I happen to have a headache.'

'And *I've* got a toothache!' said Tweedledee, who had overheard the remark. 'I'm far worse than you!'

'Then you'd better not fight to-day,' said Alice thinking it a good opportunity to make peace.

'We *must* have a bit of a fight, but I don't care about going on long,' said Tweedledum. 'What's the time now?'

Tweedledee looked at his watch, and said 'Half-past four.'

'Let's fight till six, and then have dinner,' said Tweedledum.

'Very well,' the other said, rather sadly: 'and *she* can watch us – only you'd better not come *very* close,' he added: 'I generally hit everything I can see – when I get really excited.'

'And *I* hit everything within reach,' cried Tweedledum, 'whether I can see it or not.'

Alice laughed. 'You must hit the *trees* pretty often, I should think,' she said.

Tweedledum looked round him with a satisfied smile. 'I don't suppose,' he said, 'there'll be a tree left standing, for ever so far round, by the time we've finished!'

'And all about a rattle!' said Alice still hoping to make them a *little* ashamed of fighting for such a trifle.

'I shouldn't have minded it so much,' said Tweedledum, 'if it hadn't been a new one.'

'I wish the monstrous crow would come!' thought Alice.

'There's only one sword, you know,' Tweedledum said to his brother: 'but you can have the umbrella – it's quite as sharp. Only we must begin quick. It's getting as dark as it can.'

'And darker,' said Tweedledee.

It was getting dark so suddenly that Alice thought there must be a thunderstorm coming on. 'What a thick black cloud that is!' she said. 'And how fast it comes! Why, I do believe it's got wings!'

'It's the crow!' Tweedledum cried out in a shrill voice of alarm: and the two brothers took to their heels and were out of sight in a moment.

Alice ran a little way into the wood, and stopped under a large tree. 'It can never get at me *here*,' she thought: 'it's far too large to squeeze itself in among the trees. But I wish it wouldn't flap its wings so – it makes quite a hurricane in the wood – here's somebody's shawl being blown away!'

CHAPTER FIVE

WOOL AND WATER

S he caught the shawl as she spoke, and looked about for the owner: in another moment the White Queen came running wildly through the wood, with both arms stretched out wide, as if she were flying, and Alice very civilly went to meet her with the shawl.

'I'm very glad I happened to be in the way,' Alice said, as she helped her to put on her shawl again.

The White Queen only looked at her in a helpless frightened sort of way, and kept repeating something in a whisper to herself that sounded like 'Bread-and-butter, bread-and butter,' and Alice felt that if there was to be any conversation at all, she must manage it herself. So she began rather timidly: 'Am I addressing the White Queen?'

'Well, yes, if you call that a-dressing,' the Queen said. 'It isn't *my* notion of the thing, at all.'

Alice thought it would never do to have an argument at the very beginning of their conversation, so she smiled and said, 'If your Majesty will only tell me the right way to begin, I'll do it as well as I can.'

'But I don't want it done at all!' groaned the poor Queen. 'I've been a-dressing myself for the last two hours.'

It would have been all the better, as it seemed to Alice, if she had got some one else to dress her, she was so dreadfully untidy. 'Every single thing's crooked,'

Alice thought to herself, 'and she's all over pins! – May I put your shawl straight for you?' she added aloud.

'I don't know what's the matter with it!' the Queen said, in a melancholy voice. 'It's out of temper, I think. I've pinned it here, and I've pinned it there, but there's no pleasing it!'

'It *can't* go straight, you know, if you pin it all on one side,' Alice said, as she gently put it right for her; 'and, dear me, what a state your hair is in!'

'The brush has got entangled in it!' the Queen said with a sigh. 'And I lost the comb yesterday.'

Alice carefully released the brush, and did her best to get the hair into order. 'Come, you look rather better now!' she said, after altering most of the pins. 'But really you should have a lady's-maid!'

'I'm sure I'll take you with pleasure!' the Queen said. 'Twopence a week, and jam every other day.'

Alice couldn't help laughing, as she said, 'I don't want you to hire *me* – and I don't care for jam.'

'It's very good jam,' said the Queen.

'Well, I don't want any *to-day*, at any rate.'

'You couldn't have if it you *did* want it,' the Queen said. 'The rule is, jam to-morrow and jam yesterday – but never jam to-day.'

'It *must* come sometimes to "jam to-day,"' Alice objected.

'No, it can't,' said the Queen. 'It's jam every *other* day: to-day isn't any *other* day, you know.'

'I don't understand you,' said Alice. 'It's dreadfully confusing!'

'That's the effect of living backwards,' the Queen said kindly: 'it always makes one a little giddy at first –'

'Living backwards!' Alice repeated in great astonishment. 'I never heard of such a thing!'

'– but there's one great advantage in it, that one's memory works both ways.'

'I'm sure *mine* only works one way,' Alice remarked. 'I can't remember things before they happen.'

'It's a poor sort of memory that only works backwards,' the Queen remarked.

'What sorts of things do *you* remember best?' Alice ventured to ask.

'Oh, things that happened the week after next,' the Queen replied in a careless tone. 'For instance, now,' she went on, sticking a large piece of plaster on her finger as she spoke, 'there's the King's Messenger. He's in prison now, being punished; and the trial doesn't even begin till next Wednesday: and of course the crime comes last of all.'

'Suppose he never commits the crime?' said Alice.

'That would be all the better, wouldn't it?' the Queen said, as she bound the plaster round her finger with a bit of ribbon.

Alice felt there was no denying *that*. 'Of course it would be all the better,' she said: 'but it wouldn't be all the better his being punished.'

'You're wrong *there*, at any rate,' said the Queen: 'were *you* ever punished?'

'Only for faults,' said Alice.

'And you were all the better for it, I know!' the Queen said triumphantly.

'Yes, but then I *had* done the things I was punished for,' said Alice: 'that makes all the difference.'

'But if you *hadn't* done them,' the Queen said, 'that would have been better still; better, and better, and better!' Her voice went higher with each 'better,' till it got quite to a squeak at last.

Alice was just beginning to say 'There's a mistake somewhere −', when the Queen began screaming so loud that she had to leave the sentence unfinished. 'Oh, oh, oh!' shouted the Queen, shaking her hand about as if she wanted to shake it off. 'My finger's bleeding! Oh, oh, oh, oh!'

Her screams were so exactly like the whistle of a steam-engine, that Alice had to hold both her hands over her ears.

'What is the matter?' she said, as soon as there was a chance of making herself heard. 'Have you pricked your finger?'

'I haven't pricked it *yet*,' the Queen said, 'but I soon shall – oh, oh, oh!'

'When do you expect to do it?' Alice asked, feeling very much inclined to laugh.

'When I fasten my shawl again,' the poor Queen groaned out: 'the brooch will come undone directly. Oh, oh!' As she said the words the brooch flew open, and the Queen clutched wildly at it, and tried to clasp it again.

'Take care!' cried Alice. 'You're holding it all crooked!' And she caught at the brooch: but it was too late: the pin had slipped, and the Queen had pricked her finger.

'That accounts for the bleeding, you see,' she said to Alice with a smile. 'Now you understand the way things happen here.'

'But why don't you scream now?' Alice asked, holding her hands ready to put over her ears again.

'Why, I've done all the screaming already,' said the Queen. 'What would be the good of having it all over again?'

By this time it was getting light. 'The crow must have flown away, I think,' said Alice: 'I'm so glad it's gone. I thought it was the night coming on.'

'I wish *I* could manage to be glad!' the Queen said. 'Only I never can remember the rule. You must be very happy, living in this wood, and being glad whenever you like!'

'Only it is so *very* lonely here!' Alice said in a melancholy voice; and at the thought of her loneliness two large tears came rolling down her cheeks.

'Oh, don't go on like that!' cried the poor Queen, wringing her hands in despair. 'Consider what a great girl you are. Consider what a long way you've come to-day. Consider what o'clock it is. Consider anything, only don't cry!'

Alice could not help laughing at this, even in the midst of her tears. 'Can *you* keep from crying by considering things?' she asked.

'That's the way it's done,' the Queen said with great decision: 'nobody can do two things at once, you know. Let's consider your age to begin with – how old are you?'

'I'm seven and a half exactly.'

'You needn't say "exactually,"' the Queen remarked: 'I can believe it without that. Now I'll give you something to believe. I'm just one hundred and one, five months and a day.'

'I can't believe *that*!' said Alice.

'Can't you?' the Queen said in a pitying tone. 'Try again: draw a long breath, and shut your eyes.'

Alice laughed. 'There's no use trying,' she said: 'one *can't* believe impossible things.'

'I daresay you haven't had much practice,' said the Queen. 'When I was your age, I always did it for half-an-hour a day. Why, sometimes I've believed as many as six impossible things before breakfast. There goes the shawl again!'

The brooch had come undone as she spoke, and a sudden gust of wind blew the Queen's shawl across a little brook. The Queen spread out her arms again, and went flying after it, and this time she succeeded in catching it for herself. 'I've got it!' she cried in a triumphant tone. 'Now you shall see me pin it on again, all by myself!'

'Then I hope your finger is better now?' Alice said very politely, as she crossed the little brook after the Queen.

*   *   *   *   *   *

*   *   *   *   *

*   *   *   *   *   *

'Oh, much better!' cried the Queen, her voice rising into a squeak as she went on. 'Much be-etter! Be-etter! Be-e-e-etter! Be-e-ehh!' The last word ended in a long bleat, so like a sheep that Alice quite started.

She looked at the Queen, who seemed to have suddenly wrapped herself up in wool. Alice rubbed her eyes, and looked again. She couldn't make out what had happened at all. Was she in a shop? And was that really – was it really a *sheep* that was sitting on the other side of the counter? Rub as she would, she could make nothing more of it: she was in a little dark shop, leaning with her elbows on the counter, and opposite to her was an old Sheep, sitting in an arm-chair knitting, and every now and then leaving off to look at her through a great pair of spectacles.

'What is it you want to buy?' the Sheep said at last, looking up for a moment from her knitting.

'I don't *quite* know yet,' Alice said, very gently. 'I should like to look all round me first, if I might.'

'You may look in front of you, and on both sides, if you like,' said the Sheep: 'but you can't look *all* round you – unless you've got eyes at the back of your head.'

But these, as it happened, Alice had *not* got: so she contented herself with turning round, looking at the shelves as she came to them.

The shop seemed to be full of all manner of curious things – but the oddest part of it all was, that whenever she looked hard at any shelf, to make out exactly what it had on it, that particular shelf was always quite empty: though the others round it were crowded as full as they could hold.

'Things flow about so here!' she said at last in a plaintive tone, after she had spent a minute or so in vainly pursuing a large bright thing, that looked sometimes like a doll and sometimes like a work-box, and was always in the shelf next above the one she was looking at. 'And this one is the most provoking of all – but I'll tell you what –' she added, as a sudden thought struck her, 'I'll follow it up to the very top shelf of all. It'll puzzle it to go through the ceiling, I expect!'

But even this plan failed: the 'thing' went through the ceiling as quietly as possible, as if it were quite used to it.

'Are you a child or a teetotum?' the Sheep said, as she took up another pair of needles. 'You'll make me giddy soon, if you go on turning round like that.' She was now working with fourteen pairs at once, and Alice couldn't help looking at her in great astonishment.

'How *can* she knit with so many?' the puzzled child thought to herself. 'She gets more and more like a porcupine every minute!'

'Can you row?' the Sheep asked, handing her a pair of knitting-needles as she spoke.

'Yes, a little – but not on land – and not with needles –' Alice was beginning to say, when suddenly the needles turned into oars in her hands, and she

found they were in a little boat, gliding along between banks: so there was nothing for it but to do her best.

'Feather!' cried the Sheep, as she took up another pair of needles.

This didn't sound like a remark that needed any answer, so Alice said nothing, but pulled away. There was something very queer about the water, she thought, as every now and then the oars got fast in it, and would hardly come out again.

'Feather! Feather!' the Sheep cried again, taking more needles. 'You'll be catching a crab directly.'

'A dear little crab!' thought Alice. 'I should like that.'

'Didn't you hear me say "Feather"?' the Sheep cried angrily, taking up quite a bunch of needles.

'Indeed I did,' said Alice: 'you've said it very often – and very loud. Please, where are the crabs?'

'In the water, of course!' said the Sheep, sticking some of the needles into her hair, as her hands were full. 'Feather, I say!'

'*Why* do you say "Feather" so often?' Alice asked at last, rather vexed. 'I'm not a bird!'

'You are,' said the Sheep: 'You're a little goose.'

This offended Alice a little, so there was no more conversation for a minute or two, while the boat glided gently on, sometimes among beds of weeds (which made the oars stick fast in the water, worse than ever), and sometimes under trees, but always with the same tall riverbanks frowning over their heads.

'Oh, please! There are some scented rushes!' Alice cried in a sudden transport of delight. 'There really are – and *such* beauties!'

'You needn't say "please" to *me* about 'em,' the Sheep said, without looking up from her knitting: 'I didn't put 'em there, and I'm not going to take 'em away.'

'No, but I meant – please, may we wait and pick some?' Alice pleaded. 'If you don't mind stopping the boat for a minute.'

'How am *I* to stop it?' said the Sheep. 'If you leave off rowing, it'll stop of itself.'

So the boat was left to drift down the stream as it would, till it glided gently in among the waving rushes. And then the little sleeves were carefully rolled up, and the little arms were plunged in elbow-deep, to get hold of the rushes a good long way down before breaking them off – and for a while Alice forgot all about the Sheep and the knitting, as she bent over the side of the boat, with just the ends of her tangled hair dipping in the water – while with bright eager eyes she caught at one bunch after another of the darling scented rushes.

'I only hope the boat won't tipple over!' she said to herself. 'Oh, *what* a lovely one! Only I couldn't quite reach it.' And it certainly *did* seem a little provoking ('almost as if it happened on purpose,' she thought) that, though she managed to pick plenty of beautiful rushes as the boat glided by, there was always a more lovely one that she couldn't reach.

'The prettiest are always further!' she said at last, with a sigh at the obstinacy of the rushes in growing so far off, as, with flushed cheeks and dripping hair and hands, she scrambled back into her place, and began to arrange her new-found treasures.

What mattered it to her just then that the rushes had begun to fade, and to lose all their scent and beauty, from the very moment that she picked them? Even real scented rushes, you know, last only a very little while – and these, being dream-rushes, melted away almost like snow, as they lay in heaps at her feet – but Alice hardly noticed this, there were so many other curious things to think about.

They hadn't gone much farther before the blade of one of the oars got fast in the water and *wouldn't* come out again (so Alice explained it afterwards), and the consequence was that the handle of it caught her under the chin, and, in spite of a series of little shrieks of 'Oh, oh, oh!' from poor Alice, it swept her straight off the seat, and down among the heap of rushes.

However, she wasn't a bit hurt, and was soon up again: the Sheep went on with her knitting all the while, just as if nothing had happened. 'That was a nice crab you caught!' she remarked, as Alice got back into her place, very much relieved to find herself still in the boat.

'Was it? I didn't see it,' said Alice, peeping cautiously over the side of the boat into the dark water. 'I wish it hadn't let go – I should so like a little crab to take home with me!' But the Sheep only laughed scornfully, and went on with her knitting.

'Are there many crabs here?' said Alice.

'Crabs, and all sorts of things,' said the Sheep: 'plenty of choice, only make up your mind. Now, what *do* you want to buy?'

'To buy!' Alice echoed in a tone that was half astonished and half frightened – for the oars, and the boat, and the river, had vanished all in a moment, and she was back again in the little dark shop.

'I should like to buy an egg, please,' she said timidly. 'How do you sell them?'

'Fivepence farthing for one – twopence for two,' the Sheep replied.

'Then two are cheaper than one?' Alice said in a surprised tone, taking out her purse.

'Only you *must* eat them both, if you buy two,' said the Sheep.

'Then I'll have *one* please,' said Alice, as she put the money down on the counter. For she thought to herself, 'They mightn't be at all nice, you know.'

The Sheep took the money, and put it away in a box: then she said 'I never put things into people's hands – that would never do – you must get it for yourself.' And so saying, she went off to the other end of the shop, and set the egg upright on a shelf.

'I wonder *why* it wouldn't do?' thought Alice, as she groped her way among the tables and chairs, for the shop was very dark towards the end. 'The egg seems to get further away the more I walk towards it. Let me see, is this a chair? Why, it's got branches, I declare! How very odd to find trees growing here! And actually here's a little brook! Well, this is the very queerest shop I ever saw!'

*   *   *   *   *   *

*   *   *   *   *

*   *   *   *   *   *

So she went on, wondering more and more at every step, as everything turned into a tree the moment she came up to it, and she quite expected the egg to do the same.

CHAPTER SIX

HUMPTY DUMPTY

However, the egg only got larger and larger, and more and more human: when she had come within a few yards of it, she saw that it had eyes and a nose and mouth; and when she had come close to it, she saw clearly that it was HUMPTY DUMPTY himself. 'It can't be anybody else!' she said to herself. 'I'm as certain of it, as if his name were written all over his face.'

It might have been written a hundred times, easily, on that enormous face. Humpty Dumpty was sitting with his legs crossed, like a Turk, on the top of a high wall – such a narrow one that Alice quite wondered how he could keep his balance – and, as his eyes were steadily fixed in the opposite direction, and he didn't take the least notice of her, she thought he must be a stuffed figure after all.

'And how exactly like an egg he is!' she said aloud, standing with her hands ready to catch him, for she was every moment expecting him to fall.

'It's *very* provoking,' Humpty Dumpty said after a long silence, looking away from Alice as he spoke, 'to be called an egg – *very*!'

'I said you *looked* like an egg, Sir,' Alice gently explained. 'And some eggs are very pretty, you know,' she added, hoping to turn her remark into a sort of compliment.

'Some people,' said Humpty Dumpty, looking away from her as usual, 'have no more sense than a baby!'

CHAPTER SIX: HUMPTY DUMPTY

Alice didn't know what to say to this: it wasn't at all like conversation, she thought, as he never said anything to *her*; in fact, his last remark was evidently addressed to a tree – so she stood and softly repeated to herself:–

> *'Humpty Dumpty sat on a wall:*
> *Humpty Dumpty had a great fall.*
> *All the King's horses and all the King's men*
> *Couldn't put Humpty Dumpty in his place again.'*

'That last line is much too long for the poetry,' she added, almost out loud, forgetting that Humpty Dumpty would hear her.

'Don't stand chattering to yourself like that,' Humpty Dumpty said, looking at her for the first time, 'but tell me your name and your business.'

'My *name* is Alice, but –'

'It's a stupid name enough!' Humpty Dumpty interrupted impatiently. 'What does it mean?'

'*Must* a name mean something?' Alice asked doubtfully.

'Of course it must,' Humpty Dumpty said with a short laugh: '*my* name means the shape I am – and a good handsome shape it is, too. With a name like yours, you might be any shape, almost.'

'Why do you sit out here all alone?' said Alice, not wishing to begin an argument.

'Why, because there's nobody with me!' cried Humpty Dumpty. 'Did you think I didn't know the answer to *that*? Ask another.'

'Don't you think you'd be safer down on the ground?' Alice went on, not with any idea of making another riddle, but simply in her good-natured anxiety for the queer creature. 'That wall is so *very* narrow!'

'What tremendously easy riddles you ask!' Humpty Dumpty growled out. 'Of course I don't think so! Why, if ever I *did* fall off – which there's no chance of – but *if* I did –' Here he pursed up his lips and looked so solemn and grand

that Alice could hardly help laughing. '*If I did fall*,' he went on, 'the King has promised me – ah, you may turn pale, if you like! You didn't think I was going to say that, did you? *The King has promised me – with his very own mouth to – to –*'

'To send all his horses and all his men,' Alice interrupted, rather unwisely.

'Now I declare that's too bad!' Humpty Dumpty cried, breaking into a sudden passion. 'You've been listening at doors – and behind trees – and down chimneys – or you couldn't have known it!'

'I haven't, indeed!' Alice said very gently. 'It's in a book.'

'Ah, well! They may write such things in a *book*,' Humpty Dumpty said in a calmer tone. 'That's what you call a History of England, that is. Now, take a good look at me! I'm one that has spoken to a King, *I* am: mayhap you'll never see such another: and to show you I'm not proud, you may shake hands with me!' And he grinned almost from ear to ear, as he leant forwards (and as nearly as possible fell off the wall in doing so) and offered Alice his hand. She watched

him a little anxiously as she took it. 'If he smiled much more, the ends of his mouth might meet behind,' she thought: 'and then I don't know what would happen to his head! I'm afraid it would come off!'

'Yes, all his horses and all his men,' Humpty Dumpty went on. 'They'd pick me up again in a minute, *they* would! However, this conversation is going on a little too fast: let's go back to the last remark but one.'

'I'm afraid I can't quite remember it,' Alice said very politely.

'In that case we start fresh,' said Humpty Dumpty, 'and it's my turn to choose a subject –' ('He talks about it just as if it was a game!' thought Alice.) 'So here's a question for you. How old did you say you were?'

Alice made a short calculation, and said 'Seven years and six months.'

'Wrong!' Humpty Dumpty exclaimed triumphantly. 'You never said a word like it!'

'I thought you meant "How old *are* you?"' Alice explained.

'If I'd meant that, I'd have said it,' said Humpty Dumpty.

Alice didn't want to begin another argument, so she said nothing.

'Seven years and six months!' Humpty Dumpty repeated thoughtfully. 'An uncomfortable sort of age. Now if you'd asked *my* advice, I'd have said "Leave off at seven" – but it's too late now.'

'I never ask advice about growing,' Alice said indignantly.

'Too proud?' the other enquired.

Alice felt even more indignant at this suggestion. 'I mean,' she said, 'that one can't help growing older.'

'*One* can't, perhaps,' said Humpty Dumpty, 'but *two* can. With proper assistance, you might have left off at seven.'

'What a beautiful belt you've got on!' Alice suddenly remarked. (They had had quite enough of the subject of age, she thought: and if they really were to take turns in choosing subjects, it was her turn now.) 'At least,' she corrected herself on second thoughts, 'a beautiful cravat, I should have said – no, a belt,

I mean – I beg your pardon!' she added in dismay, for Humpty Dumpty looked thoroughly offended, and she began to wish she hadn't chosen that subject. 'If only I knew,' she thought to herself, 'which was neck and which was waist!'

Evidently Humpty Dumpty was very angry, though he said nothing for a minute or two. When he did speak again, it was in a deep growl.

'It is a – *most – provoking –* thing,' he said at last, 'when a person doesn't know a cravat from a belt!'

'I know it's very ignorant of me,' Alice said, in so humble a tone that Humpty Dumpty relented.

'It's a cravat, child, and a beautiful one, as you say. It's a present from the White King and Queen. There now!'

'Is it really?' said Alice, quite pleased to find that she *had* chosen a good subject, after all.

'They gave it me,' Humpty Dumpty continued thoughtfully, as he crossed one knee over the other and clasped his hands round it, 'they gave it me – for an unbirthday present.'

'I beg your pardon?' Alice said with a puzzled air.

'I'm not offended,' said Humpty Dumpty.

'I mean, what *is* an un-birthday present?'

'A present given when it isn't your birthday, of course.'

Alice considered a little. 'I like birthday presents best,' she said at last.

'You don't know what you're talking about!' cried Humpty Dumpty. 'How many days are there in a year?'

'Three hundred and sixty-five,' said Alice.

'And how many birthdays have you?'

'One.'

'And if you take one from three hundred and sixty-five, what remains?'

'Three hundred and sixty-four, of course.'

Humpty Dumpty looked doubtful. 'I'd rather see that done on paper,' he said.

Alice couldn't help smiling as she took out her memorandum-book, and worked the sum for him:

$$\begin{array}{r} 365 \\ 1 \\ \hline 364 \end{array}$$

Humpty Dumpty took the book, and looked at it carefully. 'That seems to be done right –' he began.

'You're holding it upside down!' Alice interrupted.

'To be sure I was!' Humpty Dumpty said gaily, as she turned it round for him. 'I thought it looked a little queer. As I was saying, that *seems* to be done right – though I haven't time to look it over thoroughly just now – and that shows that there are three hundred and sixty-four days when you might get un-birthday presents –'

'Certainly,' said Alice.

'And only *one* for birthday presents, you know. There's glory for you!'

'I don't know what you mean by "glory,"' Alice said.

Humpty Dumpty smiled contemptuously. 'Of course you don't – till I tell you. I meant "there's a nice knock-down argument for you!"'

'But "glory" doesn't mean "a nice knock-down argument,"' Alice objected.

'When *I* use a word,' Humpty Dumpty said in rather a scornful tone, 'it means just what I choose it to mean – neither more nor less.'

'The question is,' said Alice, 'whether you *can* make words mean so many different things.'

'The question is,' said Humpty Dumpty, 'which is to be master – that's all.'

Alice was too much puzzled to say anything, so after a minute Humpty Dumpty began again. 'They've a temper, some of them – particularly verbs, they're the proudest – adjectives you can do anything with, but not verbs – however, *I* can manage the whole lot of them! Impenetrability! That's what *I* say!'

'Would you tell me, please,' said Alice, 'what that means?'

CHAPTER SIX: HUMPTY DUMPTY

'Now you talk like a reasonable child,' said Humpty Dumpty, looking very much pleased. 'I meant by "impenetrability" that we've had enough of that subject, and it would be just as well if you'd mention what you mean to do next, as I suppose you don't mean to stop here all the rest of your life.'

'That's a great deal to make one word mean,' Alice said in a thoughtful tone.

'When I make a word do a lot of work like that,' said Humpty Dumpty, 'I always pay it extra.'

'Oh!' said Alice. She was too much puzzled to make any other remark.

'Ah, you should see 'em come round me of a Saturday night,' Humpty Dumpty went on, wagging his head gravely from side to side: 'for to get their wages, you know.'

(Alice didn't venture to ask what he paid them with; and so you see I can't tell you.)

'You seem very clever at explaining words, Sir,' said Alice. 'Would you kindly tell me the meaning of the poem called "Jabberwocky"?'

'Let's hear it,' said Humpty Dumpty. 'I can explain all the poems that ever were invented – and a good many that haven't been invented just yet.'

This sounded very hopeful, so Alice repeated the first verse:

> *"Twas brillig, and the slithy toves*
> *Did gyre and gimble in the wabe:*
> *All mimsy were the borogoves,*
> *And the mome raths outgrabe.'*

'That's enough to begin with,' Humpty Dumpty interrupted: 'there are plenty of hard words there. "*Brillig*" means four o'clock in the afternoon – the time when you begin broiling things for dinner.'

'That'll do very well,' said Alice: 'and "*slithy*"?'

'Well, "*slithy*" means "lithe and slimy." "Lithe" is the same as "active." You see it's like a portmanteau – there are two meanings packed up into one word.'

'I see it now,' Alice remarked thoughtfully: 'and what are "*toves*"?'

'Well, "*toves*" are something like badgers – they're something like lizards – and they're something like corkscrews.'

'They must be very curious-looking creatures.'

'They are that,' said Humpty Dumpty: 'also they make their nests under sun-dials – also they live on cheese.'

'And what's to "*gyre*" and to "*gimble*"?'

'To "*gyre*" is to go round and round like a gyroscope. To "*gimble*" is to make holes like a gimblet.'

'And "*the wabe*" is the grass-plot round a sun-dial I suppose?' said Alice, surprised at her own ingenuity.

'Of course it is. It's called "*wabe*" you know, because it goes a long way before it, and a long way behind it –'

'And a long way beyond it on each side,' Alice added.

'Exactly so. Well then, "*mimsy*" is "flimsy and miserable" (there's another portmanteau for you). And a "*borogove*" is a thin shabby-looking bird with its feathers sticking out all round – something like a live mop.'

'And then "*mome raths*"?' said Alice. 'I'm afraid I'm giving you a great deal of trouble.'

'Well, a "*rath*" is a sort of green pig: but "*mome*" I'm not certain about. I think it's short for "from home" – meaning that they'd lost their way, you know.'

'And what does "*outgrabe*" mean?'

'Well, "*outgribing*" is something between bellowing and whistling, with a kind of sneeze in the middle: however, you'll hear it done, maybe – down in the wood yonder – and when you've once heard it you'll be *quite* content. Who's been repeating all that hard stuff to you?'

'I read it in a book,' said Alice. 'But I had some poetry repeated to me, much easier than that, by – Tweedledee, I think it was.'

'As to poetry, you know,' said Humpty Dumpty, stretching out one of his great hands, '*I* can repeat poetry as well as other folk, if it comes to that –'

'Oh, it needn't come to that!' Alice hastily said, hoping to keep him from beginning.

'The piece I'm going to repeat,' he went on without noticing her remark, 'was written entirely for your amusement.'

Alice felt that in that case she really *ought* to listen to it, so she sat down, and said 'Thank you' rather sadly.

> *'In winter, when the fields are white,*
> *I sing this song for your delight –*

only I don't sing it,' he added, as an explanation.

'I see you don't,' said Alice.

'If you can *see* whether I'm singing or not, you've sharper eyes than most,' Humpty Dumpty remarked severely. Alice was silent.

> *'In spring, when woods are getting green,*
> *I'll try and tell you what I mean.'*

'Thank you very much,' said Alice.

> *'In summer, when the days are long,*
> *Perhaps you'll understand the song:*
>
> *In autumn, when the leaves are brown,*
> *Take pen and ink, and write it down.'*

'I will, if I can remember it so long,' said Alice.

'You needn't go on making remarks like that,' Humpty Dumpty said: 'they're not sensible, and they put me out.'

> *'I sent a message to the fish:*
> *I told them "This is what I wish."*
>
> *The little fishes of the sea,*
> *They sent an answer back to me.*
>
> *The little fishes' answer was*
> *"We cannot do it, Sir, because —"'*

'I'm afraid I don't quite understand,' said Alice.

'It gets easier further on,' Humpty Dumpty replied.

> *'I sent to them again to say*
> *"It will be better to obey."*
>
> *The fishes answered with a grin,*
> *"Why, what a temper you are in!"*

CHAPTER SIX: HUMPTY DUMPTY

> *I told them once, I told them twice:*
> *They would not listen to advice.*
>
> *I took a kettle large and new,*
> *Fit for the deed I had to do.*
>
> *My heart went hop, my heart went thump;*
> *I filled the kettle at the pump.*
>
> *Then some one came to me and said,*
> *"The little fishes are in bed."*
>
> *I said to him, I said it plain,*
> *"Then you must wake them up again."*
>
> *I said it very loud and clear;*
> *I went and shouted in his ear.'*

Humpty Dumpty raised his voice almost to a scream as he repeated this verse, and Alice thought with a shudder, 'I wouldn't have been the messenger for *anything*!'

> *'But he was very stiff and proud;*
> *He said "You needn't shout so loud!"*
>
> *And he was very proud and stiff;*
> *He said "I'd go and wake them, if—"*
>
> *I took a corkscrew from the shelf:*
> *I went to wake them up myself.*
>
> *And when I found the door was locked,*
> *I pulled and pushed and kicked and knocked.*
>
> *And when I found the door was shut,*
> *I tried to turn the handle, but—'*

CHAPTER SIX: HUMPTY DUMPTY

There was a long pause.

'Is that all?' Alice timidly asked.

'That's all,' said Humpty Dumpty. 'Good-bye.'

This was rather sudden, Alice thought: but, after such a *very* strong hint that she ought to be going, she felt that it would hardly be civil to stay. So she got up, and held out her hand. 'Good-bye, till we meet again!' she said as cheerfully as she could.

'I shouldn't know you again if we *did* meet,' Humpty Dumpty replied in a discontented tone, giving her one of his fingers to shake; 'you're so exactly like other people.'

'The face is what one goes by, generally,' Alice remarked in a thoughtful tone.

'That's just what I complain of,' said Humpty Dumpty. 'Your face is the same as everybody has – the two eyes, so –' (marking their places in the air with his thumb) 'nose in the middle, mouth under. It's always the same. Now if you had the two eyes on the same side of the nose, for instance – or the mouth at the top – that would be *some* help.'

'It wouldn't look nice,' Alice objected. But Humpty Dumpty only shut his eyes and said 'Wait till you've tried.'

Alice waited a minute to see if he would speak again, but as he never opened his eyes or took any further notice of her, she said 'Good-bye!' once more, and, getting no answer to this, she quietly walked away: but she couldn't help saying to herself as she went, 'Of all the unsatisfactory –' (she repeated this aloud, as it was a great comfort to have such a long word to say) 'of all the unsatisfactory people I *ever* met –' She never finished the sentence, for at this moment a heavy crash shook the forest from end to end.

CHAPTER SEVEN

THE LION AND THE
UNICORN

T he next moment soldiers came running through the wood, at first in twos and threes, then ten or twenty together, and at last in such crowds that they seemed to fill the whole forest. Alice got behind a tree, for fear of being run over, and watched them go by.

She thought that in all her life she had never seen soldiers so uncertain on their feet: they were always tripping over something or other, and whenever one went down, several more always fell over him, so that the ground was soon covered with little heaps of men.

Then came the horses. Having four feet, these managed rather better than the foot-soldiers: but even *they* stumbled now and then; and it seemed to be a regular rule that, whenever a horse stumbled, the rider fell off instantly. The confusion got worse every moment, and Alice was very glad to get out of the wood into an open place, where she found the White King seated on the ground, busily writing in his memorandum-book.

'I've sent them all!' the King cried in a tone of delight, on seeing Alice. 'Did you happen to meet any soldiers, my dear, as you came through the wood?'

'Yes, I did,' said Alice: 'several thousand, I should think.'

'Four thousand two hundred and seven, that's the exact number,' the King said, referring to his book. 'I couldn't send all the horses, you know, because two of them are wanted in the game. And I haven't sent the two Messengers,

either. They're both gone to the town. Just look along the road, and tell me if you can see either of them.'

'I see nobody on the road,' said Alice.

'I only wish *I* had such eyes,' the King remarked in a fretful tone. 'To be able to see Nobody! And at that distance too! Why, it's as much as I can do to see real people, by this light!'

All this was lost on Alice, who was still looking intently along the road, shading her eyes with one hand. 'I see somebody now!' she exclaimed at last. 'But he's coming very slowly – and what curious attitudes he goes into!' (For the Messenger kept skipping up and down, and wriggling like an eel, as he came along, with his great hands spread out like fans on each side.)

'Not at all,' said the King. 'He's an Anglo-Saxon Messenger – and those are Anglo-Saxon attitudes. He only does them when he's happy. His name is Haigha.' (He pronounced it so as to rhyme with 'mayor.')

'I love my love with an H,' Alice couldn't help beginning, 'because he is Happy. I hate him with an H, because he is Hideous. I fed him with – with – with Ham sandwiches and Hay. His name is Haigha, and he lives –'

'He lives on the Hill,' the King remarked simply, without the least idea that he was joining in the game, while Alice was still hesitating for the name of a town beginning with H. 'The other Messenger's called Hatta. I must have *two*, you know – to come and go. One to come, and one to go.'

'I beg your pardon?' said Alice.

'It isn't respectable to beg,' said the King.

'I only meant that I didn't understand,' said Alice. 'Why one to come and one to go?'

'Don't I tell you?' the King repeated impatiently. 'I must have *two* – to fetch and carry. One to fetch, and one to carry.'

At this moment the Messenger arrived: he was far too much out of breath to say a word, and could only wave his hands about, and make the most fearful faces at the poor King.

'This young lady loves you with an H,' the King said, introducing Alice in the hope of turning off the Messenger's attention from himself – but it was no use – the Anglo-Saxon attitudes only got more extraordinary every moment, while the great eyes rolled wildly from side to side.

'You alarm me!' said the King. 'I feel faint – Give me a ham sandwich!'

On which the Messenger, to Alice's great amusement, opened a bag that hung round his neck, and handed a sandwich to the King, who devoured it greedily.

'Another sandwich!' said the King.

'There's nothing but hay left now,' the Messenger said, peeping into the bag.

'Hay, then,' the King murmured in a faint whisper.

Alice was glad to see that it revived him a good deal. 'There's nothing like eating hay when you're faint,' he remarked to her, as he munched away.

'I should think throwing cold water over you would be better,' Alice suggested: '– or some sal-volatile.'

'I didn't say there was nothing *better*,' the King replied. 'I said there was nothing *like* it.' Which Alice did not venture to deny.

CHAPTER SEVEN: THE LION AND THE UNICORN

'Who did you pass on the road?' the King went on, holding out his hand to the Messenger for some more hay. 'Nobody,' said the Messenger.

'Quite right,' said the King: 'this young lady saw him too. So of course Nobody walks slower than you.'

'I do my best,' the Messenger said in a sulky tone. 'I'm sure nobody walks much faster than I do!'

'He can't do that,' said the King, 'or else he'd have been here first. However, now you've got your breath, you may tell us what's happened in the town.'

'I'll whisper it,' said the Messenger, putting his hands to his mouth in the shape of a trumpet, and stooping so as to get close to the King's ear. Alice was sorry for this, as she wanted to hear the news too. However, instead of whispering, he simply shouted at the top of his voice 'They're at it again!'

'Do you call *that* a whisper?' cried the poor King, jumping up and shaking himself. 'If you do such a thing again, I'll have you buttered! It went through and through my head like an earthquake!'

'It would have to be a very tiny earthquake!' thought Alice. 'Who are at it again?' she ventured to ask.

'Why, the Lion and the Unicorn, of course,' said the King.

'Fighting for the crown?'

'Yes, to be sure,' said the King: 'and the best of the joke is, that it's *my* crown all the while! Let's run and see them.' And they trotted off, Alice repeating to herself, as she ran, the words of the old song:

> *'The Lion and the Unicorn were fighting for the crown:*
> *The Lion beat the Unicorn all round the town.*
> *Some gave them white bread, some gave them brown;*
> *Some gave them plum-cake and drummed them out of town.'*

'Does – the one – that wins – get the crown?' she asked, as well as she could, for the run was putting her quite out of breath.

'Dear me, no!' said the King. 'What an idea!'

'Would you – be good enough,' Alice panted out, after running a little further, 'to stop a minute – just to get – one's breath again?'

'I'm *good* enough,' the King said, 'only I'm not strong enough. You see, a minute goes by so fearfully quick. You might as well try to stop a Bandersnatch!'

Alice had no more breath for talking, so they trotted on in silence, till they came in sight of a great crowd, in the middle of which the Lion and Unicorn were fighting. They were in such a cloud of dust, that at first Alice could not make out which was which: but she soon managed to distinguish the Unicorn by his horn.

They placed themselves close to where Hatta, the other Messenger, was standing watching the fight, with a cup of tea in one hand and a piece of bread-and-butter in the other.

'He's only just out of prison, and he hadn't finished his tea when he was sent in,' Haigha whispered to Alice: 'and they only give them oyster-shells in there – so you see he's very hungry and thirsty. How are you, dear child?' he went on, putting his arm affectionately round Hatta's neck.

Hatta looked round and nodded, and went on with his bread-and-butter.

'Were you happy in prison, dear child?' said Haigha.

Hatta looked round once more, and this time a tear or two trickled down his cheek: but not a word would he say.

'Speak, can't you!' Haigha cried impatiently. But Hatta only munched away, and drank some more tea.

'Speak, won't you!' cried the King. 'How are they getting on with the fight?'

Hatta made a desperate effort, and swallowed a large piece of bread-and-butter. 'They're getting on very well,' he said in a choking voice: 'each of them has been down about eighty-seven times.'

'Then I suppose they'll soon bring the white bread and the brown?' Alice ventured to remark.

'It's waiting for 'em now,' said Hatta: 'This is a bit of it as I'm eating.'

There was a pause in the fight just then, and the Lion and the Unicorn sat down, panting, while the King called out 'Ten minutes allowed for refreshments!' Haigha and Hatta set to work at once, carrying round trays of white and brown bread. Alice took a piece to taste, but it was *very* dry.

'I don't think they'll fight any more to-day,' the King said to Hatta: 'go and order the drums to begin.' And Hatta went bounding away like a grasshopper.

For a minute or two Alice stood silent, watching him. Suddenly she brightened up. 'Look, look!' she cried, pointing eagerly. 'There's the White Queen running across the country! She came flying out of the wood over yonder – How fast those Queens *can* run!'

'There's some enemy after her, no doubt,' the King said, without even looking round. 'That wood's full of them.'

'But aren't you going to run and help her?' Alice asked, very much surprised at his taking it so quietly.

'No use, no use!' said the King. 'She runs so fearfully quick. You might as well try to catch a Bandersnatch! But I'll make a memorandum about her, if you like – She's a dear good creature,' he repeated softly to himself, as he opened his memorandum-book. 'Do you spell "creature" with a double "e"?'

At this moment the Unicorn sauntered by them, with his hands in his pockets. 'I had the best of it this time?' he said to the King, just glancing at him as he passed.

'A little – a little,' the King replied, rather nervously. 'You shouldn't have run him through with your horn, you know.'

'It didn't hurt him,' the Unicorn said carelessly, and he was going on, when his eye happened to fall upon Alice: he turned round instantly, and stood for some time looking at her with an air of the deepest disgust.

'What – is – this?' he said at last.

'This is a child!' Haigha replied eagerly, coming in front of Alice to introduce her, and spreading out both his hands towards her in an Anglo-Saxon attitude. 'We only found it to-day. It's as large as life, and twice as natural!'

'I always thought they were fabulous monsters!' said the Unicorn. 'Is it alive?'

'It can talk,' said Haigha, solemnly.

The Unicorn looked dreamily at Alice, and said 'Talk, child.'

Alice could not help her lips curling up into a smile as she began: 'Do you know, I always thought Unicorns were fabulous monsters, too! I never saw one alive before!'

'Well, now that we *have* seen each other,' said the Unicorn, 'if you'll believe in me, I'll believe in you. Is that a bargain?'

'Yes, if you like,' said Alice.

'Come, fetch out the plum-cake, old man!' the Unicorn went on, turning from her to the King. 'None of your brown bread for me!'

'Certainly – certainly!' the King muttered, and beckoned to Haigha. 'Open the bag!' he whispered. 'Quick! Not that one – that's full of hay!'

Haigha took a large cake out of the bag, and gave it to Alice to hold, while he got out a dish and carving-knife. How they all came out of it Alice couldn't guess. It was just like a conjuring-trick, she thought.

The Lion had joined them while this was going on: he looked very tired and sleepy, and his eyes were half shut. 'What's this!' he said, blinking lazily at Alice, and speaking in a deep hollow tone that sounded like the tolling of a great bell.

'Ah, what *is* it, now?' the Unicorn cried eagerly. 'You'll never guess! *I* couldn't.'

The Lion looked at Alice wearily. 'Are you animal – or vegetable – or mineral?' he said, yawning at every other word.

'It's a fabulous monster!' the Unicorn cried out, before Alice could reply.

'Then hand round the plum-cake, Monster,' the Lion said, lying down and putting his chin on his paws. 'And sit down, both of you,' (to the King and the Unicorn): 'fair play with the cake, you know!'

The King was evidently very uncomfortable at having to sit down between the two great creatures; but there was no other place for him.

'What a fight we might have for the crown, *now*!' the Unicorn said, looking slyly up at the crown, which the poor King was nearly shaking off his head, he trembled so much.

'I should win easy,' said the Lion.

'I'm not so sure of that,' said the Unicorn.

'Why, I beat you all round the town, you chicken!' the Lion replied angrily, half getting up as he spoke.

Here the King interrupted, to prevent the quarrel going on: he was very nervous, and his voice quite quivered. 'All round the town?' he said. 'That's a good long way. Did you go by the old bridge, or the market-place? You get the best view by the old bridge.'

'I'm sure I don't know,' the Lion growled out as he lay down again. 'There was too much dust to see anything. What a time the Monster is, cutting up that cake!'

Alice had seated herself on the bank of a little brook, with the great dish on her knees, and was sawing very diligently with the knife. 'It's very provoking!' she said, in reply to the Lion (she was getting quite used to being called 'the Monster'). 'I've cut several slices already, but they always join on again!'

'You don't know how to manage Looking-glass cakes,' the Unicorn remarked. 'Hand it round first, and cut it afterwards.'

This sounded nonsense, but Alice very obediently got up, and carried the dish round, and the cake divided itself into three pieces as she did so. '*Now* cut it up,' said the Lion, as she returned to her place with the empty dish.

'I say, this isn't fair!' cried the Unicorn, as Alice sat with the knife in her hand, very much puzzled how to begin. 'The Monster has given the Lion twice as much as me.'

'She's kept none for herself, anyhow,' said the Lion. 'Do you like plum-cake, Monster?'

But before Alice could answer him, the drums began.

Where the noise came from, she couldn't make out: the air seemed full of it, and it rang through and through her head till she felt quite deafened. She started to her feet and sprang across the little brook in terror,

*　　*　　*　　*　　*　　*

　*　　*　　*　　*　　*

*　　*　　*　　*　　*　　*

and had just time to see the Lion and the Unicorn rise to their feet, with angry looks at being interrupted in their feast, before she dropped to her knees, and put her hands over her ears, vainly trying to shut out the dreadful uproar.

'If *that* doesn't "drum them out of town,"' she thought to herself, 'nothing ever will!'

CHAPTER EIGHT

'IT'S MY OWN INVENTION'

After a while the noise seemed gradually to die away, till all was dead silence, and Alice lifted up her head in some alarm. There was no one to be seen, and her first thought was that she must have been dreaming about the Lion and the Unicorn and those queer Anglo-Saxon Messengers. However, there was the great dish still lying at her feet, on which she had tried to cut the plum-cake, 'So I wasn't dreaming, after all,' she said to herself, 'unless – unless we're all part of the same dream. Only I do hope it's *my* dream, and not the Red King's! I don't like belonging to another person's dream,' she went on in a rather complaining tone: 'I've a great mind to go and wake him, and see what happens!'

At this moment her thoughts were interrupted by a loud shouting of 'Ahoy! Ahoy! Check!' and a Knight, dressed in crimson armour, came galloping down upon her, brandishing a great club. Just as he reached her, the horse stopped suddenly: 'You're my prisoner!' the Knight cried, as he tumbled off his horse.

Startled as she was, Alice was more frightened for him than for herself at the moment, and watched him with some anxiety as he mounted again. As soon as he was comfortably in the saddle, he began once more 'You're my –' but here another voice broke in 'Ahoy! Ahoy! Check!' and Alice looked round in some surprise for the new enemy.

CHAPTER EIGHT: 'IT'S MY OWN INVENTION'

This time it was a White Knight. He drew up at Alice's side, and tumbled off his horse just as the Red Knight had done: then he got on again, and the two Knights sat and looked at each other for some time without speaking. Alice looked from one to the other in some bewilderment.

'She's *my* prisoner, you know!' the Red Knight said at last.

'Yes, but then I came and rescued her!' the White Knight replied.

'Well, we must fight for her, then,' said the Red Knight, as he took up his helmet (which hung from the saddle, and was something the shape of a horse's head), and put it on.

'You will observe the Rules of Battle, of course?' the White Knight remarked, putting on his helmet too.

'I always do,' said the Red Knight, and they began banging away at each other with such fury that Alice got behind a tree to be out of the way of the blows.

'I wonder, now, what the Rules of Battle are,' she said to herself, as she watched the fight, timidly peeping out from her hiding-place: 'one Rule seems to be, that if one Knight hits the other, he knocks him off his horse, and if he misses, he tumbles off himself – and another Rule seems to be that they hold their clubs with their arms, as if they were Punch and Judy – What a noise they make when they tumble! Just like a whole set of fire-irons falling into the fender! And how quiet the horses are! They let them get on and off them just as if they were tables!'

Another Rule of Battle, that Alice had not noticed, seemed to be that they always fell on their heads, and the battle ended with their both falling off in this way, side by side: when they got up again, they shook hands, and then the Red Knight mounted and galloped off.

'It was a glorious victory, wasn't it?' said the White Knight, as he came up panting.

'I don't know,' Alice said doubtfully. 'I don't want to be anybody's prisoner. I want to be a Queen.'

'So you will, when you've crossed the next brook,' said the White Knight. 'I'll see you safe to the end of the wood – and then I must go back; you know. That's the end of my move.'

'Thank you very much,' said Alice. 'May I help you off with your helmet?' It was evidently more than he could manage by himself; however, she managed to shake him out of it at last.

'Now one can breathe more easily,' said the Knight, putting back his shaggy hair with both hands, and turning his gentle face and large mild eyes to Alice. She thought she had never seen such a strange-looking soldier in all her life.

He was dressed in tin armour, which seemed to fit him very badly, and he had a queer-shaped little deal box fastened across his shoulders, upside-down, and with the lid hanging open. Alice looked at it with great curiosity.

'I see you're admiring my little box,' the Knight said in a friendly tone. 'It's my own invention – to keep clothes and sandwiches in. You see I carry it upside-down, so that the rain can't get in.'

'But the things can get *out*,' Alice gently remarked. 'Do you know the lid's open?'

'I didn't know it,' the Knight said, a shade of vexation passing over his face. 'Then all the things must have fallen out! And the box is no use without them.' He unfastened it as he spoke, and was just going to throw it into the bushes, when a sudden thought seemed to strike him, and he hung it carefully on a tree.

'Can you guess why I did that?' he said to Alice.

Alice shook her head.

'I hope some bees may make a nest in it – then I should get the honey.'

'But you've got a bee-hive – or something like one – fastened to the saddle,' said Alice.

'Yes, it's a very good bee-hive,' the Knight said in a discontented tone, 'one of the best kind. But not a single bee has come near it yet. And the other thing is a mouse-trap. I suppose the mice keep the bees out – or the bees keep the mice out, I don't know which.'

'I was wondering what the mouse-trap was for,' said Alice. 'It isn't very likely there would be any mice on the horse's back.'

'Not very likely, perhaps,' said the Knight; 'but if they do come, I don't choose to have them running all about.'

'You see,' he went on after a pause, 'it's as well to be provided for *everything*. That's the reason the horse has all those anklets round his feet.'

'But what are they for?' Alice asked in a tone of great curiosity.

'To guard against the bites of sharks,' the Knight replied. 'It's an invention of my own. And now help me on. I'll go with you to the end of the wood – What's that dish for?'

'It's meant for plum-cake,' said Alice.

'We'd better take it with us,' the Knight said. 'It'll come in handy if we find any plum-cake. Help me to get it into this bag.'

This took a long time to manage, though Alice held the bag open very carefully, because the Knight was so *very* awkward in putting in the dish: the first two or three times that he tried he fell in himself instead. 'It's rather a tight fit, you see,' he said, as they got it in at last; 'there are so many candlesticks in the bag.' And he hung it to the saddle, which was already loaded with bunches of carrots, and fire-irons, and many other things.

'I hope you've got your hair well fastened on?' he continued, as they set off.

'Only in the usual way,' Alice said, smiling.

'That's hardly enough,' he said, anxiously. 'You see the wind is so *very* strong here. It's as strong as soup.'

'Have you invented a plan for keeping the hair from being blown off?' Alice enquired.

'Not yet,' said the Knight. 'But I've got a plan for keeping it from *falling* off.'

'I should like to hear it, very much.'

'First you take an upright stick,' said the Knight. 'Then you make your hair creep up it, like a fruit-tree. Now the reason hair falls off is because it hangs *down* – things never fall *upwards*, you know. It's a plan of my own invention. You may try it if you like.'

It didn't sound a comfortable plan, Alice thought, and for a few minutes she walked on in silence, puzzling over the idea, and every now and then stopping to help the poor Knight, who certainly was *not* a good rider.

Whenever the horse stopped (which it did very often), he fell off in front; and whenever it went on again (which it generally did rather suddenly), he fell off behind. Otherwise he kept on pretty well, except that he had a habit of now and then falling off sideways; and as he generally did this on the side on which Alice was walking, she soon found that it was the best plan not to walk *quite so* close to the horse.

'I'm afraid you've not had much practice in riding,' she ventured to say, as she was helping him up from his fifth tumble.

The Knight looked very much surprised, and a little offended at the remark. 'What makes you say that?' he asked, as he scrambled back into the saddle, keeping hold of Alice's hair with one hand, to save himself from falling over on the other side.

'Because people don't fall off quite so often, when they've had much practice.'

'I've had plenty of practice,' the Knight said very gravely: 'plenty of practice!'

Alice could think of nothing better to say than 'Indeed?' but she said it

as heartily as she could. They went on a little way in silence after this, the Knight with his eyes shut, muttering to himself, and Alice watching anxiously for the next tumble.

'The great art of riding,' the Knight suddenly began in a loud voice, waving his right arm as he spoke, 'is to keep –' Here the sentence ended as suddenly as it had begun, as the Knight fell heavily on the top of his head exactly in the path where Alice was walking. She was quite frightened this time, and said in an anxious tone, as she picked him up, 'I hope no bones are broken?'

'None to speak of,' the Knight said, as if he didn't mind breaking two or three of them. 'The great art of riding, as I was saying, is – to keep your balance properly. Like this, you know –'

He let go the bridle, and stretched out both his arms to show Alice what he meant, and this time he fell flat on his back, right under the horse's feet.

'Plenty of practice!' he went on repeating, all the time that Alice was getting him on his feet again. 'Plenty of practice!'

'It's too ridiculous!' cried Alice, losing all her patience this time. 'You ought to have a wooden horse on wheels, that you ought!'

'Does that kind go smoothly?' the Knight asked in a tone of great interest, clasping his arms round the horse's neck as he spoke, just in time to save himself from tumbling off again.

'Much more smoothly than a live horse,' Alice said, with a little scream of laughter, in spite of all she could do to prevent it.

'I'll get one,' the Knight said thoughtfully to himself. 'One or two – several.'

There was a short silence after this, and then the Knight went on again. 'I'm a great hand at inventing things. Now, I daresay you noticed, the last time you picked me up, that I was looking rather thoughtful?'

'You were a little grave,' said Alice.

'Well, just then I was inventing a new way of getting over a gate – would you like to hear it?'

'Very much indeed,' Alice said politely.

'I'll tell you how I came to think of it,' said the Knight. 'You see, I said to myself, "The only difficulty is with the feet: the *head* is high enough already." Now, first I put my head on the top of the gate – then the head's high enough – then I stand on my head – then the feet are high enough, you see – then I'm over, you see.'

'Yes, I suppose you'd be over when that was done,' Alice said thoughtfully: 'but don't you think it would be rather hard?'

'I haven't tried it yet,' the Knight said, gravely: 'so I can't tell for certain – but I'm afraid it *would* be a little hard.'

He looked so vexed at the idea, that Alice changed the subject hastily. 'What a curious helmet you've got!' she said cheerfully. 'Is that your invention too?'

The Knight looked down proudly at his helmet, which hung from the saddle. 'Yes,' he said, 'but I've invented a better one than that – like a sugar-loaf. When I used to wear it, if I fell off the horse, it always touched the ground directly. So I had a *very* little way to fall, you see – But there *was* the danger of falling *into* it, to be sure. That happened to me once – and the worst of it was, before I could get out again, the other White Knight came and put it on. He thought it was his own helmet.'

The Knight looked so solemn about it that Alice did not dare to laugh. 'I'm afraid you must have hurt him,' she said in a trembling voice, 'being on the top of his head.'

'I had to kick him, of course,' the Knight said, very seriously. 'And then he took the helmet off again – but it took hours and hours to get me out. I was as fast as – as lightning, you know.'

'But that's a different kind of fastness,' Alice objected.

The Knight shook his head. 'It was all kinds of fastness with me, I can assure you!' he said. He raised his hands in some excitement as he said this, and instantly rolled out of the saddle, and fell headlong into a deep ditch.

Alice ran to the side of the ditch to look for him. She was rather startled by the fall, as for some time he had kept on very well, and she was afraid that he really *was* hurt this time. However, though she could see nothing but the soles of his feet, she was much relieved to hear that he was talking on in his usual tone. 'All kinds of fastness,' he repeated: 'but it was careless of him to put another man's helmet on – with the man in it, too.'

'How *can* you go on talking so quietly, head downwards?' Alice asked, as she dragged him out by the feet, and laid him in a heap on the bank.

The Knight looked surprised at the question. 'What does it matter where my body happens to be?' he said. 'My mind goes on working all the same. In fact, the more head downwards I am, the more I keep inventing new things.'

'Now the cleverest thing of the sort that I ever did,' he went on after a pause, 'was inventing a new pudding during the meat-course.'

'In time to have it cooked for the next course?' said Alice. 'Well, that *was* quick work, certainly!'

'Well, not the *next* course,' the Knight said in a slow thoughtful tone: 'no, certainly not the next *course*.'

'Then it would have to be the next day. I suppose you wouldn't have two pudding-courses in one dinner?'

'Well, not the *next* day,' the Knight repeated as before: 'not the next *day*. In fact,' he went on, holding his head down, and his voice getting lower and lower, 'I don't believe that pudding ever *was* cooked! In fact, I don't believe that pudding ever *will* be cooked! And yet it was a very clever pudding to invent.'

'What did you mean it to be made of?' Alice asked, hoping to cheer him up, for the poor Knight seemed quite low-spirited about it.

'It began with blotting-paper,' the Knight answered with a groan.

'That wouldn't be very nice, I'm afraid –'

'Not very nice *alone*,' he interrupted, quite eagerly: 'but you've no idea what a difference it makes mixing it with other things – such as gun-powder and sealing-wax. And here I must leave you.' They had just come to the end of the wood.

Alice could only look puzzled: she was thinking of the pudding.

'You are sad,' the Knight said in an anxious tone: 'let me sing you a song to comfort you.'

'Is it very long?' Alice asked, for she had heard a good deal of poetry that day.

'It's long,' said the Knight, 'but it's very, *very* beautiful. Everybody that hears me sing it – either it brings the *tears* into their eyes, or else –'

'Or else what?' said Alice, for the Knight had made a sudden pause.

'Or else it doesn't, you know. The name of the song is called "*Haddocks' Eyes*."'

'Oh, that's the name of the song, is it?' Alice said, trying to feel interested.

'No, you don't understand,' the Knight said, looking a little vexed. 'That's what the name is *called*. The name really is "*The Aged Aged Man*."'

'Then I ought to have said "That's what the *song* is called"?' Alice corrected herself.

'No, you oughtn't: that's quite another thing! The *song* is called "*Ways and Means*": but that's only what it's *called*, you know!'

'Well, what *is* the song, then?' said Alice, who was by this time completely bewildered.

'I was coming to that,' the Knight said. 'The song really is "*A-sitting On A Gate*": and the tune's my own invention.'

So saying, he stopped his horse and let the reins fall on its neck: then, slowly beating time with one hand, and with a faint smile lighting up his gentle foolish face, as if he enjoyed the music of his song, he began.

Of all the strange things that Alice saw in her journey Through The Looking Glass, this was the one that she always remembered most clearly. Years afterwards she could bring the whole scene back again, as if it had been only yesterday – the mild blue eyes and kindly smile of the Knight – the setting sun gleaming through his hair, and shining on his armour in a blaze of light that quite dazzled her – the horse quietly moving about, with the reins hanging loose on his neck, cropping the grass at her feet – and the black shadows of the forest behind – all this she took in like a picture, as, with one hand shading her eyes, she leant against a tree, watching the strange pair, and listening, in a half dream, to the melancholy music of the song.

'But the tune isn't his own invention,' she said to herself: 'it's "*I give thee all, I can no more*."' She stood and listened very attentively, but no tears came into her eyes.

'I'll tell thee everything I can;
There's little to relate.
I saw an aged aged man,
A-sitting on a gate.
"Who are you, aged man?" I said.
"And how is it you live?"
And his answer trickled through my head
Like water through a sieve.

He said "I look for butterflies
That sleep among the wheat:
I make them into mutton-pies,
And sell them in the street.
I sell them unto men," he said,
"Who sail on stormy seas;
And that's the way I get my bread –
A trifle, if you please."

But I was thinking of a plan
To dye one's whiskers green,
And always use so large a fan
That they could not be seen.
So, having no reply to give
To what the old man said,
I cried, "Come, tell me how you live!"
And thumped him on the head.

His accents mild took up the tale:
He said "I go my ways,
And when I find a mountain-rill,
I set it in a blaze;
And thence they make a stuff they call
Rowlands' Macassar Oil –
Yet twopence-halfpenny is all
They give me for my toil."

But I was thinking of a way
  To feed oneself on batter,
And so go on from day to day
  Getting a little fatter.
I shook him well from side to side,
  Until his face was blue:
"Come, tell me how you live," I cried,
  "And what it is you do!"

He said "I hunt for haddocks' eyes
  Among the heather bright,
And work them into waistcoat-buttons
  In the silent night.
And these I do not sell for gold
  Or coin of silvery shine,
But for a copper halfpenny,
  And that will purchase nine.

"I sometimes dig for buttered rolls,
  Or set limed twigs for crabs;
I sometimes search the grassy knolls
  For wheels of Hansom-cabs.
And that's the way" (he gave a wink)
  "By which I get my wealth –
And very gladly will I drink
  Your Honour's noble health."

I heard him then, for I had just
Completed my design
To keep the Menai bridge from rust
By boiling it in wine.
I thanked him much for telling me
The way he got his wealth,
But chiefly for his wish that he
Might drink my noble health.

And now, if e'er by chance I put
My fingers into glue,
Or madly squeeze a right-hand foot
Into a left-hand shoe
Or if I drop upon my toe
A very heavy weight,
I weep, for it reminds me so,
Of that old man I used to know –

Whose look was mild, whose speech was slow,
Whose hair was whiter than the snow,
Whose face was very like a crow,
With eyes, like cinders, all aglow,
Who seemed distracted with his woe,
Who rocked his body to and fro,
And muttered mumblingly and low,
As if his mouth were full of dough,
Who snorted like a buffalo –
That summer evening, long ago,
A-sitting on a gate.'

As the Knight sang the last words of the ballad, he gathered up the reins, and turned his horse's head along the road by which they had come. 'You've only a few yards to go,' he said, 'down the hill and over that little brook, and then you'll be a Queen – But you'll stay and see me off first?' he added as Alice turned with an eager

look in the direction to which he pointed. 'I shan't be long. You'll wait and wave your handkerchief when I get to that turn in the road? I think it'll encourage me, you see.'

'Of course I'll wait,' said Alice: 'and thank you very much for coming so far – and for the song – I liked it very much.'

'I hope so,' the Knight said doubtfully: 'but you didn't cry so much as I thought you would.'

So they shook hands, and then the Knight rode slowly away into the forest. 'It won't take long to see him *off*, I expect,' Alice said to herself, as she stood watching him. 'There he goes! Right on his head as usual! However, he gets on again pretty easily – that comes of having so many things hung round the horse –' So she went on talking to herself, as she watched the horse walking leisurely along the road, and the Knight tumbling off, first on one side and then on the other. After the fourth or fifth tumble he reached the turn, and then she waved her handkerchief to him, and waited till he was out of sight.

'I hope it encouraged him,' she said, as she turned to run down the hill: 'and now for the last brook, and to be a Queen! How grand it sounds!' A very few steps brought her to the edge of the brook. 'The Eighth Square at last!' she cried as she bounded across,

and threw herself down to rest on a lawn as soft as moss, with little flower-beds dotted about it here and there. 'Oh, how glad I am to get here! And what *is* this on my head?' she exclaimed in a tone of dismay, as she put her hands up to something very heavy, that fitted tight all round her head.

'But how *can* it have got there without my knowing it?' she said to herself, as she lifted it off, and set it on her lap to make out what it could possibly be.

It was a golden crown.

CHAPTER NINE

QUEEN ALICE

'Well, this *is* grand!' said Alice. 'I never expected I should be a Queen so soon – and I'll tell you what it is, your Majesty,' she went on in a severe tone (she was always rather fond of scolding herself), 'it'll never do for you to be lolling about on the grass like that! Queens have to be dignified, you know.'

So she got up and walked about – rather stiffly just at first, as she was afraid that the crown might come off: but she comforted herself with the thought that there was nobody to see her, 'and if I really am a Queen,' she said as she sat down again, 'I shall be able to manage it quite well in time.'

Everything was happening so oddly that she didn't feel a bit surprised at finding the Red Queen and the White Queen sitting close to her, one on each side: she would have liked very much to ask them how they came there, but

she feared it would not be quite civil. However, there would be no harm, she thought, in asking if the game was over. 'Please would you tell me –' she began, looking timidly at the Red Queen.

'Speak when you're spoken to!' the Queen sharply interrupted her.

'But if everybody obeyed that rule,' said Alice, who was always ready for a little argument, 'and if you only spoke when you were spoken to, and the other persons always waited for *you* to begin, you see nobody would ever say anything, so that –'

'Ridiculous!' cried the Queen. 'Why, don't you see, child –' here she broke off with a frown, and, after thinking for a minute, suddenly changed the subject of the conversation. 'What do you mean by "If you really are a Queen"? What right have you to call yourself so? You can't be a Queen, you know, till you've passed the proper examination, and the sooner we begin it, the better.'

'I only said "if"!' poor Alice pleaded in a piteous tone. The two Queens looked at each other, and the Red Queen remarked, with a little shudder, 'She *says* she only said "if" –'

'But she said a great deal more than that!' the White Queen moaned, wringing her hands. 'Oh, ever so much more than that!'

'So you did, you know,' the Red Queen said to Alice. 'Always speak the truth – think before you speak – and write it down afterwards.'

'I'm sure I didn't mean –' Alice was beginning, but the Red Queen interrupted her impatiently.

'That's just what I complain of! You *should* have meant! What do you suppose is the use of a child without any meaning? Even a joke should have some meaning – and a child's more important than a joke, I hope. You couldn't deny that, even if you tried with both hands.'

'I don't deny things with my *hands*,' Alice objected.

'Nobody said you did,' said the Red Queen. 'I said you couldn't if you tried.'

'She's in that state of mind,' said the White Queen, 'that she wants to deny *something* – only she doesn't know what to deny!'

'A nasty, vicious temper,' the Red Queen remarked; and then there was an uncomfortable silence for a minute or two.

The Red Queen broke the silence by saying to the White Queen, 'I invite you to Alice's dinner-party this afternoon.'

The White Queen smiled feebly, and said 'And I invite *you*.'

'I didn't know I was to have a party at all,' said Alice; 'but if there is to be one, I think *I* ought to invite the guests.'

'We gave you the opportunity of doing it,' the Red Queen remarked: 'but I daresay you've not had many lessons in manners yet?'

'Manners are not taught in lessons,' said Alice. 'Lessons teach you to do sums, and things of that sort.'

'Can you do Addition?' the White Queen asked. 'What's one and one and one and one and one and one and one and one and one and one?'

'I don't know,' said Alice. 'I lost count.'

'She can't do Addition,' the Red Queen interrupted. 'Can you do Subtraction? Take nine from eight.'

'Nine from eight I can't, you know,' Alice replied very readily: 'but –'

'She can't do Subtraction,' said the White Queen. 'Can you do Division? Divide a loaf by a knife – what's the answer to that?'

'I suppose –' Alice was beginning, but the Red Queen answered for her. 'Bread-and-butter, of course. Try another Subtraction sum. Take a bone from a dog: what remains?'

Alice considered. 'The bone wouldn't remain, of course, if I took it – and the dog wouldn't remain; it would come to bite me – and I'm sure *I* shouldn't remain!'

'Then you think nothing would remain?' said the Red Queen.

'I think that's the answer.'

'Wrong, as usual,' said the Red Queen: 'the dog's temper would remain.'

'But I don't see how –'

'Why, look here!' the Red Queen cried. 'The dog would lose its temper, wouldn't it!'

'Perhaps it would,' Alice replied cautiously.

'Then if the dog went away, its temper would remain!' the Queen exclaimed triumphantly.

Alice said, as gravely as she could, 'They might go different ways.' But she couldn't help thinking to herself, 'What dreadful nonsense we *are* talking!'

'She can't do sums a *bit*!' the Queens said together, with great emphasis.

'Can *you* do sums?' Alice said, turning suddenly on the White Queen, for she didn't like being found fault with so much.

The Queen gasped and shut her eyes. 'I can do Addition,' she said, 'if you give me time – but I can't do Subtraction, under *any* circumstances!'

'Of course you know your A B C?' said the Red Queen.

'To be sure I do,' said Alice.

'So do I,' the White Queen whispered: 'we'll often say it over together, dear. And I'll tell you a secret – I can read words of one letter! Isn't *that* grand!

However, don't be discouraged. You'll come to it in time.'

Here the Red Queen began again. 'Can you answer useful questions?' she said. 'How is bread made?'

'I know *that*!' Alice cried eagerly. 'You take some flour −'

'Where do you pick the flower?' the White Queen asked. 'In a garden, or in the hedges?'

'Well, it isn't *picked* at all,' Alice explained: 'it's *ground* −'

'How many acres of ground?' said the White Queen. 'You mustn't leave out so many things.'

'Fan her head!' the Red Queen anxiously interrupted. 'She'll be feverish after so much thinking.' So they set to work and fanned her with bunches of leaves, till she had to beg them to leave off, it blew her hair about so.

'She's all right again now,' said the Red Queen. 'Do you know Languages? What's the French for fiddle-de-dee?'

'Fiddle-de-dee's not English,' Alice replied gravely.

'Who ever said it was?' said the Red Queen.

Alice thought she saw a way out of the difficulty this time. 'If you'll tell me what language "fiddle-de-dee" is, I'll tell you the French for it!' she exclaimed triumphantly.

But the Red Queen drew herself up rather stiffly, and said 'Queens never make bargains.'

'I wish Queens never asked questions', Alice thought to herself.

'Don't let us quarrel,' the White Queen said in an anxious tone. 'What is the cause of lightning?'

'The cause of lightning,' Alice said very decidedly, for she felt quite certain about this, 'is the thunder − no, no!' she hastily corrected herself. 'I meant the other way.'

'It's too late to correct it,' said the Red Queen: 'when you've once said a thing, that fixes it, and you must take the consequences.'

'Which reminds me –' the White Queen said, looking down and nervously clasping and unclasping her hands, 'we had *such* a thunderstorm last Tuesday – I mean one of the last set of Tuesdays, you know.'

Alice was puzzled. 'In *our* country,' she remarked, 'there's only one day at a time.'

The Red Queen said 'That's a poor thin way of doing things. Now *here*, we mostly have days and nights two or three at a time, and sometimes in the winter we take as many as five nights together – for warmth, you know.'

'Are five nights warmer than one night, then?' Alice ventured to ask.

'Five times as warm, of course.'

'But they should be five times as *cold*, by the same rule –'

'Just so!' cried the Red Queen. 'Five times as warm, *and* five times as cold – just as I'm five times as rich as you are, *and* five times as clever!'

Alice sighed and gave it up. 'It's exactly like a riddle with no answer!' she thought.

'Humpty Dumpty saw it too,' the White Queen went on in a low voice, more as if she were talking to herself.

'He came to the door with a corkscrew in his hand –'

'What did he want?' said the Red Queen.

'He said he *would* come in,' the White Queen went on, 'because he was looking for a hippopotamus. Now, as it happened, there wasn't such a thing in the house, that morning.'

'Is there generally?' Alice asked in an astonished tone.

'Well, only on Thursdays,' said the Queen.

'I know what he came for,' said Alice: 'he wanted to punish the fish, because –'

Here the White Queen began again. 'It was *such* a thunderstorm, you can't think!' ('She *never* could you know,' said the Red Queen.) 'And part of the roof came off, and ever so much thunder got in – and it went rolling round the room in great lumps – and knocking over the tables and things – till I was so frightened, I couldn't remember my own name!'

Alice thought to herself, 'I never should *try* to remember my name in the middle of an accident! Where would be the use of it?' but she did not say this aloud, for fear of hurting the poor Queen's feelings.

'Your Majesty must excuse her,' the Red Queen said to Alice, taking one of the White Queen's hands in her own, and gently stroking it: 'she means well, but she can't help saying foolish things, as a general rule.'

The White Queen looked timidly at Alice, who felt she *ought* to say something kind, but really couldn't think of anything at the moment.

'She never was really well brought up,' the Red Queen went on: 'but it's amazing how good-tempered she is! Pat her on the head, and see how pleased she'll be!' But this was more than Alice had courage to do.

'A little kindness – and putting her hair in papers – would do wonders with her –'

The White Queen gave a deep sigh, and laid her head on Alice's shoulder. 'I *am* so sleepy!' she moaned.

'She's tired, poor thing!' said the Red Queen. 'Smooth her hair – lend her your nightcap – and sing her a soothing lullaby.'

'I haven't got a nightcap with me,' said Alice, as she tried to obey the first direction: 'and I don't know any soothing lullabies.'

'I must do it myself, then,' said the Red Queen, and she began:

> *'Hush-a-by lady, in Alice's lap!*
> *Till the feast's ready, we've time for a nap:*
> *When the feast's over, we'll go to the ball –*
> *Red Queen, and White Queen, and Alice, and all!'*

'And now you know the words,' she added, as she put her head down on Alice's other shoulder, 'just sing it through to *me*. I'm getting sleepy, too.' In another moment both Queens were fast asleep, and snoring loud.

CHAPTER NINE: QUEEN ALICE

'What *am* I to do?' exclaimed Alice, looking about in great perplexity, as first one round head, and then the other, rolled down from her shoulder, and lay like a heavy lump in her lap. 'I don't think it *ever* happened before, that anyone had to take care of two Queens asleep at once! No, not in all the History of England – it couldn't, you know, because there never was more than one Queen at a time. Do wake up, you heavy things!' she went on in an impatient tone; but there was no answer but a gentle snoring.

The snoring got more distinct every minute, and sounded more like a tune: at last she could even make out words, and she listened so eagerly that, when the two great heads suddenly vanished from her lap, she hardly missed them.

She was standing before an arched doorway over which were the words QUEEN ALICE in large letters, and on each side of the arch there was a bell-handle; one was marked 'Visitors' Bell,' and the other 'Servants' Bell.'

'I'll wait till the song's over,' thought Alice, 'and then I'll ring – the – *which* bell must I ring?' she went on, very much puzzled by the names. 'I'm not a visitor, and I'm not a servant. There *ought* to be one marked "Queen" you know –'

Just then the door opened a little way, and a creature with a long beak put its head out for a moment and said 'No admittance till the week after next!' and shut the door again with a bang.

Alice knocked and rang in vain for a long time, but at last a very old Frog, who was sitting under a tree, got up and hobbled slowly towards her: he was dressed in bright yellow, and had enormous boots on.

'What is it, now?' the Frog said in a deep hoarse whisper.

Alice turned round, ready to find fault with anybody. 'Where's the servant whose business it is to answer the door?' she began angrily.

'Which door?' said the Frog.

Alice almost stamped with irritation at the slow drawl in which he spoke. '*This* door, of course!'

CHAPTER NINE: QUEEN ALICE

The Frog looked at the door with his large dull eyes for a minute: then he went nearer and rubbed it with his thumb, as if he were trying whether the paint would come off; then he looked at Alice.

'To answer the door?' he said. 'What's it been asking of?' He was so hoarse that Alice could scarcely hear him.

'I don't know what you mean,' she said.

'I speaks English, doesn't I?' the Frog went on. 'Or are you deaf? What did it ask you?'

'Nothing!' Alice said impatiently. 'I've been knocking at it!'

'Shouldn't do that – shouldn't do that –' the Frog muttered. 'Wexes it, you know.' Then he went up and gave the door a kick with one of his great feet. 'You let *it* alone,' he panted out, as he hobbled back to his tree, 'and it'll let *you* alone, you know.'

At this moment the door was flung open, and a shrill voice was heard singing:

> *'To the Looking-Glass world it was Alice that said,*
> *'I've a sceptre in hand, I've a crown on my head;*
> *Let the Looking-Glass creatures, whatever they be,*
> *Come and dine with the Red Queen, the White Queen, and me!''*

And hundreds of voices joined in the chorus:

> *'Then fill up the glasses as quick as you can,*
> *And sprinkle the table with buttons and bran:*
> *Put cats in the coffee, and mice in the tea –*
> *And welcome Queen Alice with thirty-times-three!'*

Then followed a confused noise of cheering, and Alice thought to herself, 'Thirty times three makes ninety. I wonder if any one's counting?' In a minute

there was silence again, and the same shrill voice sang another verse:

> *"'O Looking-Glass creatures," quoth Alice, "draw near!*
> *'Tis an honour to see me, a favour to hear:*
> *'Tis a privilege high to have dinner and tea*
> *Along with the Red Queen, the White Queen, and me!"'*

Then came the chorus again:

> *'Then fill up the glasses with treacle and ink,*
> *Or anything else that is pleasant to drink;*
> *Mix sand with the cider, and wool with the wine –*
> *And welcome Queen Alice with ninety-times-nine!'*

'Ninety times nine!' Alice repeated in despair. 'Oh, that'll never be done! I'd better go in at once –' and in she went, and there was a dead silence the moment she appeared.

Alice glanced nervously along the table, as she walked up the large hall, and noticed that there were about fifty guest, of all kinds: some were animals, some birds, and there were even a few flowers among them. 'I'm glad they've come without waiting to be asked,' she thought: 'I should never have known who were the right people to invite!'

There were three chairs at the head of the table; the Red and White Queens had already taken two of them, but the middle one was empty. Alice sat down in it, rather uncomfortable at the silence, and longing for some one to speak.

At last the Red Queen began. 'You've missed the soup and fish,' she said. 'Put on the joint!' And the waiters set a leg of mutton before Alice, who looked at it rather anxiously, as she had never had to carve a joint before.

'You look a little shy; let me introduce you to that leg of mutton,' said the Red Queen. 'Alice – Mutton; Mutton – Alice.' The leg of mutton got up in the dish and made a little bow to Alice; and Alice returned the bow, not knowing whether to be frightened or amused.

'May I give you a slice?' she said, taking up the knife and fork, and looking from one Queen to the other.

'Certainly not,' the Red Queen said, very decidedly: 'it isn't etiquette to cut any one you've been introduced to. Remove the joint!' And the waiters carried it off, and brought a large plum-pudding in its place.

'I won't be introduced to the pudding, please,' Alice said rather hastily, 'or we shall get no dinner at all. May I give you some?'

But the Red Queen looked sulky, and growled 'Pudding – Alice; Alice – Pudding. Remove the pudding!' and the waiters took it away so quickly that Alice couldn't return its bow.

However, she didn't see why the Red Queen should be the only one to give orders, so, as an experiment, she called out 'Waiter! Bring back the pudding!'

and there it was again in a moment, like a conjuring-trick. It was so large that she couldn't help feeling a *little* shy with it, as she had been with the mutton; however, she conquered her shyness by a great effort and cut a slice and handed it to the Red Queen.

'What impertinence!' said the Pudding. 'I wonder how you'd like it, if I were to cut a slice out of *you*, you creature!'

It spoke in a thick, suety sort of voice, and Alice hadn't a word to say in reply: she could only sit and look at it and gasp.

'Make a remark,' said the Red Queen: 'it's ridiculous to leave all the conversation to the pudding!'

'Do you know, I've had such a quantity of poetry repeated to me to-day,' Alice began, a little frightened at finding that, the moment she opened her lips, there was dead silence, and all eyes were fixed upon her; 'and it's a very curious thing, I think – every poem was about fishes in some way. Do you know why they're so fond of fishes, all about here?'

She spoke to the Red Queen, whose answer was a little wide of the mark. 'As to fishes,' she said, very slowly and solemnly, putting her mouth close to Alice's ear, 'her White Majesty knows a lovely riddle – all in poetry – all about fishes. Shall she repeat it?'

'Her Red Majesty's very kind to mention it,' the White Queen murmured into Alice's other ear, in a voice like the cooing of a pigeon. 'It would be *such* a treat! May I?'

'Please do,' Alice said very politely.

The White Queen laughed with delight, and stroked Alice's cheek. Then she began:

> *"First, the fish must be caught."*
> *That is easy: a baby, I think, could have caught it.*
> *"Next, the fish must be bought."*
> *That is easy: a penny, I think, would have bought it.*

"Now cook me the fish!"
That is easy, and will not take more than a minute.
"Let it lie in a dish!"
That is easy, because it already is in it.

"Bring it here! Let me sup!"
It is easy to set such a dish on the table.
"Take the dish-cover up!"
Ah, that is so hard that I fear I'm unable!

For it holds it like glue –
Holds the lid to the dish, while it lies in the middle:
Which is easiest to do,
Un-dish-cover the fish, or dishcover the riddle?'

'Take a minute to think about it, and then guess,' said the Red Queen. 'Meanwhile, we'll drink your health – Queen Alice's health!' she screamed at the top of her voice, and all the guests began drinking it directly, and very queerly they managed it: some of them put their glasses upon their heads like extinguishers, and drank all that trickled down their faces – others upset the decanters, and drank the wine as it ran off the edges of the table – and three of them (who looked like kangaroos) scrambled into the dish of roast mutton, and began eagerly lapping up the gravy, 'just like pigs in a trough!' thought Alice.

'You ought to return thanks in a neat speech,' the Red Queen said, frowning at Alice as she spoke.

'We must support you, you know,' the White Queen whispered, as Alice got up to do it, very obediently, but a little frightened.

'Thank you very much,' she whispered in reply, 'but I can do quite well without.'

'That wouldn't be at all the thing,' the Red Queen said very decidedly: so Alice tried to submit to it with a good grace.

('And they *did* push so!' she said afterwards, when she was telling her sister the history of the feast. 'You would have thought they wanted to squeeze me flat!')

In fact it was rather difficult for her to keep in her place while she made her speech: the two Queens pushed her so, one on each side, that they nearly lifted her up into the air: 'I rise to return thanks –' Alice began: and she really *did* rise as she spoke, several inches; but she got hold of the edge of the table, and managed to pull herself down again.

'Take care of yourself!' screamed the White Queen, seizing Alice's hair with both her hands. 'Something's going to happen!'

And then (as Alice afterwards described it) all sorts of things happened in a moment. The candles all grew up to the ceiling, looking something like a bed of rushes with fireworks at the top. As to the bottles, they each took a pair of plates, which they hastily fitted on as wings, and so, with forks for legs, went fluttering about in all directions: 'and very like birds they look,' Alice thought to herself, as well as she could in the dreadful confusion that was beginning.

At this moment she heard a hoarse laugh at her side, and turned to see what was the matter with the White Queen; but, instead of the Queen, there was the leg of mutton sitting in the chair. 'Here I am!' cried a voice from the soup-tureen, and Alice turned again, just in time to see the Queen's broad good-natured face grinning at her for a moment over the edge of the tureen, before she disappeared into the soup.

There was not a moment to be lost. Already several of the guests were lying down in the dishes, and the soup ladle was walking up the table towards Alice's chair, and beckoning to her impatiently to get out of its way.

'I can't stand this any longer!' she cried as she jumped up and seized the table-cloth with both hands: one good pull, and plates, dishes, guests, and candles came crashing down together in a heap on the floor.

'And as for *you*,' she went on, turning fiercely upon the Red Queen, whom she considered as the cause of all the mischief – but the Queen was no longer at her side – she had suddenly dwindled down to the size of a little doll, and was now on the table, merrily running round and round after her own shawl, which was trailing behind her.

At any other time, Alice would have felt surprised at this, but she was far too much excited to be surprised at anything *now*. 'As for *you*,' she repeated, catching hold of the little creature in the very act of jumping over a bottle which had just lighted upon the table, 'I'll shake you into a kitten, that I will!'

CHAPTER TEN

SHAKING

CHAPTER TEN: SHAKING

She took her off the table as she spoke, and shook her backwards and forwards with all her might.

The Red Queen made no resistance whatever; only her face grew very small, and her eyes got large and green: and still, as Alice went on shaking her, she kept on growing shorter – and fatter – and softer – and rounder – and –

CHAPTER ELEVEN

WAKING

CHAPTER ELEVEN: WAKING

– and it really *was* a kitten, after all.

CHAPTER TWELVE

WHICH DREAMED IT?

'Your Red Majesty shouldn't purr so loud,' Alice said, rubbing her eyes, and addressing the kitten, respectfully, yet with some severity. 'You woke me out of oh! such a nice dream! And you've been along with me, Kitty – all through the Looking-Glass world. Did you know it, dear?'

It is a very inconvenient habit of kittens (Alice had once made the remark) that, whatever you say to them, they *always* purr. 'If they would only purr for "yes," and mew for "no," or any rule of that sort,' she had said, 'so that one could keep up a conversation! But how *can* you talk with a person if they always say the same thing?'

On this occasion the kitten only purred: and it was impossible to guess whether it meant 'yes' or 'no.'

So Alice hunted among the chessmen on the table till she had found the Red Queen: then she went down on her knees on the hearth-rug, and put the kitten and the Queen to look at each other. 'Now, Kitty!' she cried, clapping her hands triumphantly. 'Confess that was what you turned into!'

('But it wouldn't look at it,' she said, when she was explaining the thing afterwards to her sister: 'it turned away its head, and pretended not to see it: but it looked a *little* ashamed of itself, so I think it *must* have been the Red Queen.')

CHAPTER TWELVE: WHICH DREAMED IT?

'Sit up a little more stiffly, dear!' Alice cried with a merry laugh. And curtsey while you're thinking what to – what to purr. It saves time, remember!' And she caught it up and gave it one little kiss, 'just in honour of its having been a Red Queen.'

'Snowdrop, my pet!' she went on, looking over her shoulder at the White Kitten, which was still patiently undergoing its toilet, 'when *will* Dinah have finished with your White Majesty, I wonder? That must be the reason you were so untidy in my dream – Dinah! Do you know that you're scrubbing a White Queen? Really, it's most disrespectful of you!

'And what did *Dinah* turn to, I wonder?' she prattled on, as she settled comfortably down, with one elbow on the rug, and her chin in her hand, to watch the kittens. 'Tell me, Dinah, did you turn to Humpty Dumpty? I *think* you did – however, you'd better not mention it to your friends just yet, for I'm not sure.

'By the way, Kitty, if only you'd been really with me in my dream, there was one thing you *would* have enjoyed – I had such a quantity of poetry said to me, all about fishes! To-morrow morning you shall have a real treat. All the time you're eating your breakfast, I'll repeat "The Walrus and the Carpenter" to you; and then you can make believe it's oysters, dear!

'Now, Kitty, let's consider who it was that dreamed it all. This is a serious question, my dear, and you should *not* go on licking your paw like that – as if Dinah hadn't washed you this morning! You see, Kitty, it *must* have been either me or the Red King. He was part of my dream, of course – but then I was part of his dream, too! *Was* it the Red King, Kitty? You were his wife, my dear, so you ought to know – Oh, Kitty, *do* help to settle it! I'm sure your paw can wait!' But the provoking kitten only began on the other paw, and pretended it hadn't heard the question.

Which do you think it was?

A boat beneath a sunny sky,
Lingering onward dreamily
In an evening of July –

Children three that nestle near,
Eager eye and willing ear,
Pleased a simple tale to hear –

Long has paled that sunny sky:
Echoes fade and memories die.
Autumn frosts have slain July.

Still she haunts me, phantomwise,
Alice moving under skies
Never seen by waking eyes.

Children yet, the tale to hear,
Eager eye and willing ear
Lovingly shall nestle near.

In a Wonderland they lie,
Dreaming as the days go by,
Dreaming as the summers die:

Ever drifting down the stream –
Lingering in the golden gleam –
Life, what is it but a dream?

THE END

ABOUT THE AUTHOR

CHARLES LUTWIDGE DODGSON (1832–98), known the world over by his pseudonym, Lewis Carroll, was the third of eleven children born to the Reverend Charles Dodgson and his wife, Frances Jane Lutwidge. A gifted student in many subjects, the young Charles was educated at Rugby, the famous public school immortalized in *Tom Brown's Schooldays*, and Christ Church, Oxford, where he became a Lecturer in Mathematics and spent the rest of his working life. It was there, in 1855, while taking photographs in the garden of Henry George Liddell, Dean of Christ Church, that he met Liddell's four-year-old daughter, Alice, and formed the friendship that was to transform children's literature. Alice Liddell became the rapt audience for his fantastically imaginative storytelling, and she was the inspiration for the main character in his two beloved masterpieces of the nonsensical and the absurd, *Alice's Adventures in Wonderland* and *Through the Looking Glass*.

ABOUT THE ILLUSTRATOR

Sir John Tenniel (1820–1914) was already celebrated as a cartoonist for *Punch*, England's leading satirical magazine, when, in 1864, he was approached by Lewis Carroll to illustrate *Alice's Adventures in Wonderland*. Although the collaboration between artist and author was not easy – Tenniel afterwards complained that Dodgson, 'that conceited old Don', was impossibly demanding – the resulting illustrations for *Alice* and its sequel proved such perfect realizations of the text that they have become inseparable.

PANZER GRENADIER D

Grossdeutschland

The Panzer Grenadier Division "Grossdeutschland" and Panzer-Korps Grossdeutschland • Panzer Division Brandenburg • Führer Grenadier Division • Führer Begleit Division • Panzer Division Kurmark

A Pictorial History with Text & Maps

by Horst Scheibert

Translated by Gisele Hockenberry

Edited by Bruce Culver

squadron/signal publications

[Cover] "Grossdeutschland" panzergrenadiers dismount from an SdKfz 251 halftrack in front of a resistance point, during the drive on Rzhev, Late Fall 1942. The squad leader in the foreground wears an autumn camouflage Shelter-Quarter over his issue Field Gray Feldbluse. On his right arm is the Dark Green "Grossdeutschland" cufftitle. The two grenadiers leaving the halftrack have the newly issued reversible Mouse Gray and White winter parka. While this garment was in short supply most of the Winter of 1942-43, this elite unit got them early and in sufficient quantity.

ISBN 0-89747-061-3

Originally Published by Podzun-Verlag, 636 Friedburg-3/Dorheim, Markt 9, West Germany

Contents

Preface

The intent of this book is to show the history and eventual fate of all the "GD" units. To make this pictorial history as clear as possible, the text and photographs have been arranged by year. Brief chronologies at the beginning of each yearly chapter relate the combat actions of "Grossdeutschland" and its sister units to the historical events of the period. In this way, a better understanding may be gained of the detailed information in the text, photos, and captions.

GD Monogram

From Wachkommando (Guard Command) to Motorized Infantry Regiment "GROSSDEUTSCHLAND"

The origin of all "Grossdeutschland" forces was the command of the Wachtruppe [guard troop] in Berlin, and the infantry-training regiment in Doeberitz. This photo shows a guard company of the Wachtruppe command marching through Berlin's Brandenburg gate to the honor memorial in 1934.

Table showing the development of the Grossdeutschland units

In 1934, the command of the Wachtruppe was renamed "Wachtruppe/Berlin." This guard was photographed in 1936.

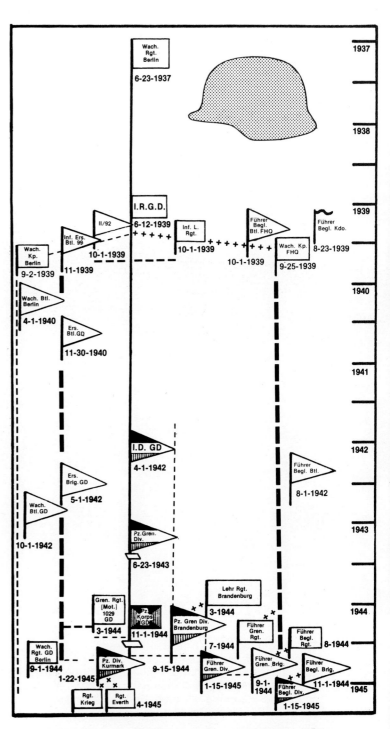

Unconditional surrender on May 8, 1945

Changing of the guard in front of the Reichschancery.

Guards on duty in Berlin, 1938.

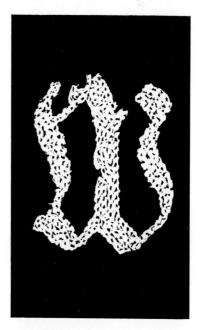

On June 23, 1937, the "Wachtruppe Berlin" was re-designated "Wachregiment" (guard regiment). At this time, all members of this unit added the "W" to their shoulder tabs and patches.

INFANTERIESCHULE

In 1937, the infantry-training battalion at Doeberitz was expanded to a regiment. The members of this unit carried an "L" on their shoulder tabs. In October 1939, nearly half of this regiment joined the newly-formed infantry regiment "Grossdeutschland".

[Above] The entrance to the infantry school in Elsgrund near Doeberitz.

[Below] Combat training in the infantry-training regiment, 1938.

The complete guard in front of the honor memorial in Berlin, 1939.

1939

In 1939, "Grossdeutschland" was reformed as a full four-battalion infantry regiment; this was the beginning of the unit's rise to divisional size. The "Wachregiment/Berlin" provided the core of the new unit, and the name "Grossdeutschland" ("Greater Germany") was chosen because members came from all different areas of Germany.
In September, 1939, the Second World War began with an attack on Poland. "GD" was still reforming and did not take part in these early actions. Only after reorganization was completed did "GD" move to the Western front after training in Grafenwöhr, and a period in the Westerwald.

Movements and Actions, 1939

1939—World History

3-14: Declaration of independence of Slovakia and Karpathian Ukraine.
3-15: German troops arrive in Czechoslovakia.
3-23: German troops enter the Memel area.
3-26: Poland declines to let Danzig return, and to allow Germany an extra-territorial road and railroad route through the corridor.
3-31: English-French declaration of guarantee for Poland.
4- 7: Italy occupies Albania; Spain joins the Anti-Comintern pact.
4-13: England and France extend their declaration of guarantee to Rumania and Greece.
5-22: Expansion of the "Berlin-Rome Axis" to the "Steel pact".
7- 1: (Approx.) Beginning of the Wehrmacht's march against Poland.
8- 1: (Approx.) Beginning of the Wehrmacht's march to the West.
8-23: German-Soviet non-aggression pact.
8-24: "Quiet" mobilization of the Wehrmacht (103 divisions).
8-25: English-Polish mutual assistance treaty.
8-30: Poland orders the mobilization of its armed forces.
9- 1: Beginning of Second World War. The German Army attacks Poland at 4:45 AM, with 37 divisions.
9- 3: Great Britain and France declare war on Germany.
9-17: The Soviet Union marches into Poland from the East.
9-29: Surrender of Warsaw.
10- 1: Beginning of transfer of available German forces in Poland to Western front.
10- 6: End of all organized resistance in Poland.
11-30: Beginning of the Soviet attack on Finland.

At the awarding of the name "Grossdeutschland" to the "Wachregiment/Berlin" on June 14, 1939, the town commander of Berlin, General-Leutnant Seifert, and the Regimental commander, Colonel von Stockhausen, inspect the regiment in the Moabiter barracks.

1939—Division Grossdeutschland

4- 6: Order to expand the "Wachregiment/Berlin" to four battalions.

4-14: The new regiment is named "Inf. Rgt. GROSSDEUTSCHLAND" (GD).

8-23: Addition of a "Führer-Escort Command". During 1939, this unit was expanded to the "Führer-Escort Battalion", outside the organization of the "GD" Regiment. As such, it took part in the Polish campaign.

9- 6: Inf. Rgt. "GD" prepares for a mission against Poland as an airborne unit. This mission was not carried out.
9-17: "GD" unit re-transferred to Berlin.
10- 1: End of "GD" reorganization; a guard troop remains in Berlin (first in company strength, later (1940) expanded to a battalion).
10-21: Transfer to the Grafenwöhr training area (southeast of Bayreuth) for completion of reorganization and retraining as a regiment.
10-25: The "Stahlhelm" (Steel helmet) insignia is adopted for use on unit vehicles.
11-11: Transfer to the Westerwald around Montabaur and Westerburg to the XIX Motorized Army Corps, commanded by General of Armor troops, Guderian.
11-15: Assault engineer battalions (motorized) assigned to "GD".

Inf.-Regt. Großdeutschland

Cuff band assigned to "GD" in 1940.

In September, the white "Stahlhelm" [Steel helmet] symbol was adopted for use on vehicles of the regimental staff - as suggested by the regimental commander. This insignia was later adopted for all vehicles in the unit.

Departure of "GD" Infantry Regiment to Grafenwöhr on October 21, 1939

At this time, Oberst [Colonel] von Stockhausen was the regimental commander.

Infanteriesturmabzeichen
(Infantry Assault Badge)

1939 was still a year of rest for the "GD" Motorized Infantry Regiment, even with the unit reorganization, reinforced training and the various transfers. From a two-battalion Guard Troop Regiment, "Grossdeutschland" had expanded to a full four-battalion Infantry Regiment, fully equipped and trained, and assigned to an Armored Corps (still called an Army Corps) on the Western front. All these units were prepared for the next campaign in the West.

In November, the Führer-Escort Command, which was formed from the "GD" Regiment, receives its cuff band, which was later changed to a different letter type.

Führerhauptquartier

1940 was the year of the first test in combat of "GD" forces, and the regiment justified the hopes of those who had organized it as an elite unit. "Grossdeutschland" benefited greatly from time to train for the attack on France, and also had its own support units available as independent forces.

Sent into action at Sedan, a crucial objective in the initial assault on France, "GD" units were attached to fight with various panzer divisions, but always under the overall command of XIX Motorized Army Corps, commanded by General Heinz Guderian. In the second part of the French campaign — breaking through the Weygand line — "GD" was assigned to von Kleist's Panzergruppe, and was reassigned to various units as required by combat conditions.

After the fall of France, and the treaty ending the conflict, "GD" was refitted and brought up to strength in Alsace and Burgundy. It then trained and prepared for two new operations-"Sealion" (invasion of England) and "Felix" (assault on Gibraltar). Neither operation was carried out.

Movements and Actions,
Spring 1940 to Summer 1941

Legend:

- ⬭ Assembly Area
- --→ Railroad Transport
- → March Route
- xxxx→ Attack
- ✂ Major Engagement

1.] - Montabaur
2.] - Zell/Mosel
3.] - Colmar
4.] - Training fields-Le Valdahon and Belfort
5.] - Teschen-Troppau
6.] - Zelechow

0   100   200   300 km

1940—World History	1940—Division
	1-29: March from the Montabaur area to the middle Mosel region (Rgt. staff to Zell).
3-12: Finnish-Soviet peace treaty signed in Moscow.	4- 4: "GD" receives Assault Gun Battery 640 (with 6 StuG III), and this becomes the 16th Company of the Regiment. Regiment goes on standby alert.
4- 9: Beginning of the occupation of Norway and Denmark.	
5-10: Beginning of the campaign against France, Belgium and Holland (138 German divisions). British troops land in Iceland.	5-10: "GD" regiment, supported by artillery and engineers from the 10th Panzer Division, attacks through Luxembourg to move against the southern Belgian fortifications. Simultaneously, elements of "GD" third battalion land as airborne troops.
	5-12: Early skirmishes at the Samois.
	5-13: Capture of the Maas River crossings at Sedan and breakthrough to the Maginot Line. "GD" temporarily placed under command of 1st Panzer Division.
	5-14: "GD" fights enemy tank attacks at Chemery and Bulson.
5-15: Truce with the Netherlands.	5-15/5-17: Beginning of the battles on the Stonne highlands.
	5-17/5-19: Lull in the fighting around Bulson.
5-20: von Kleist's Panzergruppe reaches the Armel Canal.	5-20/5-23: "GD" marches toward St. Omer (south of Dunkirk), and engages the enemy at Arras.
	5-24/5-26: "GD" fights the BEF south of Dunkirk, and establishes bridgeheads at St. Pierre Brouck.
	5-27/5-28: Attack on Wormhondt and Herzeele; firing continues around Dunkirk.
5-28: Belgium surrenders.	5-29: Battles on the Canal de la Colme; continued engagements at Dunkirk. Occupation of Bergnes.
6- 4: Estonia, Latvia, and Lithuania accept Soviet ultimatum and are occupied by Russian troops.	6- 4: "GD" transferred to the Amiens bridgehead.
6- 5: Start of the attack on the "Weygand Line" (Somme-Aisne positions).	6- 6: German units break through the Weygand Line; "GD" is attached to 10th PD in this action.
	6- 8: Beginning of the pursuit of enemy forces to the Oise River.
6-10: After halt in heavy fighting south of Amiens, tank forces intended for the assault on Paris were rushed further to the east. On this day, Paris was occupied.	6-11: With the destruction of the Oise Bridge, the Germans turn northeast into the area around Guiscard.
	6-13: Start of the forced march to the River Seine via Channy-Coucy-Epadrey-Ambleny-Cutry-Villers-Cotterets-Coupru-Domptin-Charly M.-Villeneuve-Sourdon.
6-14: Italy declares war against France and England.	6-15: Fighting for the Seine crossings.
	6-16: Further pursuit of retreating enemy units to Lyon via Le Creusot and Macon.
	6-19: Occupation of Lyon.
	6-20/7-4: "GD" serves as occupation security troops around Lyon.
6-22: France agrees to end military action, capitulates to Germany.	
6-27: Rumania surrenders Bukovina and Bessarabia to Russia after Soviet ultimatum.	
	7- 5: March to Paris.
	7-10: Addition of a Motorcycle Troop Company to "GD", it is formed as the 17th Company of the Rgt.
7- 4: France breaks off diplomatic relations with England.	7-19: Mass in Notre Dame Cathedral for the whole regiment.
	7-26: March to Colmar and Schlettstadt in Alsace.

The regimental commander in 1940 was Oberst (Col.) Graf von Schwerin.

GD Shoulder Strap
(Oberst)

1940—World History

8-31: Hungary receives parts of Seibenbürgen in the second Vienna partition agreement.

9- 7: Beginning of the Battle of Britain as the Luftwaffe attacks English targets.

9-27: "Dreimächtepakt" ("Tripartite Pact") - Germany, Italy, Japan - signed in Berlin.

10-28: Italian troops start from Albania and invade Greece.

11-12: V.M. Molotov visits Berlin; during his mission, Germany refuses further demands of the Soviet Union, for bases at the Dardenelles, in Bulgaria, and in Finland.

11-20: Hungary joins the Tripartite pact.

11-23: Rumania joins the Tripartite pact.

11-24: Slovakia joins the Tripartite pact.

12- 8: Italian troops suffer a disastrous failure in Greece, as counterattacking Greek troops drive the Italians out of Greece, and capture one third of Albania.

Motorcycle troops advance into Belgium at dawn on May 5, 1940.

1940—Division Grossdeutschland

7-27/10-26: "GD" remained in Alsace, preparing for "Sealion", the invasion of England.

8- 1: Organization of the Heavy Transportation Battalion as the 17th to 20th Companies of "GD".

8-24: A green cuff band with the name "Grossdeutschland" is issued to "GD" troops.

9- 5: Artillery Abteilung 400 (motorized) is added to "GD" for added support.

10- 7: A new black cuff band, with altered lettering, is issued for "GD". The Führer-Escort Battalion also receives a cuff band, the sign of an elite unit.

10-12: A Motorized Engineer's Company is added to "GD" and assigned as the 18th Company.

10-27/12-31: "GD" is transferred to the army training camp at Le Valdahon, near the Swiss border, where it remains till the end of 1940. The unit trains for operation "Felix", the assault on Gibraltar.

11-29: A Motorized Flak Company is added to the regiment as the 20th Company.

12-16: The 99th Motorized Infantry Replacement Battalion is redesignated the Motorized Infantry Replacement Regiment "Grossdeutschland" (Neuruppin).

Unit Organization of the German Panzer Forces - May 5, 1940

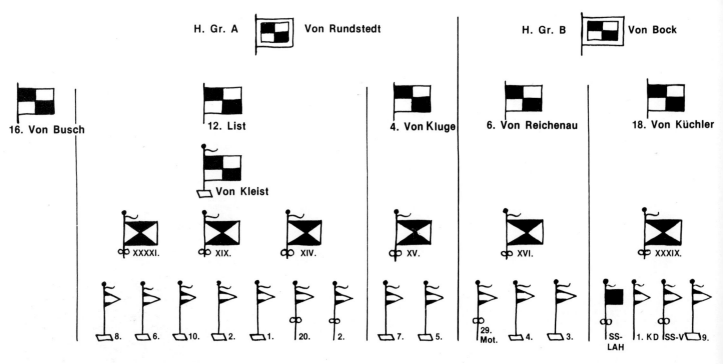

| H. Gr. A | Von Rundstedt | | H. Gr. B | Von Bock |

16. Von Busch   12. List   4. Von Kluge   6. Von Reichenau   18. Von Küchler

Von Kleist

XXXXI.   XIX.   XIV.   XV.   XVI.   XXXIX.

8.   6.   10.   2.   1.   20.   2.   7.   5.   29. Mot.   4.   3.   SS-LAH   1. KD   SS-V   9.

H. Gr. Res.

13.   SS-T   GD

The bridge over the Juliana Canal in the Netherlands was captured by the "Brandenburgers" [from which the Division "Brandenburg" was later developed].

Verwundeten- abzeichen
(Wound Badge)

The Crossing of the Maas, May 13, 1940

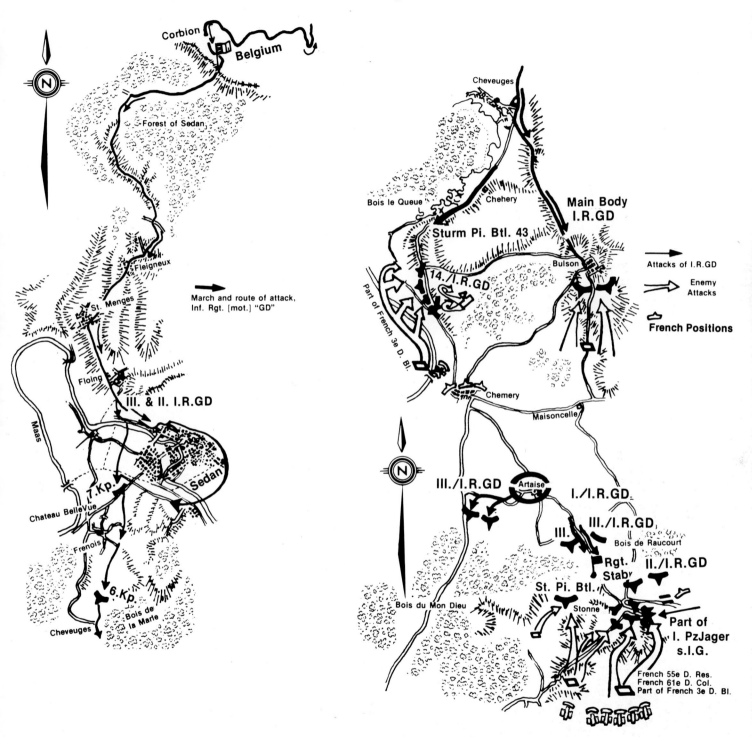

Corbion

Belgium

Forest of Sedan

Fleigneux

St. Menges

Floing

III. & II. I.R.GD

Maas

Sedan

7.Kp.

Chateau BelleVue

Frenois

6.Kp.

Cheveuges

Bois de la Marle

March and route of attack, Inf. Rgt. [mot.] "GD"

Cheveuges

Bois le Queue

Chehery

Main Body I.R.GD

Sturm Pi. Btl. 43

14./I.R.GD

Bulson

Part of French 3e D. Bl.

Chemery

Maisoncelle

Attacks of I.R.GD

Enemy Attacks

French Positions

III./I.R.GD

Artaise

I./I.R.GD

III./I.R.GD

III.

Bois de Raucourt

Rgt. Stab

II./I.R.GD

St. Pi. Btl.

Bois du Mon Dieu

Stonne

Part of I. PzJager s.I.G.

French 55e D. Res.
French 61e D. Col.
Part of French 3e D. Bl.

The Fighting South of Sedan, May 14 to May 15, 1940

"GD" Regimental Units and Commanders, May 10, 1940

I. Btl.	II. Btl.	III. Btl.	IV. Btl.

Rgt.-Stab.
  Rgt.-Fhr   Obstt. Graf von Schwerin
  Rgt.-Adj.   Hptm. Masius
  Hptm. b. Stabe   Oblt. von Kirchbach
  I b   Hpt. Gericke
  IV a   Stabszahlmeister Löw
  IV b   Stabsarzt Dr. Krummacher
  Fhr. Stabs-Kp.
  Fhr. Kradschützenzug   Oblt. Hartwig

I. (Schtz.) Bataillon   Obstlt. Köher, Hptm. Föllmer
  1. (Schtz.) Kp.   Oblt. Schwarzrock
  2. (Schtz.) Kp.   Oblt. Kolb
  3. (Schtz.) Kp.   Oblt. Fabich, Oblt. Bohrmann
  4. (MG.) Kp.   Oblt. Hänert, Lt. Schiller

II. (Schtz.) Bataillon   Major Föst, Major Greim, Adj. Oblt. Benk
  5. (Schtz.) Kp.   Oblt. Schneider
  6. (Schtz.) Kp.   Oblt. Von Courbiere
  7. (Schtz.) Kp.   Oblt. Wackernagel
  8. (MG.) Kp.   Oblt. Bethke

III. (Schtz.) Bataillon   Obstlt. Garski, Adj. Lt. Wentges
  9. (Schtz.) Kp.   Hptm. Westphal, Lt. Dr. Usadel
  10. (Schtz.) Kp.   Oblt. v. Harder, Oblt. Lucke
  11. (Schtz.) Kp.   Hptm. W. Krüger, Lt. Vogt, Lt. Obermeir
  12. (MG.) Kp.   Hptm. Grosser

IV. (Schtz.) Bataillon   Major Schneider, Adj. Oblt. Teubert
  13. (I.IG.) Kp.   Oblt. v. Massow, Oblt. Darries
  14. (Pz.-Jäg.) Kp.   Oblt. Beck-Broichsitter, Lt. Hintze, Lt. Janke
  15. (s.IG.) Kp.   Oblt. März, Oblt. Gerbener
  16. (Stu.G.) Kp.   Oblt. Frhr. v. Egloffstein, Oblt. Wirth
      Lt. Frantz, Lt. Tiarks, Lt. v. Werlhof

Stab   Stab   Stab   Stab

Schwere Kp.   Schwere Kp.   Schwere Kp.

1. Kp.   5. Kp.   9. Kp.   13. [I.I.G.] Kp.

2. Kp.   6. Kp.   10. Kp.   14. [Pz. Jäger] Kp.

3. Kp.   7. Kp.   11. Kp.   15. [s.I.G.] Kp. Nachschub-Kolonne GD

4. Kp.   8. Kp.   12. Kp.   stab

Supply column 400-with staff and 1st-3rd (later 4th) columns, and workshop unit.

Assigned to support "GD":
43rd Assault Engineers Battalion, commanded by Oberstlt. Mahler, with 3 Companies (1.-3. Pi-Kp.); and Light Bridging Column "B".

1.   2.   3.   4.

German troops and supply columns advanced through the Eifel and Ardennes all the way to the Maas River. Here, part of a panzer division, with PzKpfw III's, advances along a dusty road toward the west.

[Below] "GD" infantry take cover during an attack on a heavily defended position. Note the cuff band on the man at the right center of the photograph.

[Above] As German motorized troops make a detour, sappers clear mines from a road. Note the air identification flag on the hood of the Horch Kfz.15 car.

[Above] German troops enter Sedan after heavy fighting against Allied forces.

[Below] "GD" troops carry rubber assault boats filled with supplies during the operation to cross the Maas River.

Unit Organization of the German Panzer Forces-June 7,1940

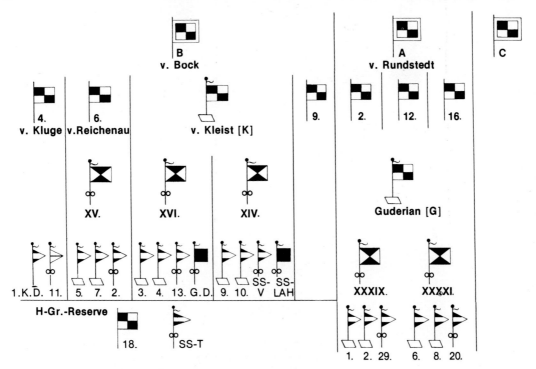

B
v. Bock

A
v. Rundstedt

C

4.
v. Kluge

6.
v. Reichenau

v. Kleist [K]

9.

2.

12.

16.

XV.

XVI.

XIV.

Guderian [G]

1.K.D. 11.

5. 7. 2.

3. 4. 13. G.D.

9. 10. SS- SS-
V LAH

XXXIX.

XXXXI.

H-Gr.-Reserve

18.

SS-T

1. 2. 29.

6. 8. 20.

The Breakthrough of the "Weygand-Line",
June 6, 1940

The Weygand Line was broken, and the Germans pursued the retreating enemy forces.

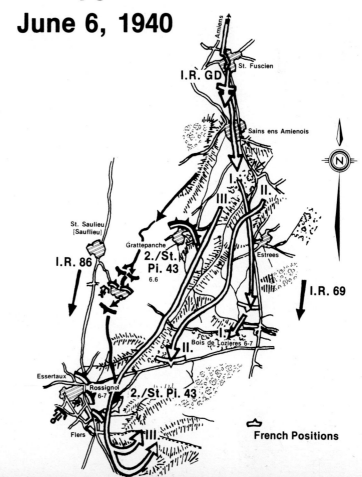

French Positions

"GD" troops march in pursuit of French units after breaking through the Weygand Line. Note the radio team in the center. The rear man carried the pack for the radio batteries; the front man carried the radio itself, while the second man operated it.

Here, one of the first assault guns to see action — in Sturmartillerie batterie 640 — advances with "GD" troops. This vehicle is a StuG III ausf A, or very early ausf B, and shows the initial configuration of this assault gun series; note the opening for the gunner's sight and the commander's binocular telescope.

The end of a defeated army, columns of French prisoners pass advancing German troops along roads and through captured villages. The truck in the lower photo is a Krupp L2H142 [Kfz 69] of an infantry company.

At this time, the ZbV 800 units developed the first units calling themselves "Brandenburgers", skilled in foreign languages and often used for advance reconnaissance and other action behind enemy lines. Later, the Panzergrenadier Division "Brandenburg" would be formed from these units.

Meanwhile, the cuffband underwent various changes in color and design (first green, then black) until the end of the war.

Infantry Regiment [mot] Grossdeutschland, December 1940

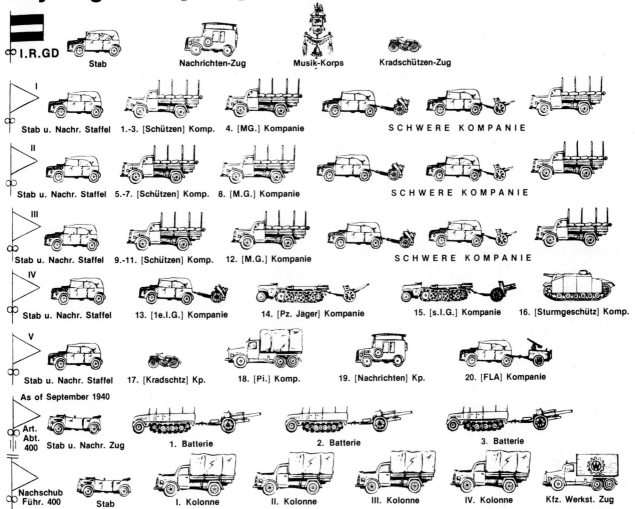

I.R.GD

Stab   Nachrichten-Zug   Musik-Korps   Kradschützen-Zug

I — Stab u. Nachr. Staffel   1.-3. [Schützen] Komp.   4. [MG.] Kompanie   S C H W E R E   K O M P A N I E

II — Stab u. Nachr. Staffel   5.-7. [Schützen] Komp.   8. [M.G.] Kompanie   S C H W E R E   K O M P A N I E

III — Stab u. Nachr. Staffel   9.-11. [Schützen] Komp.   12. [M.G.] Kompanie   S C H W E R E   K O M P A N I E

IV — Stab u. Nachr. Staffel   13. [1e.I.G.] Kompanie   14. [Pz. Jäger] Kompanie   15. [s.I.G.] Kompanie   16. [Sturmgeschütz] Komp.

V — Stab u. Nachr. Staffel   17. [Kradschtz] Kp.   18. [Pi.] Komp.   19. [Nachrichten] Kp.   20. [FLA] Kompanie

As of September 1940

Art. Abt. 400   Stab u. Nachr. Zug   1. Batterie   2. Batterie   3. Batterie

Nachschub Führ. 400   Stab   I. Kolonne   II. Kolonne   III. Kolonne   IV. Kolonne   Kfz. Werkst. Zug

1940 brought the first great test of the regiment — combat. In action during many fiercely-fought engagements and major battles, "GD" fought well and showed the value of its prolonged training, the ability of the officers, and the high morale of the men. "GD" numbered approximately 3900 officers and men at the start of the French campaign. At the end of the fighting, the regiment had sustained 1108 casualties:

	Killed in Action	Wounded	Missing	Total
Officers	8	40	1	49
NCO'S	41	128	8	177
Enlisted Men	172	662	48	882
	221	830	57	1108

Thus, unit casualties were slightly above 25%.

As was common during hard-fought actions, the men of "GD" not only gained combat experience but also formed an effective single unit. After the campaign in France, the men of "GD" no longer thought of their old units, from which they had been sent to "Grossdeutschland", "now they were "Grossdeutschland", and took pride in their new unit.

The regiment was expanded further. The addition of an Artillery Abteilung signaled the further expansion into a brigade, and eventually even a division.

1941

Molded into a close-knit fighting unit during the French campaign, and re-equipped and brought up to full strength for the training for "Sealion" and "Felix", "GD" was in excellent condition in early 1941. A second Heavy Transportation Battalion was added for greater independence and mobility.

After 3 months of intensive training in and around Belfort, April brings the first action of "GD". Involving less combat action than the French campaign, the campaign in the Balkans and Yugoslavia finds "GD" engaging in transportation, advances, and garrison duties.

In June, 1941, "GD" is assigned to the 2nd Panzerarmee for "Barbarossa", the invasion of Russia. Starting from Brest-Litovsk, the regiment attacks into Russia; during the advance, it is assigned to different units as needs dictate, often to support assaults on major objectives. "GD" is one of the German units that reaches the gates of Moscow-actually Tula, south of the city and at last at the Oka River, and then must fight in the severe winter rearguard battles as the Russians counterattack.

1941—World History

2- 6: Organization of the Deutsches Afrikakorps (D.A.K.) under General Erwin Rommel.
3- 1: Bulgaria joins the Tripartite pact.
3- 2: The 12th Army marches into Bulgaria.
3- 4: British forces land in Greece (Piraeus and Volos).
3-25: Yugoslavia joins the Tripartite pact.
4- 2: Hitler makes the final decision to attack Russia and sets the end of June for the attack.
4- 5: End of the friendship and non-aggression pacts between Yugoslavia and the Soviet Union.

4- 6: Beginning of the campaign against Yugoslavia and Greece.

4-13: Occupation of Belgrade.

4-17: Yugoslavian armed forces surrender.

4-20: Greek forces agree to truce with German forces; the battle against British troops continues.
4-27: Athens is occupied by German troops.
5- 2: Beginning of the fighting between Iraqi troops and British forces.
5-11: The British are driven out of the Greek mainland and most of the Greek Islands, except for Crete.

5-18: Italian troops in Abyssinia surrender to British armed forces.
5-20: The Germans attack Crete, including large-scale use of paratroops.
5-27: The German battleship "Bismarck" is sunk in the Atlantic by the Royal Navy.
6- 1: British troops occupy Bagdad.
6- 4: The last German Kaiser (Wilhelm II) dies in Doorn, Holland.
6- 8: British and Free French forces march into Syria.

6-18: End of the German-Turkish Friendship Agreement.

6-22: Beginning of "Barbarossa", the invasion of the Soviet Union, with 141 divisions, including 19 panzer divisions. Rumania joins the attack immediately, with 25 divisions.
6-23: Slovakia joins the battle against the Soviet Union.

6-26: Finland joins the campaign against Russia.
6-27: Hungary also enters the fight against Russia.

1941—Division Grossdeutschland

1-15: The Führer-Escort Battalion, formed from the "GD" Regiment, receives not only the "Grossdeutschland" cuffband, but also another band, inscribed "Führer-Headquarters", to be worn below the "GD" at this point.
1-27/4-4: March into Belfort area, and rest period there.

4-5/4-10: "GD" is transported by rail to Vienna - from there, the unit advances via Raab, Budapest, and Szegedin to Rumania, where it is assigned to the 41st Army Corps (motorized).

4-11: March via Arad and Temesvar into Yugoslavia.
4-12: Pursuit of enemy forces to Pancevo on the Danube River with few engagements.
4-13: "GD" 1st battalion participates in the occupation of Belgrade.
4-14/5-16: "GD" provides security troops in Yugoslavian Banat, east of the Danube around Welika, Kikinda, and Wertschetz.

4-19: Use of a broadcasting station by Oberleutnant Fabich (leader of the 3rd company) which later became famous as "Radio Belgrade".

5-17: Beginning of rail movement via Ruma, Mitrovica, Budapest, Pressburg to Oberschlesien, then into the area around Freudenstadt-Troppau.

6-15: March into area southeast of Warsaw, around Zelechow; assigned as reserve, 2nd Pz Army.

6-21: Artillery, heavy weapons, and assault guns of the 7th Panzer Division attack across the Bug River at Janow.

6-27/28: "GD" crosses the Russian frontier north of Brest-Litovsk.

1941—World History

7-12: Great Britain and the Soviet Union form an alliance to fight against Germany.

8-14: Announcement of the Atlantic Charter, but not to be extended to Germany.

1941—Division Grossdeutschland

6-29/7-3: "GD" fights in a consolidating action supporting assaults on surrounded Russian troops west of Minsk.
7-3/7-6: "GD" advances to Minsk, engaging enemy troops trying to break up the advance.
7-7/7-10: Further advances, with many individual skirmishes, via Beresina all the way to the Dnieper River. This advance enables "GD" to link up with armored units ahead. At this time, "GD" is assigned to 10th Panzer Division.
7-11/7-16: Attack across the Dnieper followed by fighting in the bridgehead.

7-16/7-20: Continuing advance, as Corps reserve (46th Panzer Korps), into the area west of Mstislavl near Yelnya.
7-21/7-22: Fighting in the Desna positions at Yelnya.
7-23/8-5: Fighting strong resistance on the road to Dorogobuzh (north of Yelnya) and on the railroad crossing south of Yelnya, at Vaskovo.
8-6/8-8: Relief and rest in the area around Dankovo-Vaskovo.
8-9/8-18: Defense actions in the Yelnya salient west of Yelnya.

8-19/8-30: End of fighting in the Vaskovo-Chochlovka-Rudnaya area.

Movements and Actions,
June 22 to December 31, 1941

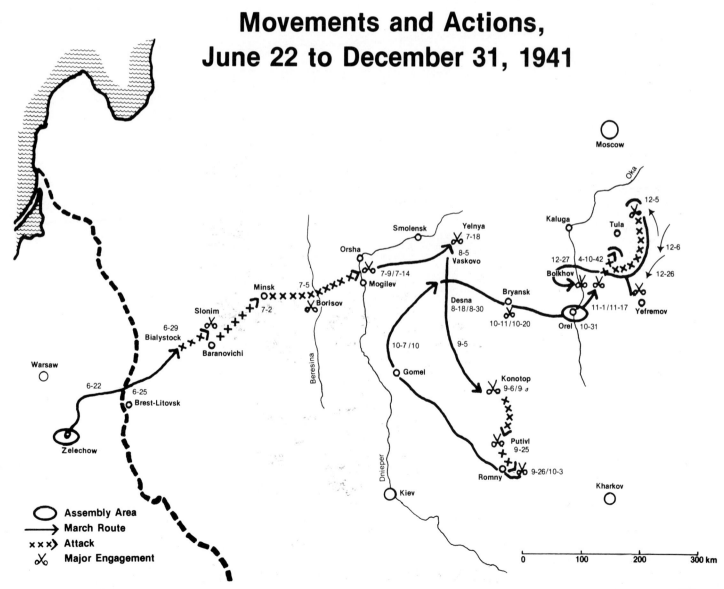

1941—World History

8-25: British and Soviet troops march into Iran.

9- 2: Beginning of material deliveries by the Americans to the Soviet Union.

9- 8: Leningrad is reached by German troops but not captured.

9-10: Greenland comes under US administration.

9-19: Kiev is occupied.

9-25: Kharkov is occupied.

10- 2: Beginning of the offensive against Moscow.

10-14: Kalinin (Tver) is reached, threatening Moscow.
10-16: The Soviet government withdraws from Moscow to Kuybyshev.

11-18: Beginning of the British counter-offensive in North Africa; the Africa Korps is thrown back onto El Agheila.
11-21: Occupation of Rostov.

11-25: Finland, Croatia, Rumania and Denmark join the Anticomintern pact.

12- 6: The offensive against Moscow is halted for good and the Soviet forces start counter-attack.
12- 7: Declaration of war by Japan against the USA (Pearl Harbor attack).

12-25: Hong Kong surrenders to the Japanese.

1941—Division Grossdeutschland

8-25: Oberleutnant Hänert (killed in action), commander of the 1st battalion, is the first man in "GD" regiment to win the Ritterkreuz (Knights Cross) in the Russian campaign.
9-1/9-4: "GD" marches south to participate in the battle for Kiev, traveling via Roslavl, Lukaviza, and Starodub. The unit crosses the Desna River at Novgorod-Seversk and secures a bridgehead.

9-5/9-8: "GD" advances south to Glukhov.

9-9/9-13: Assault across the Seym River at Putivl.

9-14/9-25: Engagements at Schilkova, Konotop, and Belopolye.

9-24: Kampfgruppe Nehring, formed from part of Führer-Escort Battalion — leaves Rastenburg in order to get into action near Volkhov, north of Leningrad, during the 1941-42 winter.

9-26/10-3: "GD" holds against Russian counterattacks east of Romny.

10-4/10-10: "GD" is transferred to the Roslavl area, via Konotop and Gomel.
10-11/10-12: Continued travel via Bryansk to Karachev, moving into a bivouac area north of the city.

10-17/10-21: Rest and recuperation in Orel.

10-22/10-23: Through the mud of the Russian autumn, "GD" reaches a concentration bivouac area northeast of Mtsensk.
10-24: "GD" attacks and dislodges well dug-in enemy troops.
10-29: The regiment advances to Tula, engaging in many battles with defending Russian Troops.
10-30/11-30: Engaged in battles around Yefremov and at Tula.
12-1/12-5: "GD" attempts to capture Tula from the north by enveloping the defenses from the east. During this assault on Ryazan and Kashira, the 17th Company (motorcycle troops) suffers a disastrous "Black Day" at Kolodesnaya.
12- 6: Beginning of a very severe cold wave (-40°C), and lessening of action at the front lines.
12-7/12-20: "GD" engages in repelling counterattacks around Yefremov and Tula. There are extensive battles from Tula to the defensive positions east of Orel, via Chern-Mtsensk.
12-21: Advance into the area around Bolkhov north of Orel.
12-22/12-31: Defensive engagements on the Oka River and north of Bolkhov. "GD" divided, with units assigned to support three different infantry divisions.

Ritterkreuz ("Knight's Cross")

A German column advances into Yugoslavia, northeast
of Belgrade. Even early in the war, a great variety of
vehicles are used in German units.

[Below] View of Pancevo.

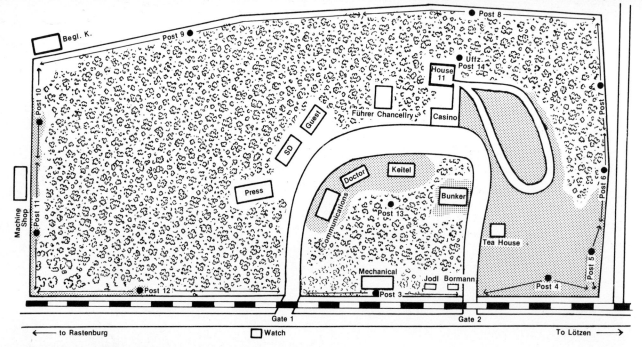

Diagram of location of units of the Führer-Escort
Battalion, formed from "GD".

Layout of the "Wolfsschanze" (Wolf's Redoubt) at Rastenburg, FHQu (Führer's Headquarters) at invasion, on June 21, 1941

[Below] Headquarters "Wolfsschanze", Gate 1.

Enlistment Papers of a "GD" Recruit.

The beginning of the Russian campaign consisted largely of rapid marches as far as the area south of Smolensk, punctuated by small battles and skirmishes against defending Russian troops. Initially, the German columns moved rapidly into Soviet territory.

Ersatz-Brigade (mot)
Großdeutschland
HGr. Hr. Hs. 12 9 5

Cottbus,   1941
Hermann-Löns-Kaserne

Darf nicht
für andere Wehrmachtteile einschl.
Waffen-SS geworben werden.

Annahmeschein

für   Ewald Schweig   geb. am 10.10.1924   Kaufm.Lehrling

Gladbeck/Westfalen, Hasselkreuzstr.2 a.

Sie werden hiermit als Bewerber für die   - Kriegsfreiwilliger - für

Inf.-Div. (mot) Großdeutschland   in   Cottbus   angenommen.

Nach Empfang dieses Annahmescheins haben Sie sich innerhalb von 4 Tagen bei dem für Sie zuständigen

Wehrbezirkskommando   Gelsenkirchen   unter Vorlage dieses Annahmescheins persönlich oder schriftlich zu melden". Schriftlicher Meldung ist dieser Annahmeschein beizufügen, außerdem der Wehrpaß, sofern Sie diesen vom Wehrbezirkskommando erhalten haben".

Sie werden später vom Wehrbezirkskommando durch Einberufungsbefehl einberufen.

Umstehende Anordnungen sind zu beachten.

Dieser Annahmeschein behält seine Gültigkeit bis zu dem Zeitpunkt, an dem Sie zur Wehrmacht einberufen werden.

Angemeldet:
Gelsenkirchen
16. März 1941

Ober i. Brig.-Kt.

Wehrbezirkskommando   Gelsenkirchen

Hauptmann

Nichtzutreffendes ist zu streichen
Falls Annahmeschein durch Wehrbezirkskommando erteilt, ist Meldung nicht erforderlich

29

The crossing of the Beresina River at Borisov brought thoughts of Napoleon's disastrous campaign of 1812. [Above] The approach to the river. [Below] The first vehicles were taken across the river by ferry.

German engineers finish assembly of a heavy pontoon bridge across the Beresina River. As can be seen, the temporary ferry on the preceding page was actually a short section of this pontoon bridge.

German infantrymen prepare for an assault on enemy positions. As the Wehrmacht advanced deeper into Russia, fighting became more frequent and more intense.

Assaults across flat, open terrain nearly always required support from artillery, armored units [tanks and assault guns], or armored half-tracks. [Above] An SPW supports infantry crossing a wheat field. [Below] A StuG III ausf B halts next to a house.

A near miss by an enemy shell forces the troops to drop down, as there is virtually no cover or protection in these flat fields.

Mobile fire support is directed against Soviet positions. Here, a Sdkfz 10/4 halftrack of a flak battery prepares to fire. Note the binocular telescope used by the officer standing by the vehicle.

The Attack from Yelnya, July 30, 1941

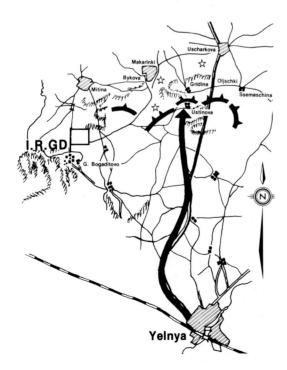

Determined enemy resistance often meant that the infantry had to dismount from the transport vehicles and advance cross-country in "open order" [advancing formation]. These troops advance on a suspected Russian position, while most of the vehicles remain on the road.

The Desna Battles, September 1 to September 4, 1941

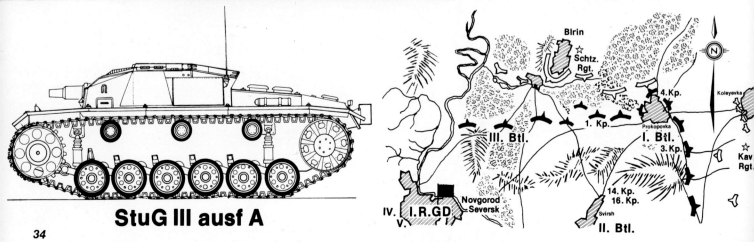

StuG III ausf A

The fighting in the area northeast of Orel continued into the fall.

After the battle: Rifles of Russian soldiers who surrendered.

Amid the burning destruction of a Russian village, German troops prepare to advance further. The two vehicles at the left are Horch Kfz 15's.

Because of delays in mounting and dismounting from trucks, fast assaults often found infantry riding directly on the tanks.

In the Russian autumn, German troops get their first taste of the bitterest enemy on the Eastern front — the weather. The numerous rivers and streams, with the very poor road conditions in bad weather, require skill and perseverance from drivers and troops. Many vehicles are lost in such poor conditions as shown here.

The higher costs of more intense fighting in the East. [Left] Obstlt. Garski [l.] and Obst. von Stockenhausen honor the dead from a recent engagement. [Below] The graves increase in number every day.

1941 was a bad year for "Grossdeutschland". The second six months brought the regiment every experience that can befall a combat unit: advance, attack, defensive fighting, great successes and terrible losses, victory and high morale, frustration and loss of morale, days of rest then bitter battles with high casualties, summer with its heat and dust, the fall with rain and mud, and winter with its bitter cold, fighting in open fields, woods, and cities.

"GD" came through this early part of the Russian campaign successfully, and earned a good reputation as a valuable fighting unit. This reputation was bought with heavy casualties; up to January 6, 1942, "GD" lost in Russia:

	Killed in Action	Wounded	Missing
Officers	36	89	--
NCO'S	129	377	4
Enlisted Men	735	2590	110
	900	3056	114

Total: 4070 men

[Above] Even in dry weather, the poor roads exacted a toll on the vehicles.

[Below] With a shortage of serviceable motor vehicles, most units had to resort to an earlier form of transport. Here, a horse-drawn wagon negotiates a crossing on the Oka River, near Bolkhov.

Scenes from the winter battles in the Yefremov-Tula area, 1941-42: vast expanses of snow-covered plains and low hills, littered with burning vehicles, guns, and frozen troops trying to keep their equipment operational.

1942 is a year of fierce and bitter fighting on the Russian front. But in 1942, "GD" is expanded to a full motorized infantry division. The orders regarding the reorganization emphasize "Grossdeutschland's" status as an elite unit. With these new orders, all new men taken into "GD" must be young, preferably volunteers, at least 1.70 meters in height, must have perfect eyesight without glasses, and must have no criminal record. It was further required that all members come up to "the ideal picture of the German soldier", a requirement held even more important for NCO's and especially officers. In addition, Inf. Div. (mot.) "Grossdeutschland" was to receive the latest and best equipment, as soon as it was released for use by front-line units.

"GD" doesn't have much time to train as a unit, for the all-important task of building morale, unit teamwork, and fighting efficiency. The second half of 1942 brings "GD" into many of the major battles and campaigns in the East, first in assult operations in the south, and later in the central sector, as a defensive unit.

The name "Grossdeutschland" in the meantime had become quite famous, and with its expansion to a full division, "GD's" fame brought more war correspondents and photographers, resulting in more thorough and better photographic coverage.

1942 — World History

1- 1: "Washington-Pact" - 26 nations decide not to make a special peace with Germany.
1- 2: Manila (Phillippines) is conquered by the Japanese.
1-11: Beginning of the Japanese attack on Dutch East Indies.
1-15: Singapore conquered by the Japanese.
1-18: Signing of a Military alliance between Germany, Italy, and Japan.

2-19: Attack on Darwin (Australia).

2-28: Landing on Java by the Japanese.
3- 1: Beginning of the British bomber offensive with attacks on German industrial cities and U-Boat bases.
3- 7: Rangoon, in Burma, captured by Japanese troops.

5- 4/5- 8: Battle of the Coral Sea, resulting in losses for the Japanese fleet.
5- 8/5-18: The Kerch peninsula in southern Russia is recaptured in the Crimean campaign.
5-17/5-28: Because of successful German counterattacks, the Russian spring offensive around Kharkov is unsuccessful in breaking the German positions.

6- 2/7-1: Battle of Sevastopol, resulting in the city's capture by siege and bombardment.

1942 — Division Grossdeutschland

1- 1/1-19: Battles on the Oka between Orel and Belev.

1-20/1-30: Engagements against enemy breakthroughs and partisans in the woods around Gorodok.
1-31/2-8: "GD" fights to secure the area around Gorodok.
2- 1: The 2nd Battalion is disbanded and the men and equipment are spread through the remaining battalions as reinforcements.
2- 9: Attack on Verch.
2-10: Battle to clear the Bolkhov-Yagodnaya railroad.
2-11/2-18: More engagements in this area, with many casualties.
2-19: The two remaining Grenadier Battalions were reformed into one unit.
2-20: "GD" attacks Kosovka and Chuchlovo.
2-21/4-8: Consolidating the gains won, and securing the area. The disbanded battalions are reformed and reorganized.

4- 1: "GD" Regiment commander, Oberst Hoernlein, is promoted to General-major, and is given command of the Division "GD" which is to be reformed from the regiment.
4- 1/5-22: Reorganization of "GD" regiment into a motorized infantry division, "GD". The newly assigned units are set up at the training schools at Doeberitz and Jüterborg (near Berlin) and Wandern/Mark Brandenburg.
4- 9/4-14: "GD" is relieved, and the old Regiment travels by truck to Orel.
4-15/4-16: The unit travels by rail to Rechitsa on the Dnieper River, at Gomel.
4-17: Unit headquarters established in Rechitsa. Here the Regiment is officially reformed as a Motorized Infantry Division, "Grossdeutschland".
5- 1: The "GD" Replacement Battalion is reformed as a Regiment and moves from Neuruppen to Cottbus at the same time.

5-23/5-31: Moving partly by rail, and the rest of the route by truck, the units which will join "GD" to expand it to a division reach the area northwest of Fatesch (NW of Kursk) via Mielau, Lomiza, Bialystok, Slutsk, Rogachev, Roslavl, Bryansk, and Orel. Here the division is assigned to the 48th Panzer Korps.
6- 1: Reformation of the Grenadier Replacement Battalion "GD" to a Motorized Replacement Brigade.

6- 4/6-7: Battle of Midway, resulting in disastrous loss by Japan of the heart of its carrier force; the turning-point of the Pacific war.
6-12: The Japanese land on Attu and Kiska in the Aleutians.
6-28: Attack of the German "Army Group South" (Operation "Blue").

7-24: Rostov is recapture by the Germans.

8- 7: U.S. troops land on Guadalcanal in the Solomon Islands.
8-14: The Canadians stage an ill-fated raid on the French coastal town of Dieppe.

8-24: The Germans reach the Volga River at the northern outskirts of Stalingrad.

8-28: German troops raise their flag on the highest mountain in the Caucasus, Mt. Elbrus.

6-28/7- 4: "GD" breaks through Russian positions at Tim, and pursues the retreating enemy all the way to the upper Don River at Voronezh.
7- 1/7-27: "GD" trains in the Fatesch area and assembles close to Shchigry for the summer offensive planned for southern Russia.
7- 5/7- 6: "GD" battles across the Don, and helps capture Voronezh.
7- 7: The Division assembles on the western bank of the Don River.
7- 8/7-13: Advance through the big bend area encompassed by the Don — without engaging the enemy — south to Olchovskii on the Olchovaya.
7-14/7-19: Forced march with light skirmishes via Tazinskaya to the Donets River, just north of its joining the Don.
7-20: "GD" crosses the Donets at Mikhailovskii.
7-21/7-23: Battles north of and around Razdorskaya on the Don River.
7-24/7-30: "GD" extends the bridgehead to the Sal River, and secures the area by taking Susatzki.
7-31: Rapid advance to the Manytsch River.
8- 1/8-14: "GD" division is relieved and assembles in Shakhty on the north bank of the Donets as OKH reserve.

8-15: "GD" begins embarking, loading equipment onto trains.
8-16/8-18: Rail transport to Smolensk.

8-25: "GD" marches northeast from Smolensk to the Rzhev area, west of Moscow.

Movements and Actions, 1942

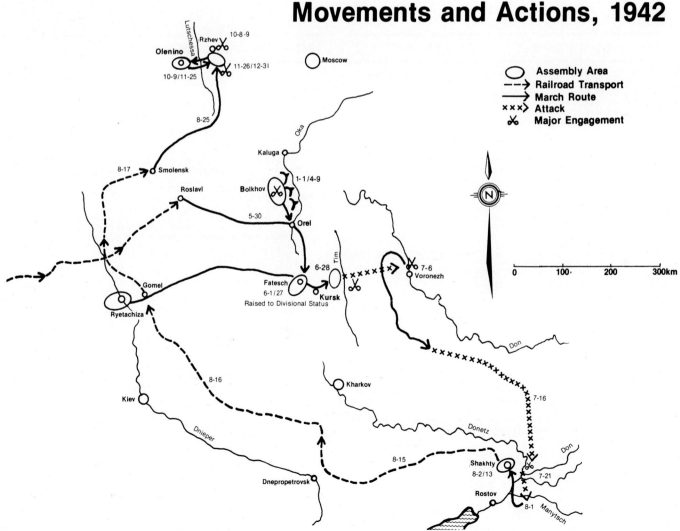

**Panzerkampfabzeichen
(Panzer Assault Badge)**

One of the churches in Bolkhov.

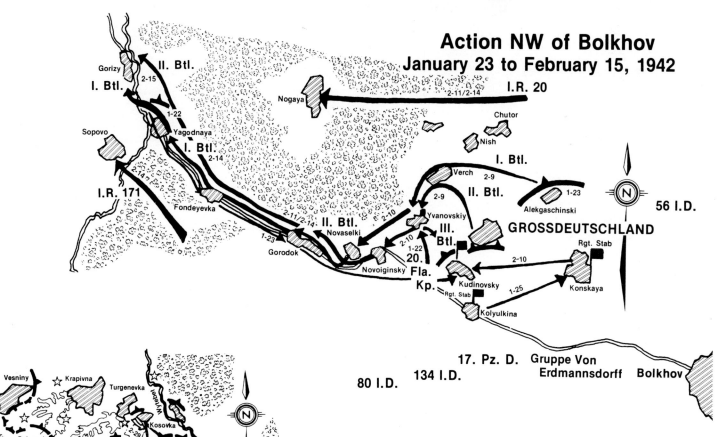

Action NW of Bolkhov
January 23 to February 15, 1942

Action around Melechovo
(near Bolkhov)
February 29, 1942

Composition of Infanterie-Division (mot) "Grossdeutschland"

Divisionsstab

Feldgendarmerie Zug

Kriegsberichter Zug

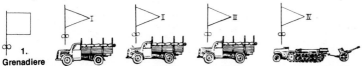

1. Grenadiere

1.-5. Kompanie 6.-10. Kompanie 11.-15. Kompanie 16.-18. Kompanie

2. Füsiliere

1.-5. Kompanie 6.-10. Kompanie 11.-15. Kompanie 16.-18. Kompanie

Sturmgeschütz Abteilung

Stab 1. Batterie 2. Batterie 3. Batterie

Panzer-Truppe

Stab 1. Kompanie 2. Kompanie 3. Kompanie Werkstatt Zug

Kradschützen Bataillon

1. Schwadron 2. Schwadron 3. Schwadron 4. Schwadron 5. Schwadron

Flak-Abteilung

1. Batterie 2. Batterie 3. Batterie 4. Batterie 5. Batterie

Artillerie Regiment

Stabsbatterie 11. [Beobachter] Batterie 10. [Werfer] Batterie [AB 1943] I.-II. Abteilung/1. Batterie I.-II. Abteilung/2. Batterie I.-II. Abteilung/3. Batterie III. Abteilung/1. and 2. Batterie

III. Abteilung/3. Batterie

Nachrichten Abteilung

Fernsprech Kompanie Funk-Kompanie Leichte Kolonne

Pioniere

1. Kompanie 2. Kompanie 3. Kompanie Brückenkolonne >K< Leichte Pionier Kolonne

Panzer Jäger

Nachrichten-Zug 1. Kompanie 2. Kompanie 3. Kompanie

Verwaltungs Dienste [Logistics Service]

Divisions-verpflegungsamt [Supply Section] Fleischerei Kompanie Bäckerei Kompanie Reifen-Kompanie

Nachschub Dienste

1.-10. Kolonne 11.-14. Kolonne 15.-18. Kolonne 1.-3. Werkstatt Kompanie Ersatz-Teil-Kompanie

Sanitätsdienste

Feldlazarett 1. Sanitäts-Kompanie 2. Sanitäts-Kompanie 1. Kranken-Kraftwagen-Zug 2. Kranken-Kraftwagen-Zug 3. Kranken-Kraftwagen-Zug Feldpost-Amt Feldersatz-Bataillon

Sonstiges (Misc.)

The "GD" divisional staff on the move, and at the command post. The division commander, Generalmajor Hoernlein, formerly the Colonel commanding "GD" as a regiment; Colonel Garski, the regimental commander, leans on a cane. Note the "GD" command pennant.

Both of these photos show vehicles of the motorcycle troop battalions of "GD", now used for reconnaissance and scouting duties. Above are two Sd Kfz 232 radio cars on railcars on the way to the training area east of Kursk. Below are Kubelwagens and heavier cars of the "GD" motorcycle troop battalion. Note the white fender markings as well as the tactical and divisional symbols. The VW's are early models, indicated by the long rear fenders.

Summer Offensive, 1942 —
First Day of Attack
June 28, 1942

9. P.D.

XXIV. Pz. A.K.

3. I.D.

I.D.GD

1.

2.

XXXXVIII.
Pz. A.K.

24. P.D.

N

4. Panzer
Armee

Gromonoya
Russanovo
Russanovo
Novyie Ssaviny
Rasschovez
Schtschigry
Ssemenovka
Ivanovka
Michailovka
Paklanovka
Pokrowskoye
Karandokovo
Manssurovo
Rakova
Kschen
Vassjutinka
Bordajevka
Kschen
Petrovskaya
Klyutshi
Alissovka
Tim
Tim
Tim

This StuG III ausf F takes on more ammunition for the 7.5 cm Stu K 40. Note the early pattern Pz Kpfw III headlamp.

[Below] All types of artillery from 15cm field artillery [Middle] to 7.5 cm infantry guns [Bottom] take part in preparations for an attack.

Ia

Early Style Ia's Pennant

47

[Opposite] The division commander looks at the enemy from a Sd Kfz 251/6 ausf B command SPW. These vehicles were fitted with command radios and usually cryptograph code machines as well.

Attack South of Olym,
June 29 to June 30, 1942

[Above] "GD" infantry, still out of enemy range, march in close file through a wheat field. The men in front carry machine gun ammunition.

[Below] A pair of Pz Kpfw IV F1's advance with the troops. Still armed with the short 7.5 cm howitzer, they were at a disadvantage fighting Russian tanks, but in infantry support actions, they were very effective.

The Russian steppes show their great beauty - sweeping endless, green fields, covered with flowers. The tanks below are decorated with garlands as camouflage. These are the newer Pz Kpfw IV ausf F2, with the long gun.

[Above] A PzKpfw IV of "GD" passes two radio cars of the division's motorcycle troop battalion. Note the extensive markings on all these vehicles.

[Right] Infantry wait for the attack to commence. Enemy fire is heavier as the attack progresses.

[Left] Heavy weapons advance with the infantry. Here, a heavy mortar team passes a flamethrower operator.

Russian tank attacks were often very large and fiercely-fought assaults. Many units, having insufficient self-propelled weapons, used towed antitank guns. Two of the best weapons were the 7.5 cm PAK 40 [above, towed by the 3-tonne SdKfz 11 tractor] and the 8.8 cm Flak 18 [below, firing on a target].

Two German PzKpfw IV's advance toward Russian positions.

[Above] A German soldier searches a Russian soldier immediately after his capture.

[Below] Interrogations by the front line troops often bring good results, which can be used in subsequent actions.

[Above] A battle-tested infantry unit marches down a dirt road. Note the great variety in the stowage of personal gear.

[Below] When the day's objective is reached, positions are dug out under protection of assault guns, in order to be safer from enemy counterattacks. These are StuG III ausf F's.

"Grossdeutschland" units attack, supported by tanks.
[Above] A PzKpfw III ausf L. [Below] A PzKpfw IV ausf
F2, followed by an F1. Again, the vast expanses of the
Russian plains are apparent in this bottom photograph.

In pursuit of retreating Russian forces, infantry ride on assault guns and tanks to keep up with the advance.

Major von Usedom, commanding officer of the Kradschützen battalion of "GD", riding in his SdKfz 250/3 armored command halftrack.

Bad roads and limited river crossings and bridges slowed many advances. This muddy road slows an advance, as many vehicles have to be manhandled through the mud.

[Below] A small temporary bridge, this one across the Tim river, creates a huge traffic jam as hundreds of vehicles line up to cross the river.

A scene common to every army: satisfying one's thirst with a drink from a helmet.

On July 5, elements of "GD" cross the Don River. Here, a SdKfz 250/3 of the Kradschützen battalion drives up the river bank after being ferried across the river.

A crewman of this 2 cm Flak 38 looks over the plains in front of the city of Voronezh. The silhouette and markings indicate that one tank and a number of other targets have been destroyed.

A StuG III ausf F crosses a rail line during the rapid march through the Don River bend sector. Proper grave crosses are prepared to replace makeshift markers.

Being in the southern Ukraine steppes during the hot summer was an uncomfortable — and unforgettable — experience.

"GD" vehicles photographed during the march south through the Don bend. [Above] A SdKfz 232 [8 rad] radio armored car of the 1st company, Kradschützen battalion. [Below] Armored halftrack SPW's of the Kradschützen [motorcycle troop] battalion. Note the small vehicle numbers on the rear corner plates.

[Opposite] Heading this column of armored halftracks is a SdKfz 247 II, based on the Horch heavy passenger car chassis. These vehicles had more limited cross-country performance, and were usually reserved for senior command or staff officers.

[Above] Men of the Kradschützen battalion during a rest. At the right is a trailer from the unit. The tent is erected from shelter quarters, carried by all German soldiers. The advance south by the Don River was marked by rapid movement, short rests, and skirmishes and heavier battles.

[Below] Artillery bursts in the middle of the flat plain show the lack of cover in the open.

A SdKfz 250/3 passes an old-fashioned wooden windmill.

The lower Don, Sal, and Manytsch Rivers were reached and partially taken in combat, but not all of these rivers were in German hands. [Above] General of the Panzer troops Kempf, commanding the 48th Panzer Korps, with [at left] "GD" Division commander Gen.-Maj. Hoernlein. [Below] A SdKfz 250/1 SPW near the Manytsch River.

A view of the ruins of Rzhev.

In the middle of August, 1942, the major Soviet counterattacks come against the old "hot spot", Rzhev. Along with other units in the Don area, "GD" is transferred north to fight this new threat. Until another transfer, to the Kharkov area in Jan. 1943, "GD" would face one of the most difficult periods its forces had ever experienced, with savage fighting and terrible weather.

A German soldier waits in a crater below a destroyed Russian "Valentine" tank.

(Left)
During the advance, "GD" enters the lime-faced mountains and hills of the Donets area.

Attack South of Rzhev,
September 10, 1942

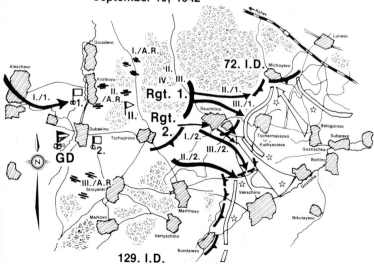

A destroyed T34/76 model 41 burns near a ruined farmhouse.

A SdKfz 250/1 of a heavy machine gun section, showing the heavy mount for the front MG 34.

Two views of the front at Chermassovo after the battles in this area were over.

Battle of the Lutschessa Valley

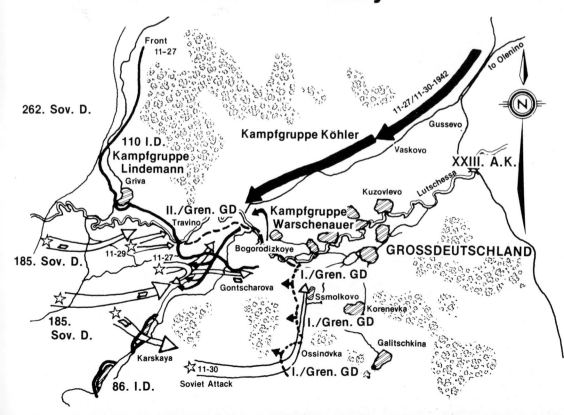

At the end of November, after 6 weeks of rest, the costly winter battle for Rzhev begins.

Note the lack of web gear and personal equipment on these two soldiers advancing over a rise.

Battles around Volchansk

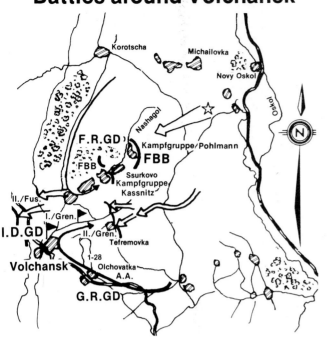

Above: An MG42 in action.

1943 — World History

9- 3: British Forces land on the Italian mainland at the southern point of Calabria.
9- 4: US Forces land on New Guinea.
9- 8: Special truce of Badoglio (Italy) with the Allies. Beginning of disarmament of the Italian Army.
9- 9: US Armed Forces land at Salerno.
9-12: Mussolini is freed on the Gran-Sasso.

9-30: The Germans evacuate Naples.

10-24: Dniepropetrovsk is evacuated by the Germans.
11- 6: Kiev is evacuated by the Germans.

11-13: Japanese naval forces suffer a serious defeat in a 3-day sea battle in the Solomon Islands.
11-28/12-1: Teheran conference. The Allied leaders agree to the position of postwar borders in Europe (demarcation line; Oder-Neisse line).
12- 6: KMS Scharnhorst is lost in the Polar Sea, sunk by the Royal Navy.

1943 — Division Grossdeutschland

8-28/9-15: "GD" fights in many areas, serving as a "fire brigade" - reinforcing critical points in the difficult battles west of Kharkov and north of Poltava.

9-16/9-19: Delaying battles to the Dnieper River (Kremenchug bridgehead). At this point, all available spare units are evacuated to the west bank of the Dnieper. "GD" reforms as separated units, fight to the German lines; "GD" then moves to France for complete refitting.
9-29: The "GD" tank regiment has only a single operational tank!
9-30/10-14: Battles at Michurin-Rog against strong forces; "GD" attacks across the Dnieper.
10-15: Start of the main Soviet offensive from the bridgehead on both sides of Michurin-Rog.
10-16/12-31: Withdrawal and defensive engagements against strong enemy forces, to the south of Sofiyevka (east of Krivoi-Rog).

11-12: Major Remer, Kdr. 1 (SPW)/Pz. Gren. Regt. "GD" receives the oak leaves to the Knight's Cross.

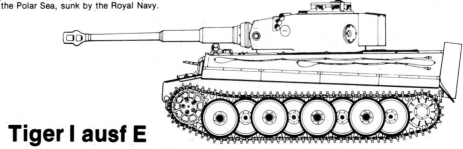

Tiger I ausf E

Light infantry gun [Above] and PAK40
[Below] in action near Byelgorod.

[Right] Destroyed Russian M3 "Stuart" light tank.

[Below Left] Infantry in snow camouflage suits use captured Russian PPSH 43 submachine guns.

[Below Right] A German 8 cm. mortar team opens fire.

For reasons of camouflage, the tanks and vehicles are painted white in winter. This painting is of little use in battle; it's more for protection against air-reconnaissance looking for troops and vehicles hidden in the few villages.

[Below] A column of tanks heading toward Borissovka, west of Byelgorod.

[Right] Oberst Graf Strachwitz, commander of the Panzer Regiment "GD" in the turret of his command tank.

On the way to Byel-gorod, a tank column halts for a rest. From left to right: Lt. Fuchs, Oberst Lorenz, Hptm. Petereit, Gefr. Schneider. Note the camouflage suits at the right.

Crewmen load a 15 cm. Nebelwerfer; the launcher is fired by remote control.

A VW type 166 "Schwimmwagen" [Kfz 1/20].

Div. Kdr. Hoernlein eats on the march.

SdKfz 9 Famo 18-tonne halftracks and a Kubel-wagen plow through mud and melting snow.

On March 23, "GD" was relieved and sent to Poltava. During this rest period, decorations for past bravery are awarded.

[Above] The Panzer regiment; [Below] The Grenadier Regiment.

In the Sturmgeschutz abteilung, the commander, Hptm. Frantz, receives the oak leaves to his Knight's Cross. [Above] Hptm. Frantz with his men. [Below] With the Unteroffizier [NCO] group, and the Division Kdr.

[Above] A Heavily camouflaged SdKfz 7 tractor tows an 8.8 cm Flak 36.

[Below] Neatly folded blouses with the distinctive "Grossdeutschland" cuffband wait for the end of a relaxing swim during a rest period.

There is time now for group photos. [Above] An intelligence unit [note the sign!] and award ceremonies and review parades. [Below] The Sturmgeschutz abteilung "GD" at the award of the Knight's Cross to its commander.

Snapshots and portraits for the relatives at home. [Left] Hptm. Magold, Kdr. 1./StuG Abt. "GD" personnel in the Army wore their cuffbands on the right sleeve; the SS formations all wore their cuffbands on the left sleeve.
[Above] Major von Wietersheim

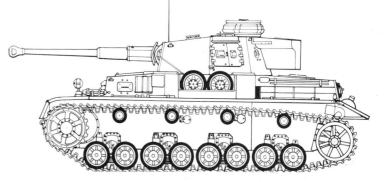

PzKpfw IV ausf F2

At this time also new weapons and tanks arrive. [Above] Panther. [Below Left] sFH on self-propelled carriage [Hummel]. [Below right] sIG on self-propelled carriage [Bison].

Operation Citadel,
July 4 to July 9, 1943

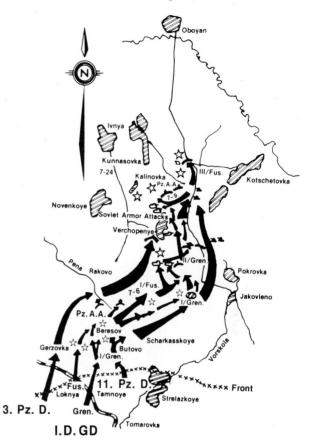

At the beginning of June 1943, a newly-equipped full-strength division — now designated "Panzer-grenadier Division GD" — is ready for action. Senior army commanders announce the plans for operation "Citadel", the assault on Kursk. [Above left] General Kempf, Kdr. of 8th Armee. [Below] Generaloberst Hoth, Kdr. of 4th Panzerarmee.

[Above] General of the Panzer troops Breith —
III./Panzer Korps [hands behind his back]; with him are
Oberst Lorenz and Hptm. Chrapkowski.

On July 4, 1943, the heavy battles between Byelgorod and
Kursk begin.

The start of operation "Zitadelle" ["Citadel"], one of the last major offensives of the German army. Infantry advances through Russian defensive positions [Above], then tanks and SPW's advance across the flat fields [Below].

The attack slows, and the infantry is forced to take cover in the flat fields.

Operation Citadel,

July 12 to July 17, 1943

Russian resistance increases steadily, and the initial rapid advance breaks down; the infantry now had to struggle for every small gain, with heavy casualties.

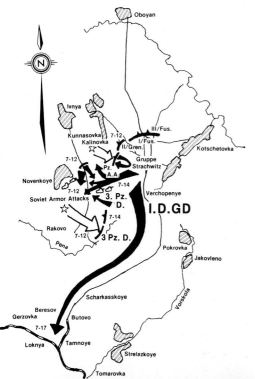

The attack stops. Casualties pile up. As fast as possible,
injured soldiers are taken to the first aid in the rear, away
from the battlefield and enemy fire.

Support troops are necessary for every action - every movement. [Above] A forward O.P. of the reconnaissance unit, served by field telephones. [Below] Trucks of a transportation company.

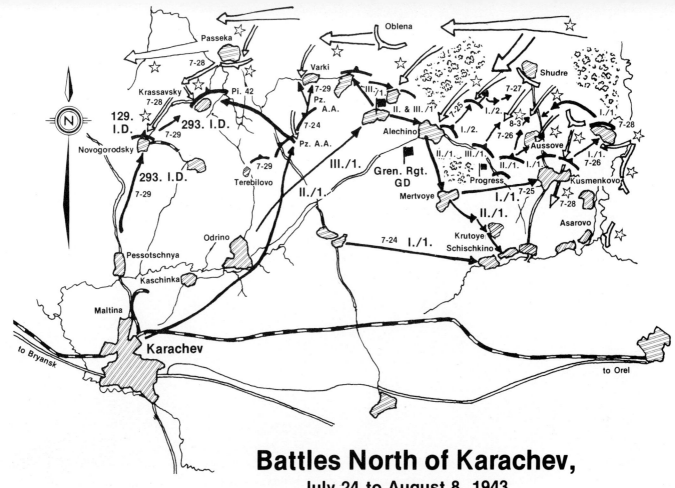

Battles North of Karachev,
July 24 to August 8, 1943

Forced by the breakthrough in Army Group Middle, "GD" is unexpectedly thrown into action in the wooded area northeast of Karachev. The action lasted 14 days.

These turned out to be difficult savagely-fought actions, fought in villages and woods with many casualties.

Fighting East of Akhtyrka,
August 7 to August 11, 1943

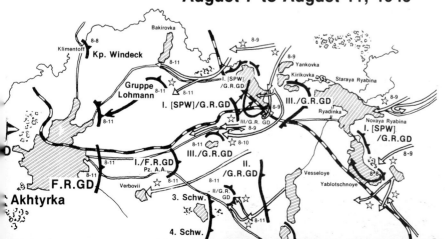

"GD" artillery units return from Karachev to the area around Akhtyrka, familiar from earlier rest and refitting periods.

"GD's" objective is to engage the Russians in an area where they have broken through, and to counterattack until the enemy forces were forced back through their lines. The division fights for days with no rest. A Tiger Abteilung joins the battle to reinforce the tank complement of the division.

Battle of Akhtyrka,
August 12 to August 16, 1943

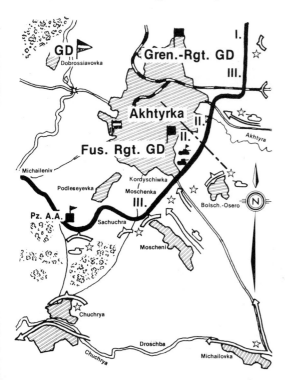

Fighting Southeast of Akhtyrka,
August 7 to August 22, 1943

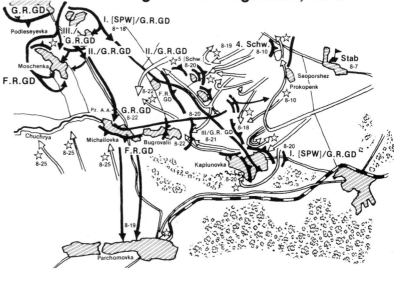

A commander of a StuG III ausf G uses binoculars and binocular telescope to observe the enemy positions. Note the field-added armor in front of the cupola.

A SdKfz 251 radio-equipped halftrack serves as a mobile command post.

Strong enemy attacks break through the German lines, and force "GD" into defensive battles on the Dnieper at Kremenchug. [Left The railroad bridge across the Dnieper River at Kremenchug. [Above] The division staff uses a large haystack as a command post.

Retreat to the Kremenchug Bridgehead,

September 20 to
September 29, 1943

Niederkampfen von Panzerkampf-wagen durch Einzelkampfer

[Special Badge for Single-Handed Destruction of a Tank]

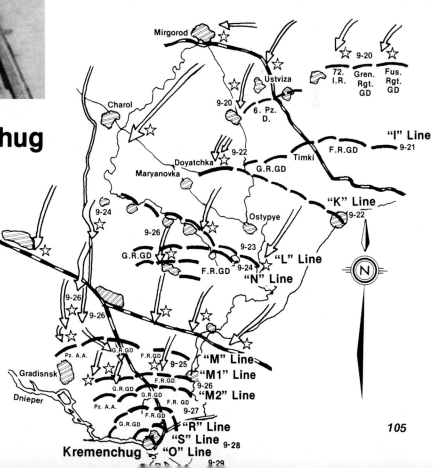

Fighting at the Mischurin Rog-Borodayevka,
September 30 to October 17, 1943

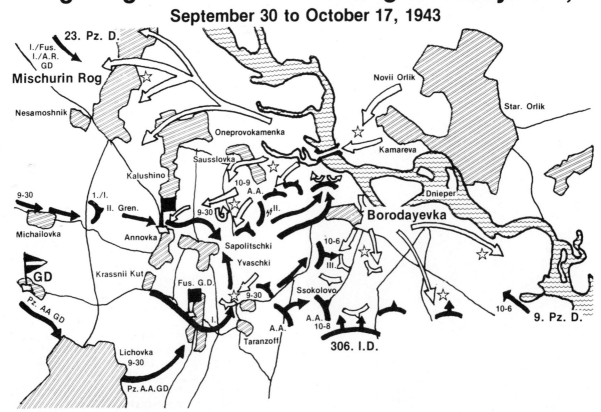

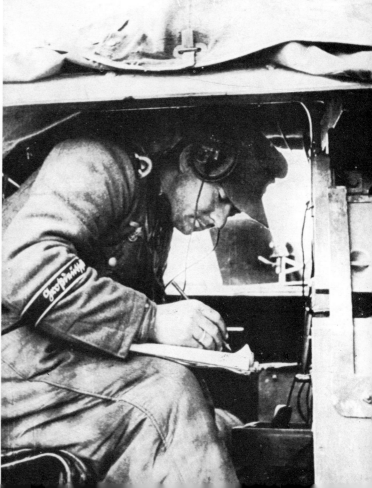

Withdrawal South of the Dnieper,
October 18 to October 25, 1943

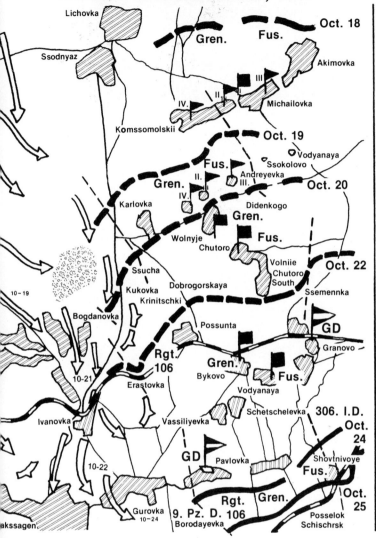

Withdrawal South of the Dnieper,
October 29 to November 26, 1943

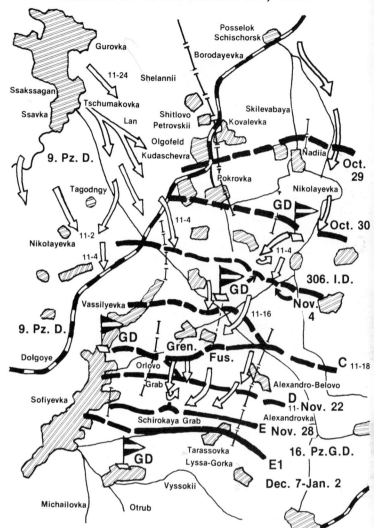

Maps above show the general chronology of the movements in this sector.

GD Shoulder Strap
(Unteroffizier)

Withdrawal actions call for artillery to break up enemy advances.

[Above] A 17 cm FK; [Below] A 10.5 cm le. FH 18.

An engineer rigs demolition charges on a wood bridge.

An O.P. reports the enemy's position.

Difficult winter battles - the third winter of the Russian campaign - take their toll of men and equipment. [Right] German troops in heavy winter clothing. [Below] Troops gather around a halftrack [SdKfz 251 ausf C].

Captured Russian soldiers are searched after the fighting has halted.

1943 had proved to be a much more difficult year than the preceeding one. The division's casualties were no longer disastrously high, but they were higher — on the average — than before. Worse, many of those lost were veterans of many actions, and with them went priceless combat experience. Outwardly, the division did not change because continual replacements flowed into all the "GD" units. The pride in the famous division instilled in the new men a good fighting spirit, and they fought well to uphold the reputation of "Grossdeutschland".

The year ended with little hope for improvement in the military situation. The heavy fighting in the Dnieper River area against superior enemy forces proved to be a preview of things to come; harder fighting, and fewer successes.

Every year, Propaganda Minister Goebbels requested the best officers in the army to report on conditions at the front lines. Here, Hptm. Konopka reports.

Movements and Actions,
July 4, to December 31, 1943

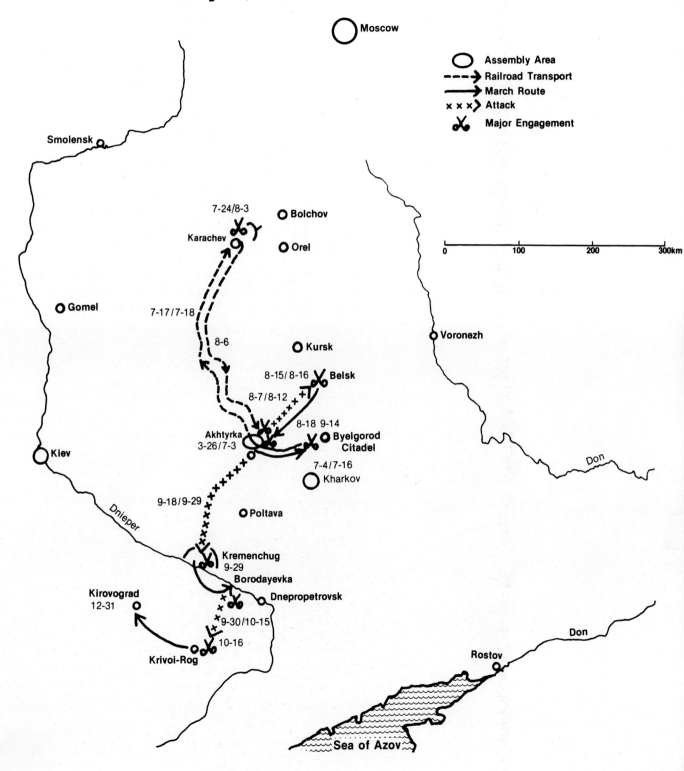

Moscow

Assembly Area
Railroad Transport
March Route
Attack
Major Engagement

Smolensk

7-24/8-3
Bolchov
Karachev
Orel

Gomel

Voronezh

7-17/7-18

8-6

Kursk

8-15/8-16 Belsk
8-7/8-12

8-18 9-14
Akhtyrka   Byelgorod
3-26/7-3   Citadel

Kiev

7-4/7-16
Kharkov

Dnieper

9-18/9-29

Poltava

Kremenchug
9-29
Borodayevka
Kirovograd   Dnepropetrovsk
12-31

9-30/10-15

10-16
Krivoi-Rog

Don

Don

Rostov

Sea of Azov

For "GD", 1944 proves to be a year of the heaviest fighting yet in the southern and northern sectors of the Eastern front. By the end of the year, parts of the German homeland will have been taken by the enemy. Only a few weeks of rest, many times only a few days at a time, were available to the division. Many other divisions were pulled out of the line and sent home, or to France, for complete refitting, but "GD" was not to be so fortunate — one disadvantage of an elite unit, expected to do the impossible at every opportunity. "Grossdeutschland" — as in the past — was continually thrown into critical battles and weak points in the lines. The unit eventually earned the nick-name "Fire Brigade" for its efforts in saving critical military situations.

Courage alone could not compensate for the overwhelming Russian superiority in men and material. Large areas of captured territory were retaken by the enemy — eventually Germany is threatened.

The sister units of the division — originally intended to be smaller forces for guard duty, or in emergencies to serve as replacement units — are now reinforced, trained, and equipped as full strength combat units to be used independently when needed in critical situations. They all carry the white "Stahlhelm" (steel helmet) as their unit insignia to show their relationship to PzGren Div. "GD". In contrast to "GD", however, they don't have their own war correspondent platoons, which is why very few photos exist of these units; in addition, these units weren't in existence very long.

1944 — World History

1- 3: Russian troops reach the pre-war Polish border.

1-22: The Allies land at Anzio and Nettuno in Italy.

3- 9: Hungary is occupied by German troops.

4- 8: Russian troops reach the former Czechoslovakian border in the Carpathians.
4- 9: Beginning of evacuation from the Crimean peninsula.

5-18: The Monte Cassino (Italy) is lost.

6- 4: Allied troops occupy Rome.

6-6: Landing by the Allies at the coast of Normandy in France.

6- 9: Beginning of the Russian offensive against Finland.
6-15: First use of V-1 rockets against England.

1944 — Division Grossdeutschland

1- 1/1-3: Defensive battles east of Krivoi-Rog.

1- 4: "GD" relieved and transferred to area west of Kirovograd.
1- 5/3-7: Defensive battles west of Kirovograd.
1-16: I./Panzer Regiment 26 (Panther) joins Pz. Rgt. "GD".

1-27: Genllt. Hasso von Manteuffel takes command of "GD", replacing Genllt. Hoernlein.
1-27/2-8: Major elements of Pz. Rgt. "GD" transferred to Cherkassy battle.
2- 5/5-18: "Kampfgruppe Böhrend" transferred to Narva front.
3- 5: From the reinforcement forces of "GD" — at Cottbus and Guben — a Replacement Grenadier Regiment (motorized) 1029 "GD" is formed.
3- 8/3-15: Defensive battles west of Kirovograd and withdrawal under fire to the bend in the Bug River.
3- 9: Rgt. 1029 "GD" transferred to Zakopane.
3-19: Rgt. 1029 "GD" participates in the occupation of Hungary.
3-16/3-30: "GD" transferred back all the way to the Dniester River.
3-31: Rgt. 1029 "GD" occupies the Carpathian mountain passes at the Hungarian-Rumanian border (at Kimpolung). Defensive battles in North Bessarabia between the Dniester and the Carpathians on both sides of Jassy.

4- 9/5-10: Rgt. 1029 "GD" fights in the Carpathians.
4-25: "GD" successfully counterattacks at Targul Frumos (Bessarabia).
5- 2/5-6: Heavy defensive fighting at Targul Frumos.
5- 7/5-31: Period of quiet at Targul Frumos. At this point, 1./Pz. Fus. Rgt. "GD" (GD2) is transferred to Germany for re-equipping with SPW's. The armored reconnaissance unit of "GD" is also re-equippped with armored vehicles. On the other hand, the size of the Pz. Gren. (Fus.) regiments are reduced, with only 3 battalions instead of the former 4 battalions, and each battalion being reduced from 5 companies to 4 companies.

6- 1: The Führer-Escort Battalion is reinforced to a regiment in East Prussia. "GD" transfers to an area north of Podul.
6- 2/6-5: "GD" counterattacks at Podul.

6- 5: Oberst Niemack, Kdr. of the Pz. Fus. Rgt. "GD" receives the swords to the oak leaves of the Knight's Cross.
6- 6: Elements of the Pz. Fus. Rgt. "GD" rejoin the regiment.
6- 7: I./Pz. Rgt. "GD", transferred to France for conversion to the Panther, is thrown into the defense of occupied France against Allied forces in Normandy.
6- 8: "GD" is pulled out of the lines.

7- 2: Minsk is lost.

7-13: Vilna is lost.
7-18: Bialystock is lost.
7-20: Attempt on Hitler's life by high-ranking Army officers.

7-27: Dünaburg and Lemberg are lost.
7-28: Brest-Litovsk is lost.
7-31: Breakthrough at Avranches begins the collapse of the Western front.
8- 1: Kovno is lost.
8- 1/10-2: Warsaw uprising, eventually broken by heavy bombardment and direct assaults.
8- 4: German troops evacuate Florence.

8-11: U.S. forces capture Guam in the Pacific.

8-15: Allies land in southern France.
8-18: Field Marshal von Kluge commits suicide.

8-20: Soviet forces stage a major offensive at Jassy; heavy fighting leads to the destruction of the German 6th Army.

8-23: State realm formed in Bucharest, Rumania.
8-25: Rumania declares war against German; General de Gaulle enters Paris; German troops begin to evacuate the Greek islands.
8-26/11-2: German troops withdraw from Greece.
9- 1: Soviet troops reach the border of Bulgaria.

9- 3: Brussels is captured by the Allies.
9- 4: Antwerp is lost; Finland agrees to a cease-fire with Russia. Kronstadt and Siebenbürgen are lost.
9- 6: Tito establishes relations with the Russians, who reach the Serbian border. Germany launches the first operational V-2 missile against an enemy target.
9-17: The Allies attempt to capture the bridges at Arnhem and Nijmegen.
9-19: Finland signs a truce with the Soviet Union.

6-15/7-24: "GD" transferred to rest area 100 km. south of Jassy; during this time Oblt. Diddens is awarded the oak leaves to the Knight's Cross. The I./Fus. Rgt. "GD" rejoins the Division equipped with SPW's. The Armored Assault Engineers Battalion is reformed as an Armored Assault Engineer Regiment in "GD". Rgt. 1029 "GD" is broken up to supply replacements for the Division.

7- 7/8-15: Kampfgruppe "von Werthern" (part of the Führer-Escort Regiment), stationed in East Prussia, engages in fighting at Vilna.
7-10: A Führer-Grenadier Brigade ("FGB") is formed from elements of the Pz. Gren. Replacement Brigade "GD", at Cottbus.

7-20: The Guard Battalion "GD", stationed in Berlin under Major Remer, gets into action in the Government Quarter during the attempt on Hitler's life.
7-25/8-2: "GD" is transferred from Rumania to East Prussia in the area near Gumbinnen.

8- 5/9-8: First counterattack by "GD" at Virballen and Vilkovischen (in Latvia).

8-12: Beginning of the march to an area west of Stauliai (Latvia).

8-18: Beginning of defensive battles to prevent Soviet breakthrough to the Baltic Sea.

8-22: "GD" marches to the north and prepares for an attack toward Tukums.

8-25: The attack begins and bogs down outside Doblen, at the Luthuanian-Latvian border.
8-26/10-2: "GD" remains in the positions gained in the attack.
9- 1: Genllt. von Manteuffel is replaced by Oberst Lorenz, formerly Kdr. of Pz. Gren. Rgt. "GD".

10- 1: The Guard Battalion "GD" in Berlin is expanded to a Guard Regiment.
10- 3: Parts of "GD" withdraw into the area west of Stauliai as a Kampfgruppe (Battle Grp.).
10- 5: Major offensive by Soviet army west of Stauliai; more units from "GD" are transferred to this area as reinforcements.
10- 6/10-9: "GD" engaged in very heavy defensive between Stauliai and Memel.
10- 6/10-14: I./Pz. Rgt. "GD" engages in first battles in East Prussia, with the 6th Panzer Division, fighting in Rozan (Narew) area of Poland. Previously, I./Pz. Rgt. "GD" (with Panthers) had fought in France, largely as an independent unit.
10-10/11-28: Defensive and holding battles in the Memel bridgehead.

Southern Front, January, 1944

10-14: Riga, in Latvia, is lost; Field Marshal Erwin Rommel commits suicide.
10-18: All physically-fit men between 16 and 60 are being called for the "Volkssturm" units.
10-19: U.S. forces begin the liberation of the Phillipines, under General MacArthur.
10-21: Aachen is captured by the Allies.

10-28: Bulgaria, after complete occupation of the country by Soviet troops, signs a truce with Russia and participates on Russian side in combat against withdrawing German troops.

11-12: Battleship "Tirpitz" sinks in the Tromsö-Fjord.
11-13: Skoplje (Serbia) is evacuated.

11-23: Strasbourg is lost.

12- 5: Ravenna is lost.
12- 7: Russian troops reach the Platten-Sea (Platten Lake).
12- 9: Budapest is surrounded.

12-16: Beginning of the Ardennes offensive.

12-27: The surrounded Bastogne is relieved by US troops.
12-31: Hungary declares war against Germany.

10-21/10-24: After transferring to East Prussia, "FGD", with replacements from "GD" division, engages the enemy — its first action — between Goldap and Gumbinnen.

11- 1: Beginning of the Panzer Korps "Grossdeutschland" in East Prussia. Besides Pz. Gren. Division "GD", and a few Korps troops, the Pz. Gren. Division "Brandenburg" (BR) was included. Pz. Korps "GD" was destined never to fight as a single unit.
11- 1/11-29: "FGB" engages in more actions in East Prussia.

11-15: I./Pz. Rgt. "GD" (Panthers) rejoins the division. I./Pz. Rgt. 26, which had fought with "GD" for much of the I./Pz. Rgt. "GD" was in France, then transfers to Hungary.

11-26/12-31: "GD" Divsion transfers via boat through Königsberg into the area around Rastenburg-Sensburg, to join Korps Staff "GD", which is being organized there.
11-27: The Führer-Escort Regiment reinforced to an armored brigade (Führer-Escort Brigade — "FBB") transfers from East Prussia into the Eifel, under Oberst Remer.
11-30: "FGB" transfers to Cottbus for rest and refitting.

12-11/12-17: "FGB", under Oberst Kahler, moves to the Western Front.
12-16: "FGB" takes part in the last great German offensive in the Ardennes, operating with the 5th Panzer Army.
12-22: "FGB" assembles in a staging area near Heiderschneid (Eifel) on the left flank of 5th Panzer Army and engages in its first actions against Allied troops.

12-31: After heavy assault combat action, resulting in heavy losses in men and equipment, "FGB" move over to defensive fighting to cover the withdrawl of German troops.

The fighting in the Dnieper bend region is undiminished.

Retreat from the Ukraine, January-April 1944

While Pz. Gren. Div. "GD" fights in the Ukraine, the first elements of the Führer-Escort Brigade arise from the Führer-Escort Btl. They transfer to the endangered Narva-Front in Estonia.

With every year, the Soviet Army has more and more excellent tanks in the field, including the T34/85 and the KV-85 and IS2. The Tiger I heavy tank becomes more important to "GD" to redress the imbalance. Note in this photo that this Tiger I is being moved by rail with the 28" full width combat tracks to save time — this vehicle can be driven directly into action upon arriving at its destination.

Retreat from Kirovograd, February 7 to March 9, 1944

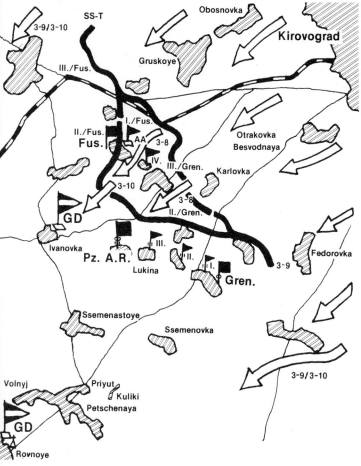

Even the best-designed vehicles could not traverse this sea of slick, sticky mud. Many trucks and tanks bogged down hopelessly in such conditions.

During the battles at Kirovograd, units of "GD" were used to reinforce other divisions. "GD" was thrown into critical situations to hold the line of force a breakthrough on many occasions — so often that the division earned the nickname "The Fire Brigade".

Oberst Lorenz with Oblt. Diddens, in front of a StuG III ausf G.

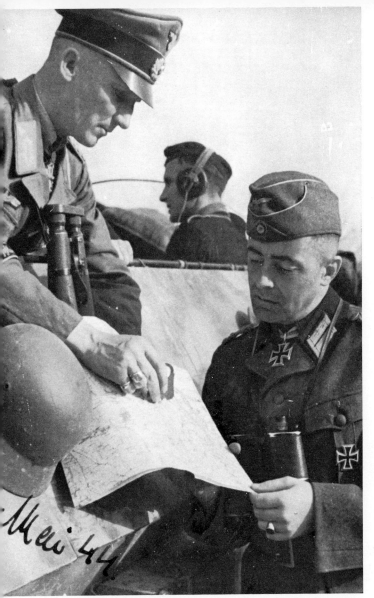

GD Command Pennant
Late Style Commander's Pennant

The end of January, Generalleutnant von Manteuffel takes over the Division - here together with his first Gen. Staff officer, Obstlt. v. Natzmer. [Below] Kdr. Pz. Gren. Rgt. "GD" Oberst Lorenz with Kdr. Pi. [engineer] Btl. "GD" Major Chrapkowski in a VW "Schwimmwagen".

Reinforced Grenadier Regiment (mot.) 1029 GD

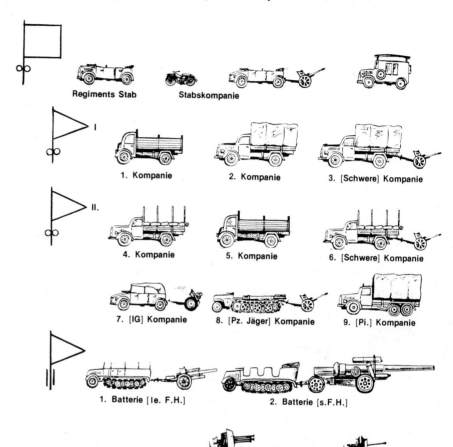

Regiments Stab   Stabskompanie

I
1. Kompanie   2. Kompanie   3. [Schwere] Kompanie

II.
4. Kompanie   5. Kompanie   6. [Schwere] Kompanie

7. [IG] Kompanie   8. [Pz. Jäger] Kompanie   9. [Pi.] Kompanie

1. Batterie [le. F.H.]   2. Batterie [s.F.H.]

3. [Fla] Batterie

It's first combat action comes about at the Carpathian passes. Later it is dissolved and made a part of Pz. Gren. Div. "GD".

Leichte Kolonne

Bivouac in a transportation company, with the men sleeping outside in the spring weather.

The Russian spring turns the dirt streets of this Ukraine village into a muddy bog. As usual, the village checkpoint has signs for traffic control. These signs are for units of "GD" and the 14th Panzer Division.

While "GD" moves over the Bug and Dniester Rivers to the west, Rgt. 1029 [mot.] "GD" — formed from the "GD" replacement battalion — moves to east. Here, elements of "GD" cross the Dniester River.

Battle for Targul Frumos, April 10 to May 5, 1944

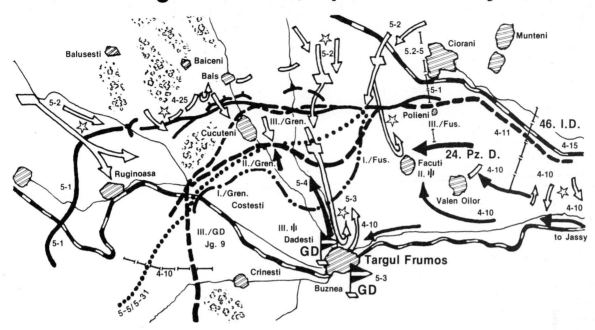

Names like Jassy, Targul Frumos, and Podul remain bitter memories because of the fierce fighting that took place there. Here, "GD" troops examine the remains of a destroyed T34/76 tank.

Vast empty plains stretched in front of the advancing "GD" units — a tremendous area that eventually proved too vast to defend.

[Opposite] A Rumanian farmer in front of his house.

[Below] The Rumanians were also engaged in this area, and were a familiar sight to the German troops here.

[Above] General von Manteuffel, Hptm. Dr. Ritter [Pz. Art. Rgt.] and Oblt. Diddens [Sturmgeschutz Abteilung], at Targul Frumos.

[Right] Panzergrenadiers ride into action on a Pz Kpfw. IV tank. Note the low combat shoes with ankle cuffs, now a standard uniform item.

[Below] A self-propelled howitzer — so heavily camouflaged that the chassis can't be identified — waits to fire on an enemy target.

[Above] During this period, the new Russian IS-2 heavy tank appears. Though very well armored, it still can be destroyed by skillful use of tanks, anti-tank guns, and aircraft.

[Below] The Luftwaffe was very active on the Eastern front, and destroyed large numbers of Soviet tanks, vehicles and strong points. Here, a Ju-87 D or G flies across a valley, past a German machine gun team.

[Above] Strong artillery fire forces the commanders [Div. Kdr. and Major Krieg, right] into ground shelters.

[Above right] In front of a T34/76, Major Chrapkowski, Kdr. of the Pz. Pioneer [Engineer] Btl., awards the tank destruction badge to one of his men.

[Right] The MG 42 was a bulkier weapon than many people realize. This model has a stamped metal buttstock; others had plastic or wood stocks.

Oberst Lorenz's command halftrack, a SdKfz 251/6.

Oblt. Dr. Boldt, the adjutant of Pz. Fus. Rgt. "GD", makes notations on a map as he receives information from a field telephone.

Casualties —

After fighting at the front, "GD" moves to a rest area 100Km south of Jassy. Here it receives reinforcements as well as weapons — especially Panthers and SPW's.

[Above] The Rgt. Kdr. of the Pz. Rgt. "GD" Oberst Langkeit in front of his tank, a Panther ausf A.

[Below] An engineer's vehicle - SdKfz 251/7 ausf D.

As usual during rest periods, the men were eager to relax, and making pets of local animals was a common practive. [Left] Oberst Niemack [Pz. Fus. Rgt. "GD"] and members of his staff.

The table of organization of Pz. Gren. Div. "GD — on the following pages — is of interest even today. It represents the ideal structure of a Panzer Division, developed after much combat experience. "GD" received more equipment than most other German Panzer Divisions — only Waffen-SS Panzer Divisions were able to obtain more or better equipment. Even so this ideal TO&E was never completely filled out, and units in the "GD" division were often separated from the main body.

As if combat action wasn't dangerous enough . . . . . !

Panzer Grenadier - Division Grossdeutschland, July, 1944

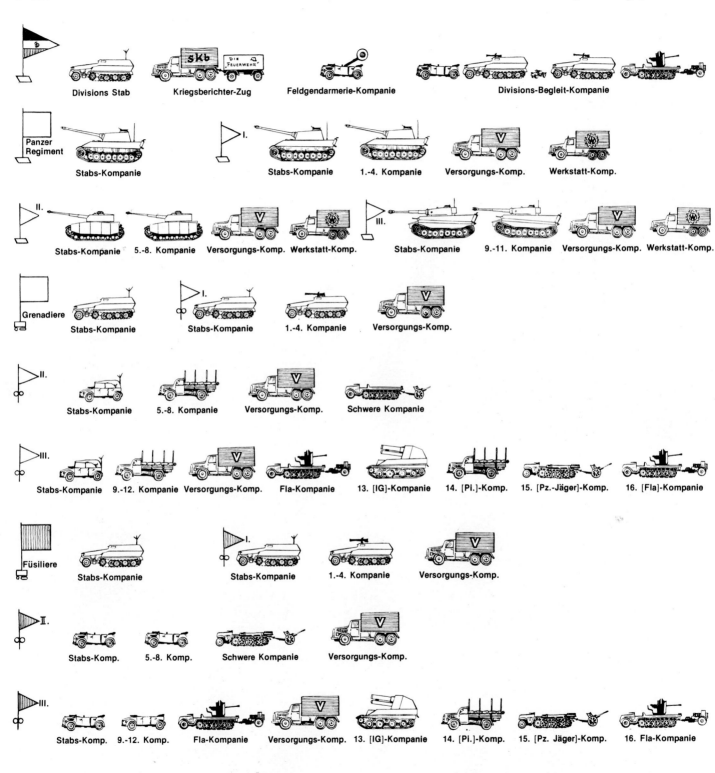

Divisions Stab   Kriegsberichter-Zug   Feldgendarmerie-Kompanie   Divisions-Begleit-Kompanie

Panzer Regiment   Stabs-Kompanie   Stabs-Kompanie   1.-4. Kompanie   Versorgungs-Komp.   Werkstatt-Komp.

Stabs-Kompanie   5.-8. Kompanie   Versorgungs-Komp.   Werkstatt-Komp.   Stabs-Kompanie   9.-11. Kompanie   Versorgungs-Komp.   Werkstatt-Komp.

Grenadiere   Stabs-Kompanie   Stabs-Kompanie   1.-4. Kompanie   Versorgungs-Komp.

Stabs-Kompanie   5.-8. Kompanie   Versorgungs-Komp.   Schwere Kompanie

Stabs-Kompanie   9.-12. Kompanie   Versorgungs-Komp.   Fla-Kompanie   13. [IG]-Kompanie   14. [Pi.]-Komp.   15. [Pz.-Jäger]-Komp.   16. [Fla]-Kompanie

Füsiliere   Stabs-Kompanie   Stabs-Kompanie   1.-4. Kompanie   Versorgungs-Komp.

Stabs-Komp.   5.-8. Komp.   Schwere Kompanie   Versorgungs-Komp.

Stabs-Komp.   9.-12. Komp.   Fla-Kompanie   Versorgungs-Komp.   13. [IG]-Kompanie   14. [Pi.]-Komp.   15. [Pz. Jäger]-Komp.   16. Fla-Kompanie

Panzer Aufklär. Abteilung   Stabs-Schwadron   Versorgungs-Schwadron   1. [Pz. SP.]-Schwadron [Pz. 38t Hetzer]   2. [SPW]-Schwadron   3. [SPW]-Schwadron   4. [Schwere] Schwadron

Heeres Flak Abteilung

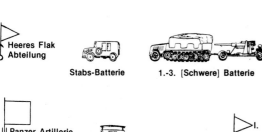

Stabs-Batterie   1.-3. [Schwere] Batterie

4. [m.] Fla-Batterie

5. [m.] Fla-Batterie

6. [le.] Batterie

Panzer Artillerie Regiment

Stabs-Batterie   Beobacht. Bttr.   Stabs-Batterie   1. [SF.] Batterie [Wespe]   2. [SF.] Batterie [Wespe]   3. [SF.] Batterie [Hummel]

II.

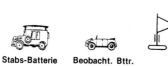

Stabs-Batterie   4. Batterie   5. Batterie   6. Batterie

III.

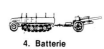
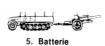

Stabs-Batterie   7. Batterie   8. Batterie   9. Batterie [10 cm Kanone]

IV.

Stabs-Batterie   10. Batterie   11. Batterie   12. Batterie

Sturmgeschütz Brigade

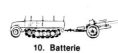

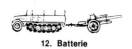

Stabs-Batterie   Versorgungs-Batterie   1. Batterie   2. Batterie   3. Batterie

Panzer Pionier Bataillon

Stabs-Kompanie   1. Kompanie   2. Kompanie   3. Kompanie   4. Kompanie   Brückenkolonne -K-   Leichte Pionier Kolonne

Panzer Nachrichten Abteilung

Fernsprech-Komp.   Funk-Kompanie   Versorgungs-Komp.

Divisions Nachschub Truppe

1.-6. Kolonne   Leichte Kolonne   Geräte-Kolonne

Kraftfahr Park Truppe

1.-3. Werkstatt-Komp.   Erastzteil-Komp.   Waffenmeisterei

Verwaltungs-Truppe

Divisions-Verpfleg. Amt   Fleischerei-KP.   Bäckerei-KP.

Feld Ersatz Bataillon

1.-6. Kompanie   Feldpost

Sanitäts-Truppe

Feldlazarett   1. San KP.   2. San. KP.   I. II. III. Kranken-Kraftwagen-Zug

The counterattack against the Russians in East Prussia begins.

[Above] Panthers roll through the flat fields near Gumbinnen toward Wolfsburg. [Below] Panzergrenadiers in SdKfz 251's — supported by a few motorcycle troops — move up with the tanks as the attacking forces make initial gains.

The end of July and beginning of August, the Division loads up and transfers to East Prussia, in order to throw itself against the Russians who are already on German ground.

[Above and Below] Panther ausf A's are loaded on railroad flat cars for the journey to the front lines.

The counter attack begins on 8-5-1944 in the area of Gumbinnen.

[Top] Last consultation. [Front Row Left] Oberst Niemack, [Middle] Generalleutnant von Manteuffel, [Right] Oberst Langkeit. Note that most of these officers wear the Knight's Cross, the highest German military decoration.

[Bottom] [Left] Oblt. Zügel; in the SdKfz 251/6, Major v. Basse [Kdr. I./Fus. Rgt.] "GD".

Attack on Wilkowischken, August 9 to August 10, 1944

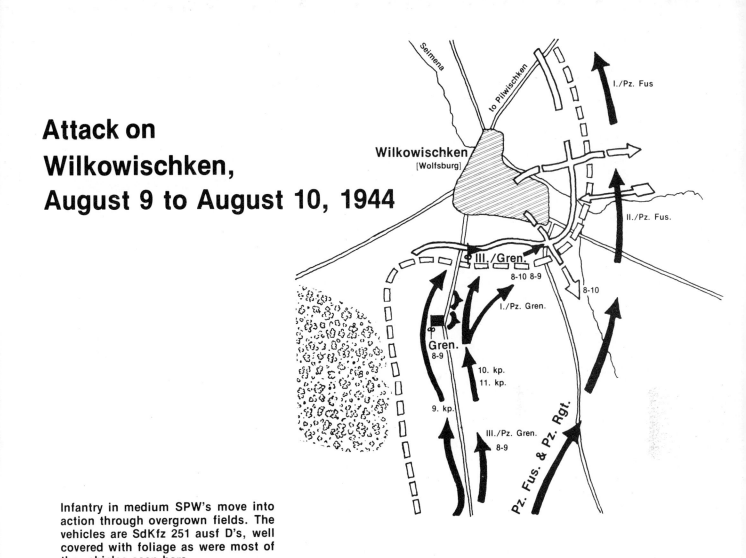

Seimena

to Pilwischken

I./Pz. Fus

Wilkowischken
[Wolfsburg]

II./Pz. Fus.

III./Gren.
8-10 8-9

8-10

I./Pz. Gren.

Gren.
8-9

10. kp.
11. kp.

9. kp.

III./Pz. Gren.
8-9

Pz. Fus. & Pz. Rgt.

Infantry in medium SPW's move into action through overgrown fields. The vehicles are SdKfz 251 ausf D's, well covered with foliage as were most of the vehicles seen here.

German troops entering Wilkowischken pass several Soviet 76.2 mm anti-tank guns abandoned by the road.

This view of the forward MG42 mount is interesting for the pinup photo and picture of a cat. Such vehicle decorations [on gun shields, etc.] were not uncommon.

In every battle, all branches are equally important and contribute to the success of the assault.

[Right] A closeup of the SPW on p. 139; [Below] A 10.5 cm FK, L/52 is prepared for firing; [Below Right] Infantry consolidate gains won in the assault.

[Above] This crew of a towed 7.5 cm PAK 40 returns small arms fire from their exposed location, the Karsenai railroad bridge.

[Below] A Pz. Rgt. 26 Panther ausf A advances past burning houses. As was common, extra spare track has been fitted to the sides of the hull and turret. "GD's" Panther Abteilung was in France at this time.

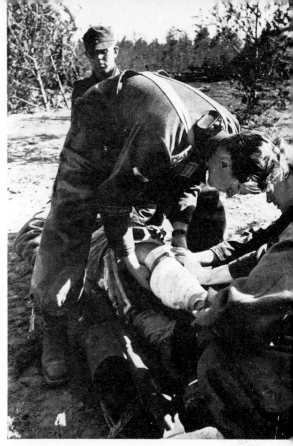

Casualties were treated quickly, and evacuated as soon as possible to protect them from further injury.

At the end of August, the Germans attack north toward Tukums and Mitau to keep open a relief corridor to the Germans fighting in the Kurland area. The attack stops in front of Doblen. At this time, Oberst [Col.] Lorenz [Front, Above] becomes "GD" division commander. [Below] Two SPW's support the advance. At the right is a late type SdKfz 251/9 ausf D "Stummel" ["Stump"], widely used for infantry fire support.

Troops in the defensive positions around Doblen.

[Above] More hand grenades are kept ready below the top wall of the trench.

[Left] These troops — relaxing here during a lull — have Panzerfaust anti-tank weapons ready for use.

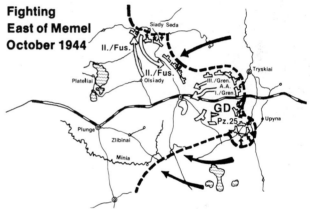

A Panther ausf G stopped during the battle.

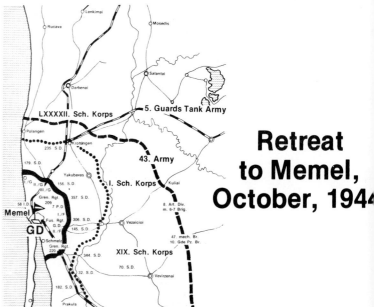

Retreat to Memel, October, 1944

In October, 1944, a massive Russian offensive forced the withdrawal of "GD" from Stauliai (Schaulen) to Memel on the coast, where a strong defensive perimeter halts the Russian advance.

"GD" is ordered to defend the perimeter at Memel for more than a month in order to cover the evacuation of German troops from the port. The evacuation begins on 11-26-1944, and after embarking by ship, "GD" is expanded to a full Panzer Korps, with Pz. Gren. Div. "Brandenburg" as a part of the whole unit. At the same time, the units are refitted and rested.

Situation, October 9, 1944

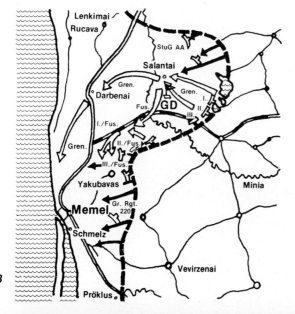

The "FBB" and "FGB" units — fully re-equipped — go into action on the Eastern and Western fronts. Both units were rebuilt from the "GD" replacement battalions, plus wounded "GD" troops being returned to service after recovery. [Right] An older SPW, a SdKfz 251 ausf C field-modified to mount a 2 cm Flak 38, provides mobile protection for the unit. This vehicle gave more protection to the crew than the SdKfz 10/5 halftracks, but movement of the gun mount was limited.

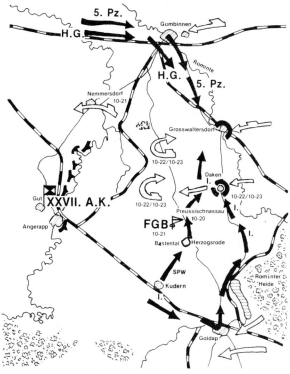

Attack of "FGB" on Daken-Grosswaltersdorf, October 21 to October 23, 1944

The following tables of organization for the Führer-Grenadier Brigade (FGB) and Führer-Begleit (Escort) Brigade (FBB) show the planned levels of troop and equipment for a brigade formation. These two units were refitted as well as possible considering shortages of the late war period, and now were well-balanced independent units with sufficient equipment to operate without extra support services.

Panzerjäger: a Marder II S. P. Pak 40, in a scruffy coat of snow camouflage paint.

Führer-Grenadier-Brigade (FGB), December, 1944

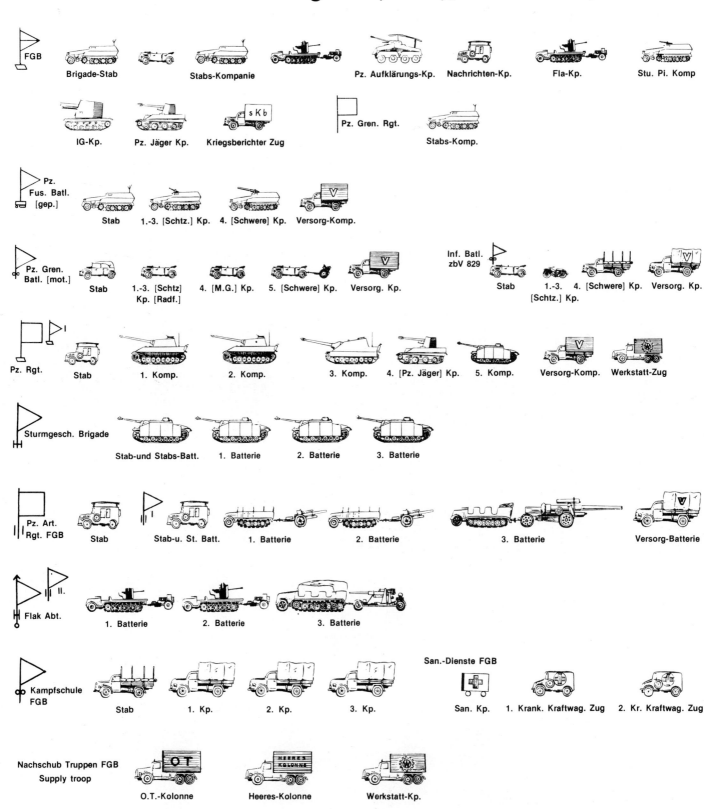

FGB
Brigade-Stab
Stabs-Kompanie
Pz. Aufklärungs-Kp.
Nachrichten-Kp.
Fla-Kp.
Stu. Pi. Komp.

IG-Kp.
Pz. Jäger Kp.
Kriegsberichter Zug
Pz. Gren. Rgt.
Stabs-Komp.

Pz. Fus. Batl. [gep.]
Stab
1.-3. [Schtz.] Kp.
4. [Schwere] Kp.
Versorg-Komp.

Pz. Gren. Batl. [mot.]
Stab
1.-3. [Schtz] Kp. [Radf.]
4. [M.G.] Kp.
5. [Schwere] Kp.
Versorg. Kp.

Inf. Batl. zbV 829
Stab
1.-3. [Schtz.] Kp.
4. [Schwere] Kp.
Versorg. Kp.

Pz. Rgt.
Stab
1. Komp.
2. Komp.
3. Komp.
4. [Pz. Jäger] Kp.
5. Komp.
Versorg-Komp.
Werkstatt-Zug

Sturmgesch. Brigade
Stab-und Stabs-Batt.
1. Batterie
2. Batterie
3. Batterie

Pz. Art. Rgt. FGB
Stab
Stab-u. St. Batt.
1. Batterie
2. Batterie
3. Batterie
Versorg-Batterie

Flak Abt.
1. Batterie
2. Batterie
3. Batterie

Kampfschule FGB
Stab
1. Kp.
2. Kp.
3. Kp.

San.-Dienste FGB
San. Kp.
1. Krank. Kraftwag. Zug
2. Kr. Kraftwag. Zug

Nachschub Truppen FGB
Supply troop
O.T.-Kolonne
Heeres-Kolonne
Werkstatt-Kp.

Führer-Begleit Brigade [FBB], December, 1944

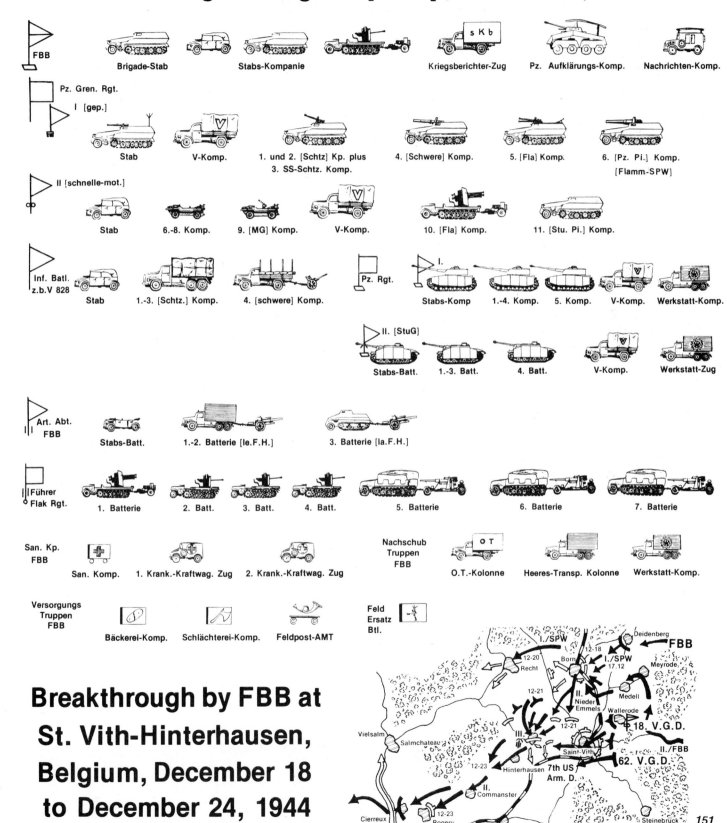

FBB

Brigade-Stab   Stabs-Kompanie   Kriegsberichter-Zug   Pz. Aufklärungs-Komp.   Nachrichten-Komp.

Pz. Gren. Rgt.

I [gep.]

Stab   V-Komp.   1. und 2. [Schtz] Kp. plus 3. SS-Schtz. Komp.   4. [Schwere] Komp.   5. [Fla] Komp.   6. [Pz. Pi.] Komp. [Flamm-SPW]

II [schnelle-mot.]

Stab   6.-8. Komp.   9. [MG] Komp.   V-Komp.   10. [Fla] Komp.   11. [Stu. Pi.] Komp.

Inf. Batl. z.b.V 828

Stab   1.-3. [Schtz.] Komp.   4. [schwere] Komp.   Pz. Rgt.   I.   Stabs-Komp   1.-4. Komp.   5. Komp.   V-Komp.   Werkstatt-Komp.

II. [StuG]

Stabs-Batt.   1.-3. Batt.   4. Batt.   V-Komp.   Werkstatt-Zug

Art. Abt. FBB

Stabs-Batt.   1.-2. Batterie [le.F.H.]   3. Batterie [la.F.H.]

Führer Flak Rgt.

1. Batterie   2. Batt.   3. Batt.   4. Batt.   5. Batterie   6. Batterie   7. Batterie

San. Kp. FBB

San. Komp.   1. Krank.-Kraftwag. Zug   2. Krank.-Kraftwag. Zug

Nachschub Truppen FBB

O.T.-Kolonne   Heeres-Transp. Kolonne   Werkstatt-Komp.

Versorgungs Truppen FBB

Bäckerei-Komp.   Schlächterei-Komp.   Feldpost-AMT

Feld Ersatz Btl.

Breakthrough by FBB at St. Vith-Hinterhausen, Belgium, December 18 to December 24, 1944

151

1944 was again a difficult year for Grossdeutschland. Excessive demands were made, and the division was able to meet these only at the cost of very heavy losses in men and material. The end of the war — once unthinkable — was now clearly in sight. Vast areas had been lost in the East and West, and German forces were being driven back to the borders of Germany. The shortages in men and equipment forced "GD" to reduce its strength and equipment establishment, and this increased casualties later. Many new units were formed, with brave patriotic names, but too often with too little equipment and training, and insufficient replacements to make up losses. To make matters worse, the infantry divisions, not motorized and usually without armor support, could not hold their positions against enemy forces increasingly well-equipped. Only the best-equipped divisions with armor components could hold the lines, and yet this capability resulted in the elite units being thrown into the worst fighting, until they were no longer capable of fighting. Many units, pushed again and again into savage defensive battles with no rest and few replacements, simply ceased to exist; the few survivors scattered to other divisions as replacements.

The Training and Reinforcement Brigade of "GD" was also brought to the end of its string. Constant replacement of "GD's" great losses, plus the establishment — and later expansion to division strength — of Führer-Begleit (Escort) Brigade (FBB) and Führer-Grenadier Brigade (FGB) had overtaxed the ability of the Replacement Brigade, along with the expansion of the "GD" Guard Battalion (at Rastenburg) to a full Regiment. As a result of the virtual collapse of "GD's" replacement organization, the Replacement and Training Regiments of the "Brandenburg" Division were placed under "GD's" control.

At year's end, the Korps staff was still being organized in East Prussia and the "GD" Division was refitting and resting near Rastenburg. "Brandenburg" was traveling by train from Hungary to East Prussia.

This Tiger I. seen in East Prussia is a late production version with steel-rimmed roadwheel and cast cupola. Again camouflage netting and foliage are necessary because of enemy air superiority.

Breakthrough at the Vistula, January 13 to January 15, 1945

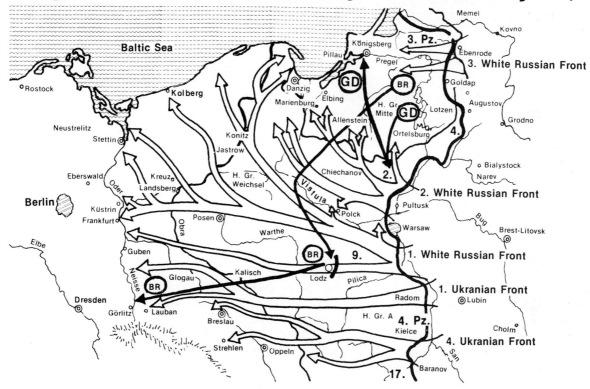

Positions of Grossdeutschland Units, February 20, 1945

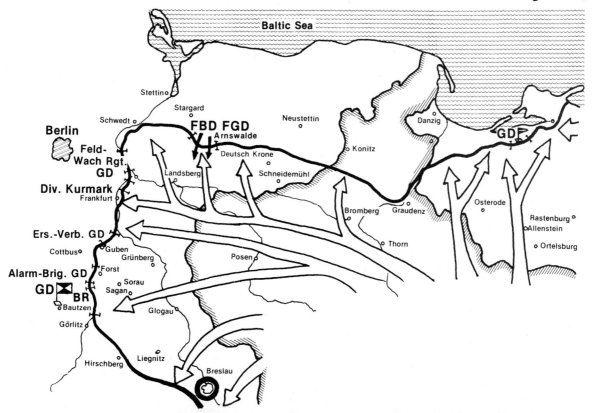

1945

At the start of this last year of the war, the Korps staff "GD" under General of Panzer Troops von Saucken and the Korps troops of "GD" Division itself, are all in East Prussia, Pz. Gren. Div. "Brandenburg" under Gen. Maj. Schulte-Heuthaus is on the way to East Prussia, and the two "Führer" brigades are fighting on the Western front.

"FBB" and "FGB" are also expanded to Panzer Divisions — more on paper than in fact — during the hurried, often extemporized reorganizations in early 1945. There is no time for adequate training or developing esprit-de-corps as a unit.

The war burns with increasing intensity as the strengthened Allied powers press in on a weakened Germany, each day coming closer to the German homeland. Allied aircraft range the length and breadth of Europe — many sport exposed metal surfaces, for camouflage is no longer necessary. Panzer Korps "GD" and its related units are shifted from battle to battle. "Brandenburg" is separated from the rest of "GD" and never returns. Even the most dedicated units cannot hold against overwhelming enemy forces and the lack of Luftwaffe air support is another critical factor in the defeats to come. Lack of replacements and equipment, and the capitulation of many of their "Allies" leaves the Germans to fight alone. Past reputations don't count in the spring of 1945, and once-proud units — Army and SS alike — are reduced to quickly reformed, poorly equipped "gap-plugging" formations, often existing officially only on paper. Survivors of one action regroup to form the next "unit" for the next desperate defensive action. Scattered groups of replacements augment the veterans but with no time for proper unit training, these groups are destroyed and in the end, they cannot even delay the inevitable end of the war in Europe. In early May, 1945, it is finished; the "1,000 year Reich" dies after 12 years and a united Germany dies with it.

1945 — World History

1-12: Soviet major offensive out of the bridgehead at Baranov (Vistula) breaks the German middle front to pieces and frees the way for Russian troops to enter East Prussia and Schlesien.

1-19: Tilsit is lost.

1-20: Allenstein (East Prussia) is lost.

1-27: Memel is lost.

2- 4/2-11: Yalta Conference (dividing of Germany after the war is agreed by the Allies).

1945 — Division Grossdeutschland

1- 1/1-11: "GD" Division and Korps staff "GD" — involved in the formation of Pz. Korps "GD" — are transferred into the Willenburg area (south of the East Prussian border) as OKH reserves.

1-12: "GD" units move south to keep open the Orzyc River bridgehead.

1-13: Pz. Gren. Div. "Brandenburg" (BR) is ordered to transfer to Litzmannstadt (Lodz).

1-14: Korps staff "GD" follows "BR" and assumes control of command over "BR" and the Luftwaffe Parachute-Panzer Div. "Hermann Goering" at Lodz.

1-15/1-30: "GD's" defensive battles in North Poland lead to a retreat into East Prussia and then to the area south of Königsberg. Eventually, "GD" is under the control of Parachute-Pz. Korps. "Hermann Goering" along with Parachute Pz. Gren. Div. "HG2".

1-17/2-20: "BR" fights in the chaos of retreat out of the Lodz-Piotrkov area in Poland to the Neisse River north of Goerlitz.

1-20: Organization of an Army Tank Destroyer Force "GD" by the Pz. Gren. replacement brigade "GD" in Cottbus; the unit goes into action on the Oder River at Steinau.

1-23: "FBB" is relieved from the lines and transferred to a rest area south of Arzfeld (south of Preum/Eifel).

1-25: "FGB" is also transferred to a rest center around Neuerburg (west of Bitburg/Eifel) after heavy defensive fighting.

1-26: Pz. Gren. Div. Kurmark ("KMK") is formed from various kampfgruppe (battle groups) and extemporized units of the "GD" replacement brigade. The commander is Oberst Langkeit, formerly Ia Major of i.G.v. Hopffgarten. "KMK" receives a divisional marking of a white "GD" helmet with the Kurmark eagle superimposed.

1-30: OKH (Army High Command) orders "FBB" and "FGB" expanded to full Panzer Divisions ("FBD" and "FGD"). Their commanders (Oberst Mäder - "FBD", and Oberst Remer - "FGD") are promoted to Generalmajor.

1-31: "GD" engages in heavy defensive battles in East Prussia.

2- 2: "FGD" transfers to the Koblenz area to complete refitting as a Panzer Division.

2- 5: The guard regiment "GD" forms a field guard regiment "GD" and sees action north of Küstrin.

2- 6/2-10: "FGD" is transferred to a staging area northeast of Stargard/Pommern; "FBD" is transferred into another area, around Freienwalde/Pommern.

1945 — World History

2-13: Budapest is in Russian hands.
2-13/2-14: Air assault on Dresden results in the city's destruction.
2-15: Breslau is surrounded.

3- 2: Trier is lost.
3- 3: Finland declares war against Germany.
3- 5: Köln is lost.
3- 7: US Forces take the Remagen railroad bridge across the Rhine River.

3-18: Kolberg is in Russian hands.

3-22: Mainz occupied by US Armed Forces.

3-24: The British cross the Rhine at Wesel in a major attack.

3-30: Danzig is lost.
4- 1: US Forces land on Okinawa.

4- 5: Major attack by the Allies brings the Appennine front to collapse.
4- 9: Königsberg is lost.

4-13: Vienna is lost.

4-18: In the Ruhr valley, the last German troops surrender.

4-20: Nürnberg is occupied.
4-25: US Forces meet with Soviet troops at Torgau on the Elbe River. Founding of the "United Nations" (UNO) in San Francisco.

4-28: Truce signed on the Italian Front. Mussolini is shot to death by partisans.
4-30: Adolf Hitler commits suicide in his Berlin bunker. Munich occupied by US Forces.
5- 1: Grossadmiral Dönitz takes over succession of Hitler.
5- 2: Berlin capitulates to invading Soviet forces.
5- 3: Salzburg occupied (US Forces).
5- 4: Capitulation (in Lüneburg) of the German Forces to the British Army in northern Germany and Holland.
5- 7: German capitulation (in Reims) to the Allies.
5- 9: German capitulation (in Karlshorst) to the Soviet Armies. Official Truce on all fronts. The war in Europe is over.

1945 — Division Grossdeutschland

2-12/2-20: Both Divisions attack from Stargard to the south. Since both units are still more Brigades than Divisions — despite their titles — they do not capture much territory, but their efforts do stabilize the front in this area.
2-12/3-10: An "Emergency" Brigade "GD" forms at Cottbus from the "GD" replacement brigade. It goes into action at Forst on the Oder River, and is later taken over by "Brandenburg" Division (3-10).

2-16/3-15: The "GD" replacement units stationed in Guben near Goerlitz engage in battles in this area.
2-21/4-15: Defensive battles fought by "Brandenburg" on the Neisse River between Muskau and Steinbach.
2-25: The "GD" replacement units not involved in combat transfer to Schleswig-Holstein and Denmark.

3-10: "FGD" and "FBD" are again relieved and transferred, "FGD" to Angermuende, and "FBD" to Langenoels.
3-15: "FGD" rejoins combat near Stettin on the Oder River.

3-17: "FGD" is transferred into an area west of Küstrin in order to relieve the encircled city. "FGD" attacks, but fails to breach the Soviet positions.

3-23: From the "GD" replacement forces in Schleswig-Holstein and Denmark, a new combat unit (Pz. Gren. Combat Force "GD") is formed, and transferred west to Bremen.
3-24/4-4: "FBD" goes into combat at Troppau and Ratibor in Oberschlesien.
3-28: Pz. Gren. Div. "Kurmark" is taken out of the lines at Frankfurt/Oder, and transferred to a rest area behind front lines.
3-29/4-12: Last remnants of "GD" division — barely 4,000 men — leave the city of Balga on the Fritsches Bay by the Baltic. The unit travels on ferries, lands at Pillau, and goes into combat in the Samland.
4- 1: "FGD" is transferred to Vienna, Austria.

4- 3/4-19: The Pz. Gren. Combat Force "GD", east of Bremen, enters combat at Lingen on the Ems River, later at Cloppenburg, and is finally absorbed by the 15th Pz. Gren. Division.
4- 5: "FBD" is also transferred to Vienna.

4-12/4-28: "Kurmark" engages in very heavy defensive combat between the Oder and Halbe.
4-13/4-25: The last remnants of "GD" are largely destroyed or dispersed in very heavy retreating battles at Pillau.
4-16/4-22: "FBD" is destroyed in battles east of, and in, the area of Spremberg. The last remnants are able to make it back to Pz. Korps "GD".
4-16/4-30: Heavy defensive fighting and retreat by "BR" and Pz. Korps "GD" between the Neisse River and Dresden.
4-19/5-2: The Guard Regiment "GD" is destroyed in the Battle of Berlin.
4-26/5-4: The last survivors of "GD" are able to cross the Hela peninsula and from there go through Bornholm to Schleswig-Holstein.

5- 1: "Brandenburg" is transferred to Olmütz.

5- 3/5-9: "BR" fights its way out of the Olmütz area to Deutschbrod. There, the division is disbanded, and individual soldiers attempt to make it through the lines back home — to captivity in U.S. or Soviet camps.

5-13: The majority of members of "FGD" — who had surrendered to the Americans — are turned over to Soviet forces in accordance with the Allied agreement to repatriate German prisoners to the forces against which they had fought.

[Above] German infantry advance across a snow-covered field in southern East Prussia.

[Below] Many German units used captured enemy vehicles — here is a T34/76 model 43. Sometimes, this was dangerous, as many gunners fired on a silhouette instead of markings.

Panzer Grenadier Division "Brandenburg", January, 1945

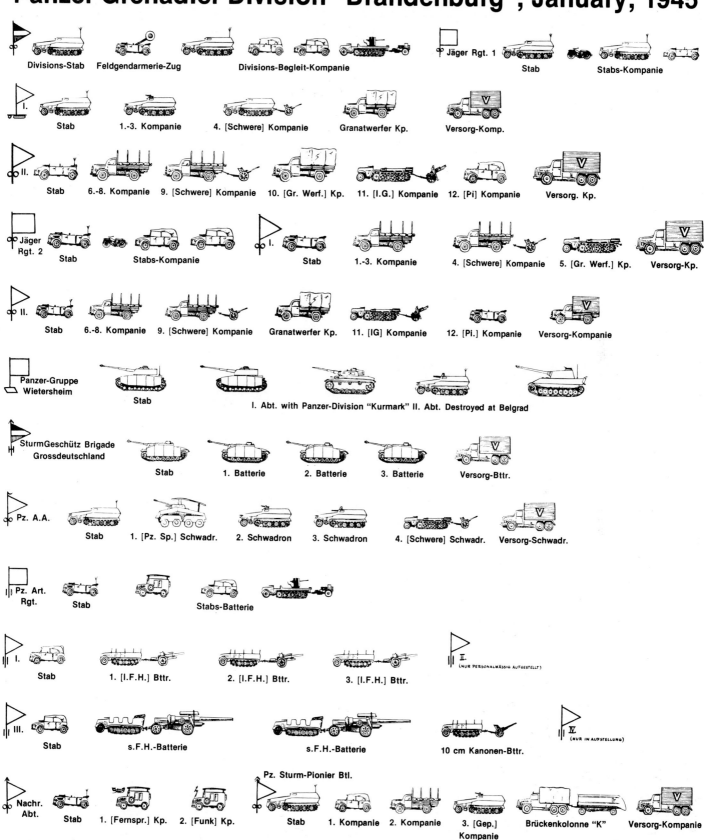

Divisions-Stab   **Feldgendarmerie-Zug**   **Divisions-Begleit-Kompanie**   **Jäger Rgt. 1**   **Stab**   **Stabs-Kompanie**

Stab   **1.-3. Kompanie**   **4. [Schwere] Kompanie**   **Granatwerfer Kp.**   **Versorg-Komp.**

Stab   **6.-8. Kompanie**   **9. [Schwere] Kompanie**   **10. [Gr. Werf.] Kp.**   **11. [I.G.] Kompanie**   **12. [Pi] Kompanie**   **Versorg. Kp.**

Jäger Rgt. 2   **Stab**   **Stabs-Kompanie**   **Stab**   **1.-3. Kompanie**   **4. [Schwere] Kompanie**   **5. [Gr. Werf.] Kp.**   **Versorg-Kp.**

Stab   **6.-8. Kompanie**   **9. [Schwere] Kompanie**   **Granatwerfer Kp.**   **11. [IG] Kompanie**   **12. [Pi.] Kompanie**   **Versorg-Kompanie**

Panzer-Gruppe Wietersheim   **Stab**

I. Abt. with Panzer-Division "Kurmark"   **II. Abt. Destroyed at Belgrad**

SturmGeschütz Brigade Grossdeutschland   **Stab**   **1. Batterie**   **2. Batterie**   **3. Batterie**   **Versorg-Bttr.**

Pz. A.A.   **Stab**   **1. [Pz. Sp.] Schwadr.**   **2. Schwadron**   **3. Schwadron**   **4. [Schwere] Schwadr.**   **Versorg-Schwadr.**

Pz. Art. Rgt.   **Stab**   **Stabs-Batterie**

I.   **Stab**   **1. [I.F.H.] Bttr.**   **2. [I.F.H.] Bttr.**   **3. [I.F.H.] Bttr.**   **II.** (NUR PERSONALMÄSSIG AUFGESTELLT)

III.   **Stab**   **s.F.H.-Batterie**   **s.F.H.-Batterie**   **10 cm Kanonen-Bttr.**   **IV.** (NUR IN AUFSTELLUNG)

Nachr. Abt.   **Stab**   **1. [Fernspr.] Kp.**   **2. [Funk] Kp.**   **Pz. Sturm-Pionier Btl.**   **Stab**   **1. Kompanie**   **2. Kompanie**   **3. [Gep.] Kompanie**   **Brückenkolonne "K"**   **Versorg-Kompanie**

 Heeres Flak Abt.
 Stab

 1. [Schwere] Batt.
2. [Schwere] Batt.
 3. Batterie
 Versorg-Batt.

 Pz. Jäger Abt.
 Stab
 1. Kompanie
 2. Kompanie
3. [mot. Zug] Kp.
 Versorg-Kp.

Verwalt-Dienste
 Divis. Verpfleg-Amt.
 Fleischerei
 Bäckerei
 Nachschub Dienste
 Kolonnen

 Feldpost-Amt
 Werkstatt-Kompanie

Sanitäts-Dienste

Fahr.-Abt.
 Stab
 1. Fahr-Schwadron
 2. Fahr-Schwadron
 3. Fahr-Schwadron
  Feldlazarett
 1. [San.] Kp.   2. [San.] Kp.
  I. Krank-KW.-Zug II. Krank-KW.-Zug
 Felderstz-Bataillon

Commanding General of Pz. Korps "GD" General der Pz.Tr. Von Sauken.

Commanding General of Pz.Gren. Div. "Brandenburg", Generalmajor Schulte-Heuthaus.

Combat in East Prussia by "GD", January 15 to January 23, 1945

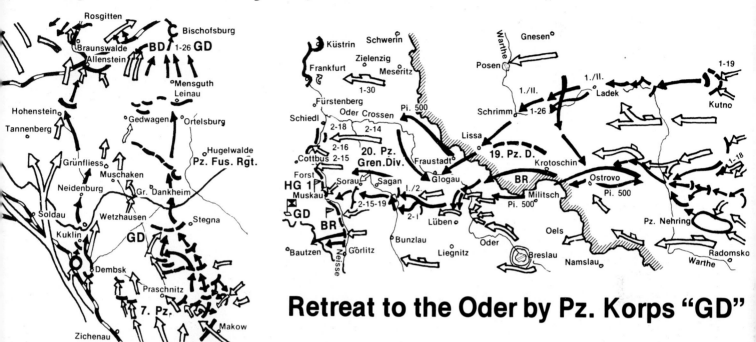

Retreat to the Oder by Pz. Korps "GD"

Pz. Korps "GD" Action, West of the Neisse, April, 1945

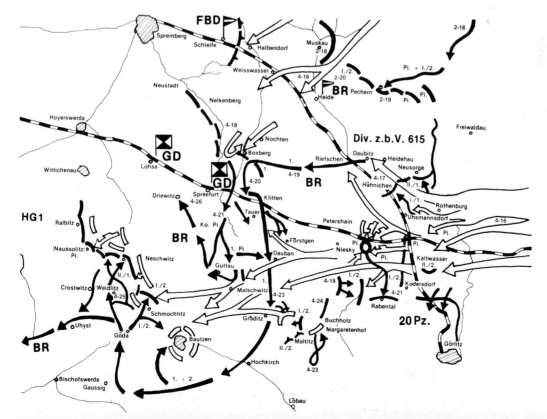

Photos from the last, difficult days.

Retreat of "GD" to Königsberg, January-February, 1945

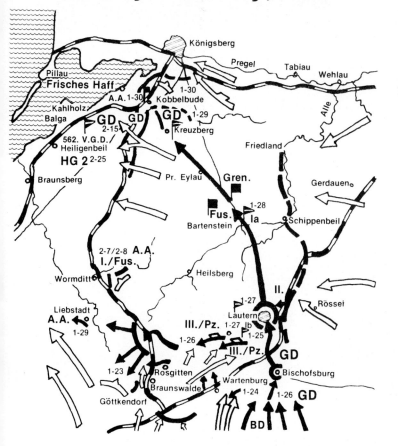

Positions South of
ebruary 6 to February 7, 1945

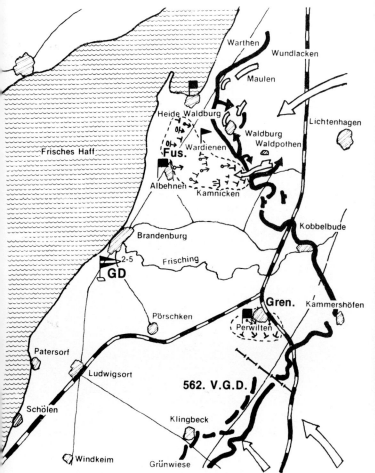

The savage retreating battles go on day after day, without rest or refitting.

162

Panzer-Grenadier Division "Kurmark" February, 1945

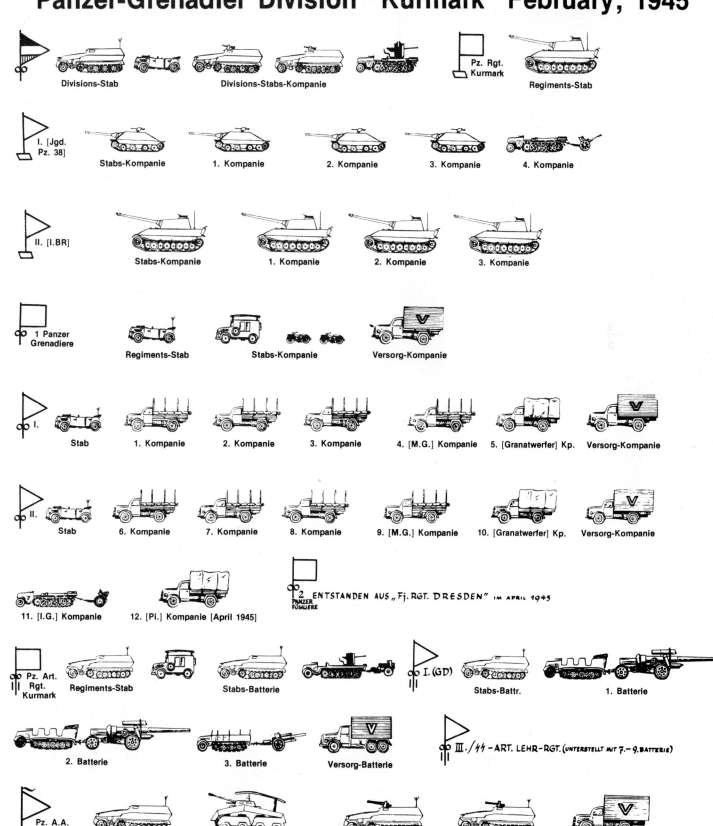

Divisions-Stab

Divisions-Stabs-Kompanie

Pz. Rgt. Kurmark

Regiments-Stab

I. [Jgd. Pz. 38]

Stabs-Kompanie 1. Kompanie 2. Kompanie 3. Kompanie 4. Kompanie

II. [I.BR]

Stabs-Kompanie 1. Kompanie 2. Kompanie 3. Kompanie

1 Panzer Grenadiere

Regiments-Stab Stabs-Kompanie Versorg-Kompanie

I.

Stab 1. Kompanie 2. Kompanie 3. Kompanie 4. [M.G.] Kompanie 5. [Granatwerfer] Kp. Versorg-Kompanie

II.

Stab 6. Kompanie 7. Kompanie 8. Kompanie 9. [M.G.] Kompanie 10. [Granatwerfer] Kp. Versorg-Kompanie

11. [I.G.] Kompanie 12. [Pi.] Kompanie [April 1945]

2 PANZER FÜSILIERE ENTSTANDEN AUS „Fj. RGT. DRESDEN" IM APRIL 1945

Pz. Art. Rgt. Kurmark

Regiments-Stab Stabs-Batterie I. (GD) Stabs-Battr. 1. Batterie

2. Batterie 3. Batterie Versorg-Batterie

III. /ϟϟ – ART. LEHR-RGT. (UNTERSTELLT MIT 7.– 9. BATTERIE)

Pz. A.A. Kurmark

Stab 1. Schwadron 2. Schwadron 3. Schwadron Versorg-Schwadr.

163

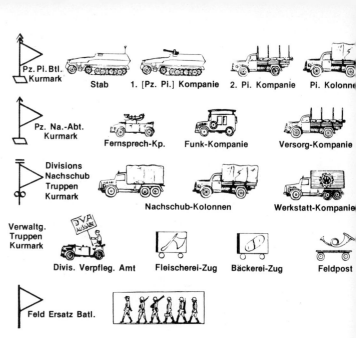

Pz. Pi. Btl. Kurmark	Stab	1. [Pz. Pi.] Kompanie	2. Pi. Kompanie	Pi. Kolonne
Pz. Na.-Abt. Kurmark	Fernsprech-Kp.	Funk-Kompanie	Versorg-Kompanie
Divisions Nachschub Truppen Kurmark	Nachschub-Kolonnen	Werkstatt-Kompanie
Verwaltg. Truppen Kurmark	Divis. Verpfleg. Amt	Fleischerei-Zug	Bäckerei-Zug	Feldpost
Feld Ersatz Batl.			
Sanitäts-Truppe	Feld Lazarett	1. San. Kp.	2. San. Kp.	I. Krank. Kraftwg-Z / II. Krank. Kraftwg-Z

The Div. Kdr. of the Panzer-Grenadier-Division "KURMARK" Generalmajor Langkeit, formerly Kdr. Pz. Rgt. "GD".

Award of the knight's Cross to Feldwebel [Sgt.] Riedmüller, I. [Pz. Jagd.] Abt./Pz. Rgt. "Kurmark". [Left] Oblt. Lützow.

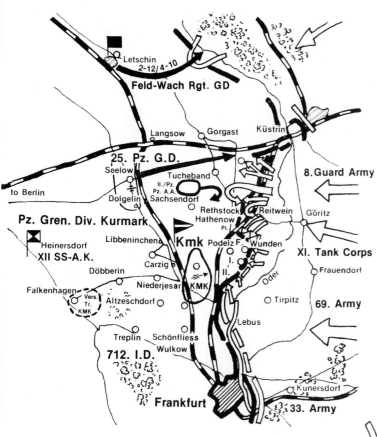

Kurmark on the Oder, February 26 to March 2, 1945

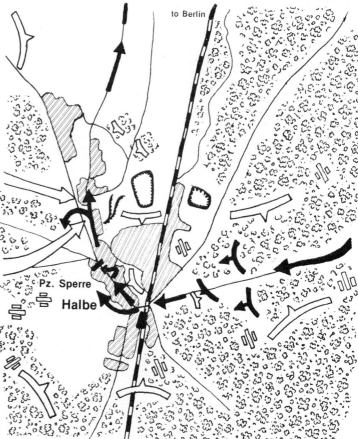

Breakthrough at Halbe, April 28 to April 29, 1945 Kurmark

Withdrawal from Balga-Kahlholz, March 16 to March 29, 1945

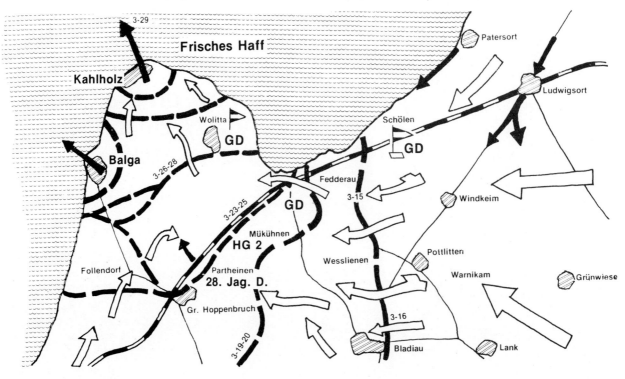

The last positions at the steep coast at Kahlholz.

Die Feuerwehr

FRONTBLATT ALLER „GROSSDEUTSCHLAND"-VERBÄNDE

Nr. 32   Erste Aprilfolge 1945   II. Jahrgang

Höchste und stolzeste Bewährung

Unsere Division während der Kämpfe an den Brennpunkten der Ostpreußenschlacht

DJ. Über zehn Wochen lang hielt unsere Division an Brennpunkten der Ostpreußenschlacht der sowjetischen Übermacht stand und band starke Kräfte des Gegners. Was diese vergangenen Wochen, — von den eisigen Winterstürmen des Januar bis in die Frühlingsnebel der Karwoche, — für jeden einzelnen von uns bedeuteten, wer vermag das in Worte zu fassen? Jeder Tag und jede Stunde, — sie hatten es in sich, sausteild und schwer! Wie oft scheinen die Fortberichten dieses Wochen, erwarteten Ecche Kampfes über unsere aufs äußerste angespannten Kräfte zu geben, mehr von uns abzufordern als menschenmöglich schien.

Wir sahen uns einer Übermacht gegenüber, die mit immer neuen, frischen Kräften ununterbrochen gegen unsere gut und verbissen verteidigten Kampflinien anstürmte, uns aus dem Feuerhagel ihrer zahllosen Artillerie überschüttete, mit ungezählten Panzerrudeln gegen uns anrannte und Bomben- und Schlachtgeschwader in zahllosen Wellen auf uns einschlugen.

Wir wußten worum es ging. Jeder Tag und jede Stunde, die wir den uns anvertrauten, durch Schweiß und Blut vieler Generationen geheiligten ostpreußischen Boden länger verteidigten, banden starke feindliche Kräfte, die nicht an anderer Stelle gegen unser schwer bedrängtes Reich anrennen konnten. Jeder Meter des ostpreußischen Erde, in den sich unsere Panzergrenadiere, Füsiliere und Musketiere mit harter Entschlossenheit festkrallten, kostete dem Gegner Ströme von Blut. Jeder Bolschewist, den unsere Scharfschützen niederstreckten, fiel aus im Kampf gegen Deutschland, bedroht nicht mehr unsere Mütter, Frauen und Mädchen mit seinem Sadismus. Jeder Panzer, den unsere mutigen Einzelkämpfer mit der Panzerfaust knackten, den unsere tapferen Bedienungen und Panzerbesatzungen abschossen, rollte nicht weiter gegen die deutsche Heimat. So wurde auch der Kampf unserer Division um Ostpreußen nach dem Eingeständnis eines bolschewistischen Offiziers zum blutigsten Überlaß dieses Krieges für die Bolschewisten".

Gerade in den letzten Wochen, als die Sowjets mit acht Armeen zum entscheidenden Stoß ansetzten, um den Durchbruch zu erzwingen und uns zu vernichten, bewies sich erneut die vorbildliche Standhaftigkeit der Männer von Großdeutschland aufs höchste. Bis zuletzt — gerade zuletzt — oft dort eingesetzt, wo die Lage am kritischsten und die Gewalt des feindlichen Massenansturms am stärksten waren, bestätigten unsere Grenadiere, Füsiliere, Sturmpioniere und Musketiere ebenso wie andere Angehörige unserer Division neu ihre unerschütterliche Kampfbereitschaft. Ob in harter Verteidigung eines Stützpunktes gegen vielfache feindliche Übermacht, ob in der dünnbesetzten Hauptkampflinie, ob nach Abriegelung eines Einbruches in der neuen Stellung, sie hielten stand. Und dort wo sie zum Gegenstoß ansetzten, da trotzten sie dem Gegner ihr Ziel ab, — wie jene neun Panzergrenadiere, die mit dem Deutschlandlied auf den Lippen in letzter Entschlossenheit eine von harten Feindkräften besetzte Höhe stürmten. Unsere Artilleristen bewahrten ruhig Blut in der glühenden Hölle wie ihre VB's Auge in Auge mit dem Feind, wie die Männer unserer Heeresflak im Feuer der Schlachter oder Panzer. Unerschüttert durch das Getöse der Bomben- und Granateinschläge taten die Nachrichtenmänner an ihren Geräten die ihnen selbstverständliche Pflicht, hielten die Männer der Narreinheiten und Trolls, wo der Kampf Mann gegen Mann ungewohnt, ihre Stellungen neben den erprobten Grabenkämpfern, stiegen die Männer aus den Schreibstuben und Werkstätten in die vordersten Gräben. Sie bewährten sich im ersten Einsatz. Und unermüdlich waren Truppenärzte und Sanitätsdienstgrade in selbstloser Hingabe helfend am Werk der Verwundetenbetreuung. Allen voran aber verteidigten und stürmten als die stolzen Vorbilder ihrer Soldaten nach alter preußischer Tradition die Offiziere der Division, ihre Kommandeure, Chefs und Einheitsführer, mit beispielhafter Tapferkeit.

Brandenburg, Fedderau, Wolittnick, Wolittic, Kahlholz — das waren die großen Phasen unseres Kampfes. Von der ersten Stunde an, da die bolschewistische Sturmwelle gegen Ostpreußen anflutete bis zur buchstäblich letzten Minute, in der die Division den Absetzungsbefehl erreichte, da sich am Strand des Kahlholzer Hornes der Kampf vollendete, waren die Männer von „Großdeutschland" am Feind. Aber der waren es die Offiziere der Division, die die Verteidigung und Absetzbewegung auf schmalem Küstenstreifen mit Umsicht und Unerschrockenheit meisterten. Nicht bevor unsere verwundeten Kameraden in Sicherheit gebracht waren, sahen sie und ihre Männer vom Kampf, verließ den General den Boden, auf dem „Großdeutschland"-Soldaten mit den Kameraden anderer Divisionen

---

Um Deutschlands Freiheit!

Soldaten meiner Division!

Ein Kampfabschnitt liegt hinter uns voll härtester Kämpfe, größter Strapazen und Entbehrungen.

Es war aber zugleich ein Kampfabschnitt, der Eure Treue, Eure Tapferkeit, Einsatzbereitschaft und Anständigkeit der Gesinnung und Haltung im hellsten Licht erstrahlen ließ.

Ich danke Euch aus tiefbewegtem Herzen für diese Eure untadelige Haltung in größter Not und Gefahr. Ihr habt aufs Neue dem Namen unserer Division Ehre gemacht und gekämpft im festen Glauben an unseren Führer und unser Volk, im Glauben an unseren Sieg, der uns trotz aller Not und Feindeslast doch werden wird.

In diesem Geiste wollen wir weiterkämpfen zur Ehre unserer gefallenen Kameraden, deren Heldentod uns Mahner ist, nicht nachzulassen im Kampf um Deutschlands Freiheit.

Heil Hitler!

Lorenz, Generalmajor

Letzte Ausgabe der Frontzeitung "Die Feuerwehr"

The Fire Brigade

[Above] One of the last artillery positions on the Balga peninsula.

[Below] Last consultation [Right, the Div. Kdr. "GD" Generalmajor Lorenz] at the steep coast at Kahlholz before crossing over to Pillau and onto the Frische peninsula.

The last remnants of "GD" from the city of Balga leave the ferry "Seasnake" in Pillau. Approximately 4,000 men reach Pillau. After further heavy defensive fighting on Samland and the Frische Peninsula, only 800 men are able to reach Schleswig-Holstein via the East Sea, Hela Peninsula, Bornholm Island, and Fehmarn.

With this final move, the "GD" division ceased to exist as a fighting force.

Samland Battles, April, 1945

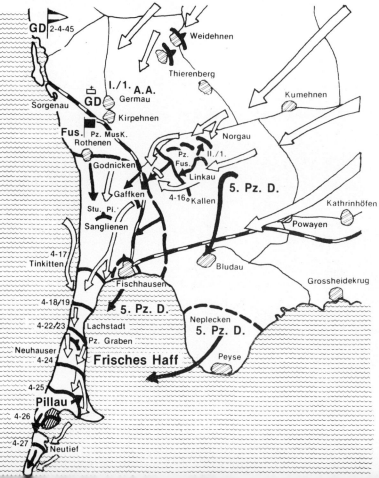

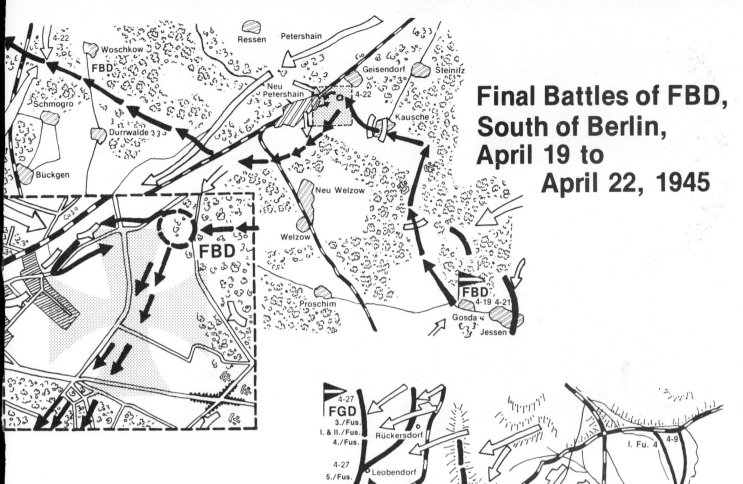

**Final Battles of FBD,
South of Berlin,
April 19 to
April 22, 1945**

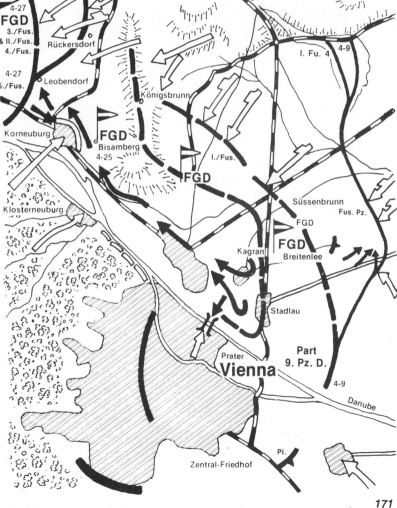

**Final Battles of FGD
near Vienna,
April, 1945**

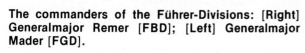

The commanders of the Führer-Divisions: [Right] Generalmajor Remer [FBD]; [Left] Generalmajor Mader [FGD].

While, at the beginning of 1944, there was still a small hope to end the war without defeat, by the beginning of 1945, there was no hope at all: the end was clearly in sight, and the most dedicated and effective military units could only delay the inevitable. The last months were marked by terribly pervasive discouragement. The brutality and ruthlessness of the Soviet enemy, the wish to protect the refugees from the evacuated eastern areas, the demand for "unconditional surrender" by the Allies — and fear of what would follow — and also the feeling of obligation to those who had died, that their sacrifices had not been in vain, all combined to convince most men to fight on regardless of the odds or the inevitable outcome of the war. Probably only those who fought under such conditions will ever understand this. "GD" members fought in 1945 in four divisions, in several temporary, hastily formed combat groups, and also as members of smaller groups or as individuals in other units of the Army. Casualties were very high for all units: "GD" Pz. Gren. Division alone suffered 16,988 casualties in all ranks from 1-15-45 to 4-22-45; Pz. Div. "FBD" was virtaully wiped out; Pz. Div. "FGD" went as a unit into Soviet captivity, and Pz. Gren. Division "Brandenburg" was scattered completely. All disappeared only after the hardest fighting of the war.

The history of the "Grossdeutschland" forces shows the usual development of all elite units. From a special detachment — usually an escort or bodyguard force — an elite formation is organized, often for purposes of propaganda of morale. As a result, such units are favored with the latest in equipment and best men, but also are asked to make greater sacrifices and suffer greater losses. Very often, such units — as happened with "GD" — exhaust themselves in overextended attempts to achieve the impossible demands of the Army High Command.

The German Army attempted to expand and reinforce "Grossdeutschland" to counterblance the growing strength — and political power — of the SS formations. "Grossdeutschland" would have been the core of the postwar German Army, had Germany won the war. Impressive names and new organizations did little good in late 1944, and no good in 1945. With all the effort that they could give on the battlefield, the men of "GD" saw the war close in on the Third Reich, in April and May 1945, all the "GD" forces ceased to exist as fighting units, destroyed by attrition or capture, with a few survivors — and most of "FGD" — surrendering to the Allies at War's end. The survivors of captivity would return years later.

The troops of the elite units like "Grossdeutschland" best typified the "ideal" German soldier, and the men lived up to that ideal as much as any other soldiers. Their battles were among the most savage, hard-fought, and brutal campaigns, and in the midst of the destruction and confusion of battle, they often made great sacrifices to save comrades, gain difficult objectives, and even to aid refugees in the final retreats. While many of their last-ditch, desperate actions seem to have been completely hopeless, their actions can only be judged and understood in terms of the period in which they occurred. Today, the spirit of the "Grossdeutschland" units is remembered by a war memorial in Kassel, Germany, and by the reputation that these famous units established in the plains of Russia, the mountains of Central Europe, and the rolling hills and coastal plains of Germany itself.

Painful duty for friends: remembering those who died.

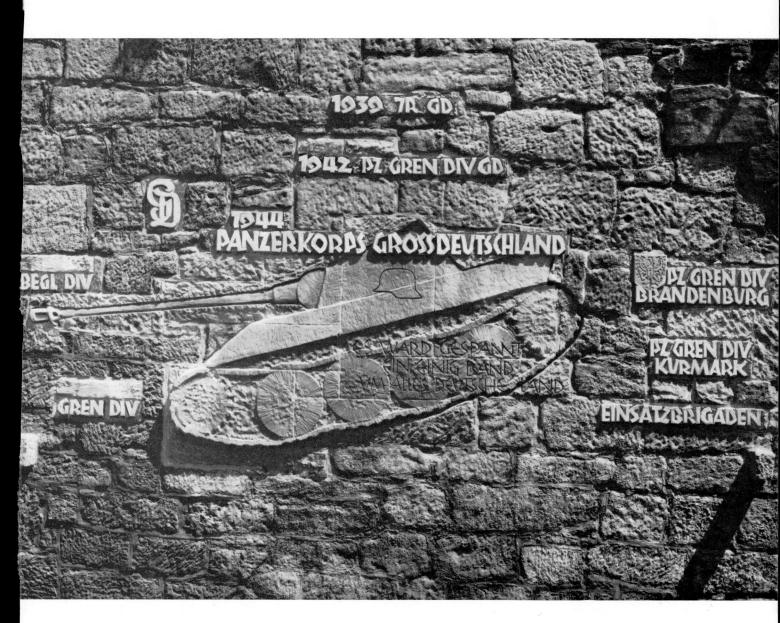